Limbic System: Amygdala, Hypothalamus, Septal Nuclei, Cingulate, Hippocampus

Emotion, Memory, Language, Development, Evolution, Love, Attachment, Sexuality, Violence, Fear, Aggression, Dreams, Hallucinations, Amnesia,

Abnormal Behavior

R. Gabriel Joseph

Limbic System:
Amygdala, Hypothalamus, Septal Nuclei, Cingulate, Hippocampus

Emotion, Memory, Language, Development, Evolution, Love, Attachment, Sexuality, Violence, Fear, Aggression, Dreams, Hallucinations, Amnesia, Abnormal Behavior

From: Neuroscience, Neuropsychiatry, Neuropsychology, 3rd & 4th Edition
Cosmology Science Publishers (Cambridge)

Published by: Cosmology Science Publishers, Cambridge, MA

ISBN: 978-1-938024-52-8

Emotion, Memory, Language, Development, Evolution, Love, Attachment, Sexuality, Violence, Aggression, Amnesia, Abnormal Behavior

Table of Contents

**Part I. Limbic System: Hypothalamus,
Amygdala, Septal Nuclei, Hippocampus**   **- 8**

functional overview -11
hypothalamus -18
sexual dimorphism in the hypothalamus -21
lateral & ventromedial hypothalamic nuclei -26
hunger & thirst - 27
pleasure & reward - 30
aversion - 31
uncontrolled laughter - hypothalamic rage - 32
circadian rhythm generation & seasonal affective disorder - 34
the hypothalamus-pituitary-adrenal axis -36
psychic manifestations of hypothalamic activity: the id - 42
the pleasure principle - 43
amygdala - 44
amygdala structural functional organization: overview - 48
evolution & embryology - 50
intrinsic & extrinsic organization: the flow of information - 54
the amygdala-striatum - 58
the medial amygdala - 60
lateral amygdala - 62
attention - 64
fear, rage & aggression - 66
case study in amygdala-aggression: charles whitman -67
docility & amygdaloid destruction - 72
social-emotional agnosia - 73
emotional language & the amygdala -74
amygdala, the anterior commissure, sexuality & emotion - 75
the limbic system & testosterone - 77
sexual orientation & heterosexual desire - 78
overview: the amygdala -80
hippocampus - 81
hippocampal arousal, attention & inhibitory influences - 82
arousal - 83
aversion & punishment - 85
attention & inhibition - 85
learning & memory: the hippocampus - 88
hippocampal & septal interactions - 90
septal nucle - 92
hippocampal & amygdaloid interactions: memory -92
temporal lobes & laterality - 95

the primary process: amygdala & pleasure - 96
amygdala & hippocampal hallucinations during infancy - 96
dreaming -98
dreams & infancy - 100
the primary process - 101
primary imagery - 101

Part II. Limbic Language & Social Emotional Development: Hypothalamus, Amygdala, Septal Nuclei, Cingulate   - 110

neonatal brainstem: functional overview - 112
sham emotions and the neonatal "smile" - 115
hypothalamus, periaqueductal gray, vocalization, quiescence, distress - 117
limbic language - 120
limbic language development - 127
limbic language hierarchical development - 128
periaqueductal gray and vocalization - 133
the medial hypothalamus: crying and screaming -136
the lateral hypothalamus and the pleasure principle - 138
the amygdala, hypothalamus, and periaqueductal gray -140
the amygdala and social-emotional vocalization - 141
the amygdala and social emotional development - 145
the amygdala, the social smile, and the human face - 147
vocalizing indices of amygdala maturation - 149
wariness, stranger fear, and the amygdala -151
the development of social behavior and stranger-fear - 154
the amygdala, fear, and attachment -156
septal social behavior - 160
septal nuclei, amygdala, social-emotional development & attachment - 161
limbic love, hate and relationships - 164
the cingulate gyrus - 166
the posterior cingulate - 167
anterior cingulate gyrus - 169
the anterior cingulate gyrus - 169
the cingulate gyrus and emotional speech - 171
the cingulate, the separation cry and "motherese" - 176
maternal behavior & the evolution of infant separation cries - 176
mother infant vocalization - 178
female superiorities in limbic language - 179
maternal behavior, attachment, and the female limbic system - 180
the male limbic system and infant care - 182
cingulate maternal infant communication - 190

babbling, limbic language, and neuroanatomical maturational events - 192
early babbling, probable meanings, and prosody - 192
maturation of the amygdala, cingulate, and early and late babbling - 195
babbling and amygdala, cingulate, neocortical maturation - 196
immaturity of the neocortical speech areas and jargon babbling - 198
right and left hemisphere language acquisition - 198

Part III: The Hippocampus, Amygdala, Memory, Amnesia, Long Term Synaptic Potentiation, and Neural Networks   -203

neural networks - 191
neural circuits & long term potentiation - 209
neural networks - 2011
synaptic growth and dendritic spine proliferation - 2012
long term potential & memory - 214
short & long term memory: the anterior & posterior hippocampus - 216
short vs long term verbal & visual memory loss & hippocampal damage - 219
bilateral hippocampal destruction & amnesia - 221
learning and memory in the absence of the hippocampus - 222
the hippocampus and entorhinal cortex - 223
the frontal lobes, hippocampus, & memory -225
the amygdala, hippocampus & memory - 226
anterograde & post-traumatic/anterograde amnesia - 227
retrograde amnesia - 229
shrinking retrograde amnesia - 231
causes of amnesia - 232
memory gaps - 233
anesthesia & unconscious learning - 234
unconscious knowledge: verbal & source amnesia - 235
the frontal lobes & the dorsal medial thalamus - 237
dorsal medial thalamus, frontal lobes, korsakoff's syndrome - 239
the hippocampus and dorsal medial nucleus - 241
hippocampus & neocortical arousal - 242
excessive hippocampal arousal & memory loss - 244
the amygdala & emotional neural networks - 245
fear, anxiety, startle, & traumatic stress - 248
fear, anticipation, & repression - 249
fear, emotional trauma, hippocampal deactivation & memory loss - 249
memory loss & amygdala dysfunction - 254
amygdala, hippocampus & dorsal medial nucleus - 254
overview: the hippocampus, amygdala & memory - 255

References   261

The Limbic System

Part I
The Limbic System:
Hypothalamus, Amygdala,
Septal Nuclei, Hippocampus

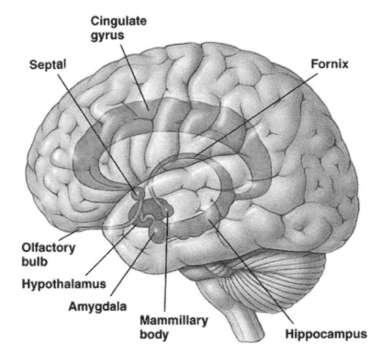

Limbic System Overview

Buried within the depths of the cerebrum are several large aggregates of limbic structures and nuclei which are preeminent in the control and mediation of memory, emotion, learning, dreaming, attention, and arousal, and the perception and expression of emotional, motivational, sexual, and social behavior including the formation of loving attachments. Indeed, the limbic system not only controls the capacity to experience love and sorrow, but it governs and monitors internal homeostasis and basic needs such as hunger and thirst, including even the cravings for pleasure-inducing drugs.

The structures and nuclei of the limbic system are exceedingly ancient, some of which began to evolve over 450 million years ago. Over the course of evolution, these emotional structures have expanded in size, some becoming increasingly cortical in response to increased environmental opportunities and demands. In fact, as the neocortical forebrain expanded and until as recently as 50 million years ago, the cerebrum of the ancestral line that would eventually give rise to humans, was dominated by the limbic system.

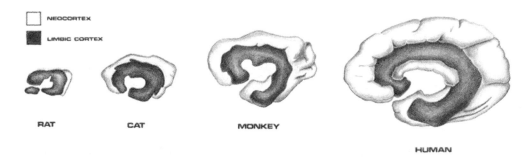

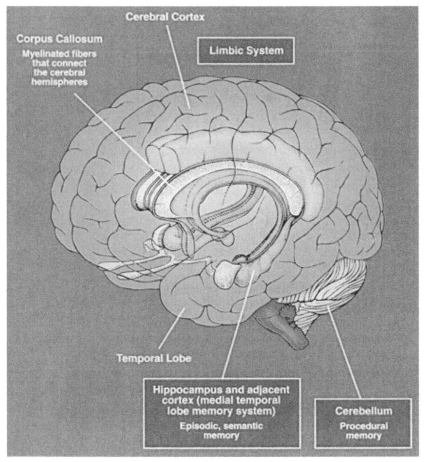

However, over the course of evolution a mantle of neocortex began to develop and enshroud the limbic system; evolving at first to serve limbic needs in a way that would maximize the survival of the organism, and to more efficiently, effectively, and safely satisfy limbic needs and impulses. In consequence, the frontal, temporal, parietal, and occipital lobes evolved covered with a neocortical mantle, that in humans would come to be associated with the conscious, rational mind. Sometimes, however, even in the most rational of humans, emotions can hijack the logical mind, and the neocortex, and even peaceful people might be impelled to murder even those they love.

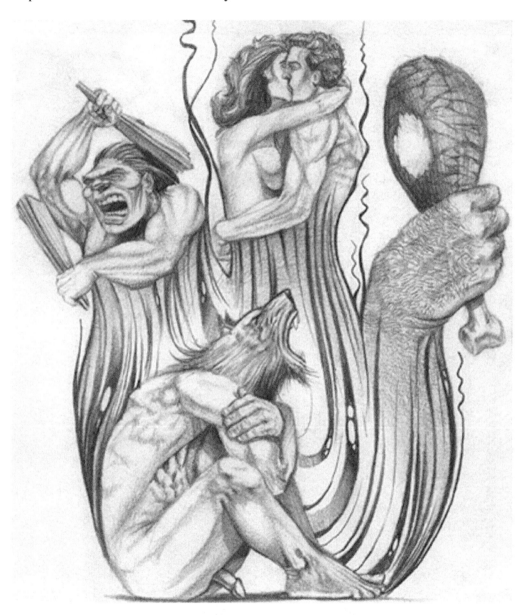

Indeed, the old limbic brain has not been replaced and is not only predominant in regard to all aspects of motivational and emotional functioning, but is capable of completely overwhelming "the rational mind" due in part to the massive axonal projections of limbic system to the neocortex. Although over the course of evolution a new brain (neocortex) has developed, Homo sapiens ("the wise may who knows he is wise") remains a creature of emotion. Humans have not completely emerged from the phylogenetic swamps of their original psychic existence.

Hence, due to these limbic roots, humans not uncommonly behave "irrationally" or in the "heat of passion," and get into fights, have sex with or scream and yell at strangers thus act at the behest of their immediate desires; sometimes falling "madly in love" and at other times, acting in a blind rage such that even those who are 'loved" may be slaughtered and murdered.

Indeed, emotion is a potentially powerful overwhelming force that warrants and yet resists control-- as something irrational that can happen to a someone ("you make me so angry") and which can temporarily hijack, overwhelm, and snuff out the "rational mind."

The schism between the rational and the emotional is real, and is due to the raw energy of emotion having it's source in the nuclei of the ancient limbic lobe -- a series of structures which first make their phylogenetic appearance over a hundred million years before humans walked upon this earth and which continue to control and direct human behavior.

FUNCTIONAL OVERVIEW

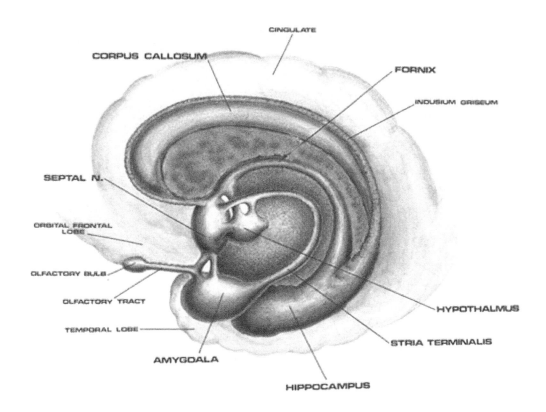

The Limbic System

In general, the primary structures of the limbic system include the hypothalamus, amygdala, hippocampus, septal nuclei, and anterior cingulate gyrus; structures which are directly interconnected by massive axonal pathways. With the exception of the cingulate which is referred to as "transitional" cortex (mesocortex) and consists of five layers, the hypothalamus, amygdala, hippocampus, septal nuclei are considered allocortex, consisting of at most, 3 layers.

The hypothalamus could be considered the most "primitive" aspect of the limbic system, though in fact the functioning of this sexually dimorphic structure is exceedingly complex (Majdic & Tobet 2011; Orikasa & Sakuma 2010; Schoenknecht et al., 2011). The hypothalamus regulates internal homeostasis including the experience of hunger and thirst, can trigger rudimentary sexual behaviors or generate aggressive behavior or feelings of extreme rage or pleasure (Blouet et al., 2009; Lin et al., 2011; Milanski et al., 2009; Motta et al., 2009; Suzuki et al., 2010). In conjunction with the pituitary the hypothalamus is a major manufacturer/secretor of hormones and other bodily humors, including those involved in the stress response and feelings of depression (Bao & Swaab 2010; Foley & Kirschbaum 2010; Kudielka & Wust, 2010).

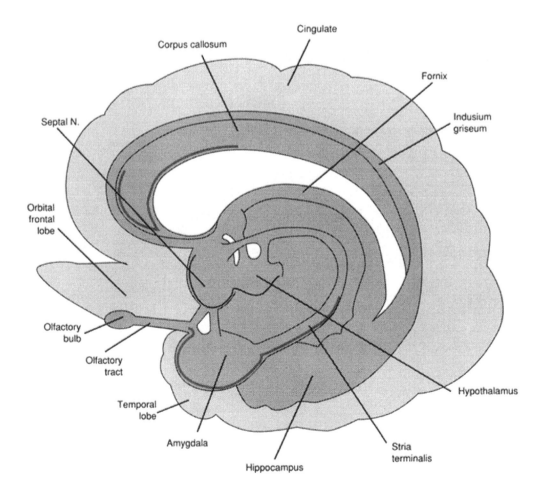

The amygdala has been implicated in the generation of the most rudimentary and the most profound of human emotions, including fear, anxiety, sexual desire, rage, religious ecstasy, or at a more basic level, determining if something might be good to eat (Nitschke et al., 2009; Pape & Pare 2010; Pessoa & Adolphs 2010; Zhang et al., 2011). The amygdala is implicated in the seeking of loving attachments (Joseph 1982, 1992; Todd & Anderson 2009) and the formation of long term emotional memories (Kensinger et al., 2011; Poulos et al., 2009; Roozendaal et al., 2009). It contains neurons which become activated in response to the human face, and which become activated in response to the direction of someone else's gaze (Blackford et al., 2009; N'Diaye, et al., 2009 Rule et al., 2010). The amygdala also acts directly on the hypothalamus via the stria terminalis, medial forebrain bundle, and amygdalafugal pathways, and in this manner can control hypothalamic impulses . The amygdala is also directly connected to the hippocampus, with which it interacts in regard to memory (Lang et al., 2009; Roozendaal et al., 2009).

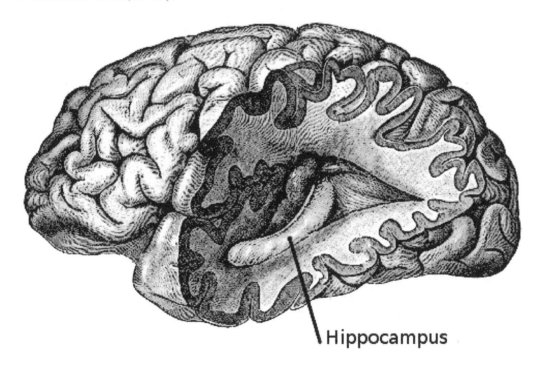

Hippocampus

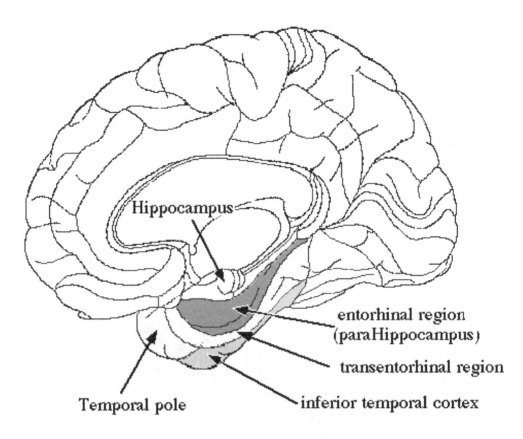

The hippocampus is unique in that unlike the amygdala and other structures, almost all of its input from the neocortex is relayed via the overlying entorhinal cortex--a five layered mesocortex. As is well known, the hippocampus is exceedingly important in memory (Chadwick et al., 2010; Warburton & Brown, 2009), acting to place various short-term memories into long-term storage Katche et al., 2010; Restivo et al., (2009). Presumably the hippocampus encodes new information during the storage and consolidation (long-term storage) phase, and assists in the gating of afferent streams of information destined for the neocortex by filtering or suppressing irrelevant sense data which may interfere with memory consolidation. Moreover, it is believed that via the development of long-term potentiation the hippocampus is able to track information as it is stored in the neocortex, and to form conjunctions between synapses and different brain regions which process and store associated memories.

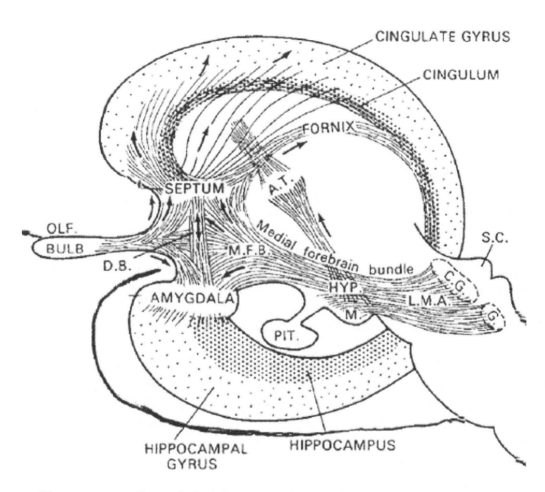

The septum and septal nuclei are associated with various extremes in social and emotional functioning (Brisch et al., 2010; Singewald et al., 2011; Thomas & Gunton 2011) and can trigger explosive violence, known as "septal rage." The septal nuclei is in part an evolutionary and developmental outgrowth of the hippocampus (Ariens Kappers, et al., 1936; Gloor, 1997), and the hypothalamus, and in fact acts to link the hippocampus with the hypothalamus as well as with the brainstem (Andy & Stephan, 1968; Risvold & Swanson, 1996; Swanson & Cowan, 1979;). It consists of both lateral and medial segments; i.e. the lateral and medial septal nuclei (Ariens Kappers, et al., 1936). Presumably, via these interconnections, the septal nuclei exerts modulatory influences on the hippocampus in regard to memory functioning and arousal. The septal nuclei is also interconnected with and shares a counterbalancing relationship with the amygdala particularly in regard to hypothalamic activity and emotional and sexual arousal (Andy & Stephan, 1968; Swanson & Cowan, 1979). For example, whereas the amygdala promotes indiscriminate contact seeking, and perhaps promiscuous sexual activity, the septal nuclei inhibits these tendencies thus assisting in the formation of selective and more enduring emotional attachments (Joseph, 1992a, 2016b).

The anterior cingulate is considered a transitional cortex, or rather, mesocortex (also referred to as "paleocortex") as it consists of five layers (Vogt 2006). The anterior cingulate is intimately interconnected with the hypothalamus, amygdala, septal nuclei, and hippocampus, and participates in memory and emotion including the experience of pain, misery, and anxiety (Cao et al., 2009; Eto et al., 2011; Shin et al., 2009), and is directly implicated in the evolution and expression of maternal behavior (Joseph 1990, 1992; MacLean 1990; Salmaso, et al., 2011) It is also the most vocal aspect of the brain, becomes active during language tasks, and generates emotional-melodic aspects of speech which is expressed via interconnections with the right and left frontal speech areas, and the vocalization center in the midbrain periaqueductal gray (Hage 2010; Joseph 1990, 1992; Jurgens 2009). Thus the anterior cingulate is implicated in the more cognitive aspects of social-emotional behavior including language and the establishment of long term attachments beginning with the mother-infant bond.

Also implicated in the functioning of the limbic system are the olfactory bulb and olfactory system, the limbic striatum (nucleus accumbens, olfactory tubercle, substantia innominata, ventral caudate and putamen), the orbital frontal and inferior temporal lobes and the midbrain monoamine system. These systems and structures are also directly connected or separated by only a single synapse, and which tend to become aroused not only as a function of emotional arousal, but in reaction to olfactory input which continues to exert profound effects on the human limbic system, and upon human behavior.

HYPOTHALAMUS

The hypothalamus is an exceedingly ancient structure and unlike most other brain regions it has remained somewhat similar in structure throughout phylogeny and apparently over the course of evolution (Crosby et al. 1966). Located in the most medial aspect of the brain, along the walls and floor of the 3rd ventricle, this nucleus is fully functional at birth and is the central core from which all emotions derive their motive force. Indeed, the hypothalamus is highly involved in all aspects of emotional, reproductive, vegetative, endocrine, hormonal, visceral and autonomic functions and mediates or exerts significant or controlling influences on eating, drinking, sleeping and the experience of pleasure, rage, and aversion including fear and aggression (Blouet et al., 2009; Lin et al., 2011; Motta et al., 2009; Siegel et al., 2010; Suzuki et al., 2010).

Nuclei of the Hypothalamus

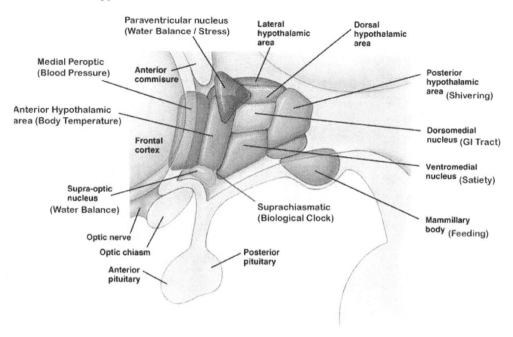

In fact, almost every region of the cerebrum interacts with and communicates with the hypothalamus and is subject to its influences (Swanson, 1987). Moreover, the hypothalamus utilizes the blood supply to transmit hormonal and humeral messages to peripheral organs as well as other brain structures and utilizes the blood supply to receive information as well, thus bypassing the synaptic route utilized by almost all other regions of the neuroaxis (Markakis & Swanson, 1997). Through the blood supply (as well as via the cerebrospinal fluid), the hypothalamus not only regulates, but is subject to feedback regulation by the same structures that it controls.

Certain areas of the diencephalon, midbrain, and brainstem, are exceedingly sensitive to hormones, humors, and peptides circulating within the blood plasma, and the cerebrospinal fluids; chemosensory information which is used for maintaining homeostasis. Broadly considered, these chemosensory sensitive areas are generally located near or surrounding the cerebral ventricles (Johnson & Gross, 1993) and they tend not to be effected by the so called "blood brain barrier;" referred to as circumventricular organs (CVOs). There are perhaps dozens of CVO's at least 8 of which are located in or near the ventricular systems which feed the brainstem and diencephalon including the hypothalamus, pineal gland and pituitary (Johnson & Gross, 1993).

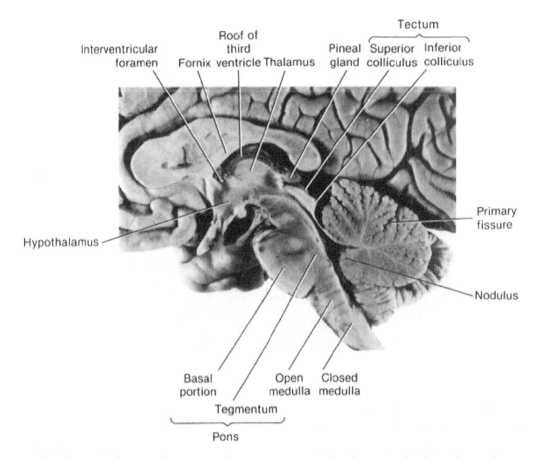

The hypothalamus, however, does not act solely through the blood supply or via cerebrospinal fluid, and its also receives sensory information synaptically, and often indirectly, as is the case with the majority of olfactory fibers. In general, sensory stimuli reach the hypothalamus from a variety of routes. These include the solitary tract of the brainstem, a structure which receives, processes, and transmits data received principally from the vagus and glosopharyngeal cranial nerves. Through this pathway the lateral hypothalamus is informed about cardiovascular activities, respiration, and taste. These pathways are also bidirectional (Swanson, 1987). Other major pathways include the medial forebrain bundle (which contains axons from a variety of different cellular groups) and the stria terminalis through which the amygdala and hypothalamus interact. The hypothalamus also maintains massive interactive pathways with the frontal lobes and septal nuclei (Risvold & Swanson, 1996).

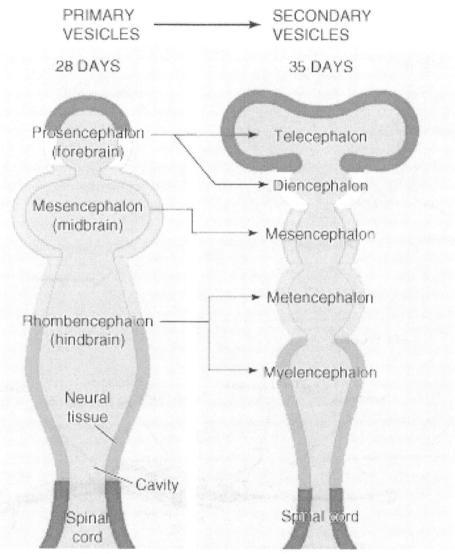

Broadly considered, the hypothalamus consists of three longitudinal subdivisions which extend along its anterior to posterior axis. These are the medial, lateral, and periventricular (Schoenknecht et al., 2011; Swanson, 1987). The periventricular zone is concerned with neuroendocrine regulation, whereas the lateral and medial zones are concerned with affective states, including hunger and thirst (Blouet et al., 2009; Lin et al., 2011; Milanski et al., 2009; Motta et al., 2009; Suzuki et al., 2010). These zones, in turn can be further subdivided into subnuclei.

Phylogenetically, structurally, and embryologically the hypothalamus is traditionally considered part of the diencephalon. During embryological development it emerges from the diencephalic vessicle of the neural tube along with those anterior-lateral evaginations which become the optic nerves and retina

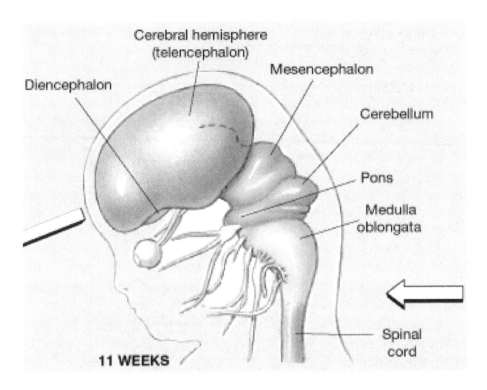

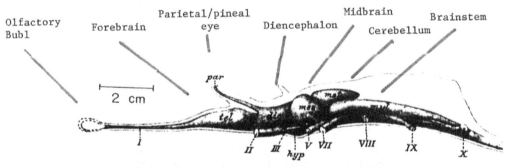

Figures (above/below) Fish brain from 500 mya

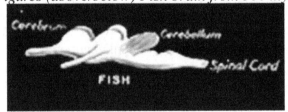

of the eye, as well as the pituitary gland (ventrally) and the pineal gland and thalamus (dorsally). There is some dispute, however, over the developmental patterns of the hypothalamus, as some scientists believe that it develops from the outside in (the "hollow hypothalamus hypothesis").

On the other hand, the hypothalamus originates from the medially situated neuroepithelium, and thus begins its developmental journey in a medial (or rather paramedial) to lateral arc, such that it appears that the medial hypothalamus is fashioned (and matures) in advance of the lateral hypothalamus.

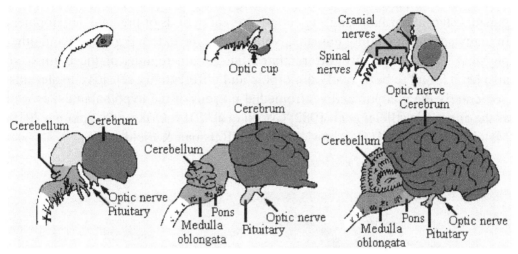

Figure: Development of the human brain.

From an evolutionary perspective, however, the hypothalamus appears to have dual (forebrain - midbrain) origins; that is emerging from the dorsal (visual) midbrain, and the olfactory forebrain, which together, and over the course of evolution, gave rise to the ventral, medial, lateral and preoptic hypothalamus. Nevertheless, in modern mammals and humans, the olfactory origins are no longer directly apparent, particularly in that most olfactory fibers reach the hypothalamus indirectly; e.g. via the amygdala and piriform cortex.

The hypothalamus is exceedingly responsive to olfactory (and pheromonal) input. Perhaps reflecting this partial and putative olfactory origin is the fact that this structure utilizes chemical (hormonal, humeral) molecules to communicate with other areas of the brain, and reacts to these same molecules as well as olfactory cues, including those directly related to sexual status.

It is this olfactory-chemical origin and sensitivity which in turn may explain why portions of the hypothalamus (like the amygdala) are also sexually dimorphic and reacts to pheromonal sensory stimuli including those which signal sexual status. That is, structurally and functionally the hypothalamus of males and females are structurally dissimilar (Bleier et al. 1982; Dorner, 1976; Gorski et al. 2014; Orikasa & Sakuma 2010; Rainbow et al. 1982; Raisman & Field, 1971, 1973) and perform different functions depending on if one is a man or a woman, and if a woman is sexually receptive, pregnant, or lactating. For example, the sexually dimorphic supraoptic and paraventricular nuclei project (via the infundibular stalk) to the posterior lobe of the pituitary which may then secrete oxytocin--a chemical which can trigger uterine contractions as well as milk production in lactating females (and which can thus make nursing a pleasurable experience). The male hypothalamus/pituitary does not perform this function.

SEXUAL DIMORPHISM IN THE HYPOTHALAMUS

Sexual differentiation is strongly influenced by the presence or absence of gonadal steroid hormones during certain critical periods of prenatal development in many species including humans. Not only are the external genitalia and other physical features sexually differentiated but certain regions of the brain have also been found to be sexually dimorphic and differentially sensitive to steroids, particularly the preoptic and ventromedial nucleus of the hypothalamus, as well as the amygdala (Bleier et al. 1982; Gorski et al. 2014; Orikasa & Sakuma 2010; Majdic & Tobet 2011; Rainbow et al. 1982; Raisman & Field, 1971, 1973).

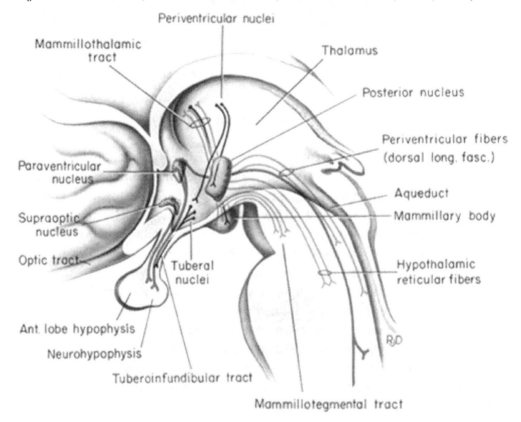

It has now been well established that the amygdala and the hypothalamus (specifically the anterior commissure, anterior-preoptic, ventromedial and suprachiasmatic nuclei) are sexually differentiated and have sex specific patterns of neuronal and dendritic development, (Majdic & Tobet 2011; Orikasa & Sakuma 2010; Rubinow et al., (2009; Whalen & Phelps 2009). This is a consequence of the presence or absence of testosterone during fetal development in humans, or soon after birth in some species such as rodents. Specifically, the presence or absence of the male hormone, testosterone during this critical neonatal period, directly effects and determines the growth and pattern of interconnections between the amygdala and hypothalamus, between axons and dendrites in these nuclei as well as the hippocampus, septal nuclei, olfactory system, and thus the organization of specific neural circuits. In the absence of testosterone, the female pattern of neuronal development occurs. Indeed, it is the presence or absence of testosterone during these early critical periods that appear to be responsible for neurological alterations which greatly effect sex differences in thinking, sexual orientation, aggression, and cognitive functioning (Barnett & Meck, 1990; Beatty, 1992; Dawson et al. 2015; Harris, 2014; Joseph, et al. 2014; Stewart et al. 2015).

For example, if the testes are removed prior to differentiation, or if a chemical blocker of testosterone is administered thus preventing this hormone from reaching target cells in the limbic system, not only does the female pattern of neuronal development occur, but males so treated behave and process information in a manner similar to females (e.g., Joseph et al. 2014); i.e. they develop female brains and think and behave in a manner similar to females. Conversely, if females are administered testosterone during this critical period, the male pattern of differentiation and behavior results (Gerall et al. 1992).

That the preoptic and other hypothalamic regions are sexually dimorphic is not surprising in that it has long been known that this area is extremely important in controlling the basal output of gonadotrophins in females prior to ovulation and is heavily involved in mediating cyclic changes in hormone levels (e.g. FSH, LH, estrogen, progesterone). Chemical and electrical stimulation of the preoptic and ventromedial hypothalamic nuclei also triggers sexual behavior and even sexual posturing in females and males (Hart et al., 2005; Lisk, 2007, 1991) and, in female primates, even maternal behavior (Numan, 2005). In fact, dendritic spine density of ventromedial hypothalamic neurons varies across the estrus cycle (Frankfurt et al., 1990) and thus presumably during pregnancy and while nursing.

In primates, electrical stimulation of the preoptic area increases sexual behavior in males, and significantly increases the frequency of erections, copulations and ejaculations, we well as pelvic thrusting followed by an explosive discharge of semen even in the absence of a mate (Hart, et al., 2005; Maclean, 1973). Conversely, lesions to the preoptic and posterior hypothalamus eliminates male sexual behavior and results in gonadal atrophy.

Hence, it is thus rather clear than the ability to sexually reproduce is dependent on the functional integrity of the hypothalamus. In fact, it is via the hypothalamus acting on the pituitary, that gonadotropins come to be released. Gonadotropins control the production and/or release of gametes; i.e. ova and sperm.

Specifically, the hypothalamic neurons secrete gonadotropin-releasing hormone, which acts on the anterior lobe of the pituitary which secretes gonadotropins. However, given that in females, this is a cyclic event, whereas in males sperms are constantly reproduced, is further evidence of the sexual dimorphism of the hypothalamus.

Hormonal Changes In Puberty

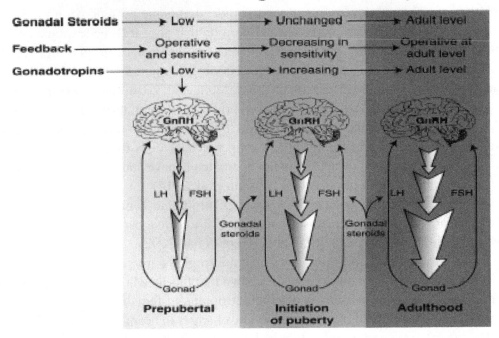

	Prepubertal	Initiation of puberty	Adulthood
Gonadal Steroids	Low	Unchanged	Adult level
Feedback	Operative and sensitive	Decreasing in sensitivity	Operative at adult level
Gonadotropins	Low	Increasing	Adult level

Sex steroids	Low	Unchanged	Adult level
Feedback	Operative and sensitive	Decreasing in sensitivity	Operative at adult level
Gonadotropins	Low	Increasing	Adult level

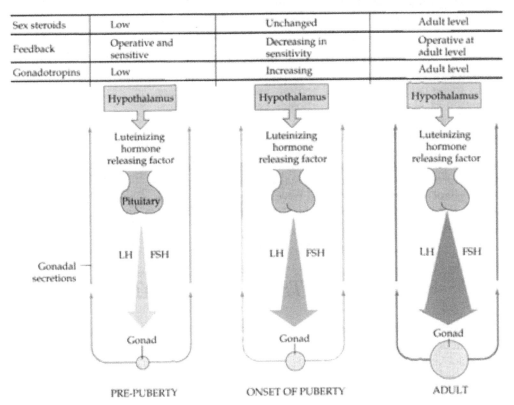

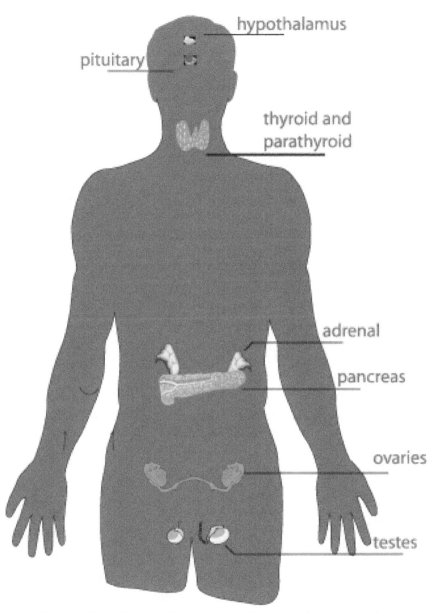

Although the etiology of homosexuality remains in question, it has been shown that the ventromedial and anterior nuclei of the hypothalamus of male homosexuals demonstrate the female pattern of development (Levay, 1991; Swaab, 1990). When coupled with the evidence of male vs female and homosexual differences in the anterior commissure which links the temporal lobe and sexually dimorphic amygdala (see below) as well as the similarity between male homosexuals and women in regard to certain cognitive attributes including spatial-perceptual capability (see below), this raises the possibility that male homosexuals are in possession of limbic system that is more "female" than "male" in functional as well as structural orientation.

Endocrine System

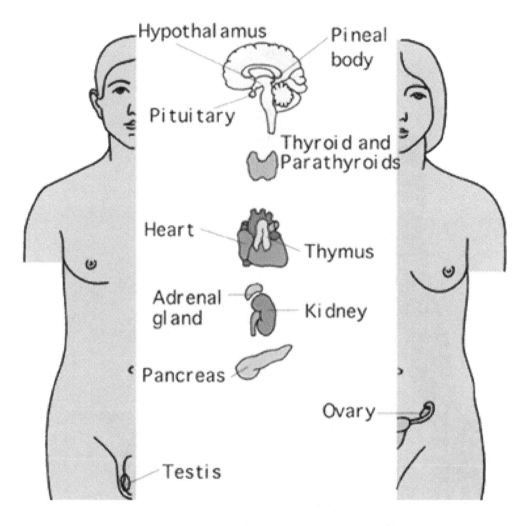

It is also interesting to note that the sexually dimorphic preoptic region contains thermosensitive neurons, and controls the physiological and behavior responses to excessive external cold or heat. That is, it is responsible for internal thermoregulation and thus heat loss or retention (Alam et al., 1995). Although we can only speculate, it may well be sex differences in this structure which accounts (at least in part) for the stereotypical differences in male vs female perceptions of cold, and why, stereotypically, females (despite their extra-layers of heat-retaining fat) are more likely to insist on elevating room temperature.

LATERAL & VENTROMEDIAL HYPOTHALAMIC NUCLEI

Although consisting of several nuclear subgroups, the lateral and medial (ventromedial) hypothalamic nuclei play particularly important roles in the control of the autonomic nervous system, the experience of pleasure and aversion, eating and drinking, and raw (undirected) emotionality (Lin et al., 2011; Milanski et al., 2009; Motta et al., 2009; Suzuki et al., 2010). They also appear to share a somewhat antagonistic relationship.

For example, the medial hypothalamus controls parasympathetic activities (e.g. reduction in heart rate, increased peripheral circulation) and exerts a dampening effect on certain forms of emotional/motivational arousal. The lateral hypothalamus mediates sympathetic activity (increasing heart rate, elevation of blood pressure) and is involved in controlling the metabolic and somatic correlates of heightened emotionality (Smith et al. 1990). In this regard, the lateral and medial region act to exert counterbalancing influences on each other.

HUNGER & THIRST

The lateral and medial region are highly involved in monitoring internal homeostasis and motivating the organism to respond to internal needs such as hunger and thirst (Bernardis & Bellinger 1987; Blouet et al., 2009; Hetherington & Ranson, 1940; Milanski et al., (2009). For example, both nuclei appear to contain receptors which are sensitive to the body's fat content (lipostatic/caloric receptors) and to circulating metabolites (e.g. glucose) which together indicate the need for food and nourishment. For example, when food is digested, the viscera secretes various hormones which act on the alimentary tract, which in turn stimulates the solitary tract (ST) which projects directly to the hypothalamus. However, in the absence of food, the viscera also begins to secrete various hormones which when coupled changes in caloric blood levels, signals to the hypothalamus the need for food.

The lateral hypothalamus also appears to contain osmoreceptors (Joynt, 1966) which determine if water intake should be altered. Electophysiologically, it has been determined that the hypothalamus not only become highly active immediately prior to and while the organism is eating or drinking, but the lateral region alters it's activity when the subject is hungry and simply looking at food (Hamburg, 1971; Rolls et. al., 1976). In fact, if the lateral hypothalamus is electrically stimulated a compulsion to eat and drink results (Delgado & Anand, 1953). Conversely, if the lateral area is destroyed bilaterally there results aphagia and adipsia so severe animals will die unless force fed (Anand & Brobeck, 1951;

Hetherington & Ranson, 1940; Teitelbaum & Epstein, 1962).

If the medial hypothalamus is surgically destroyed, inhibitory influences on the lateral region appear to be abolished such that hypothalamic hyperphagia and severe obesity result (Anand & Brobeck, 1951; Hoebel & Tetelbaum, 1966; Teitelbaum, 1961). Hence, the medial area seems to act as a satiate center; but, a center that can be overridden.

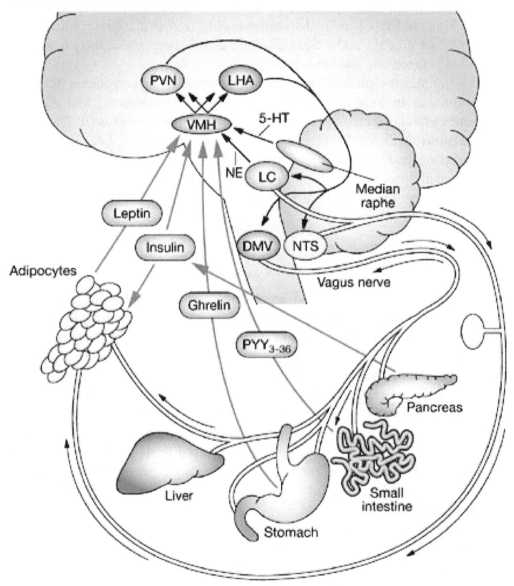

Specifically, with ventromedial lesions, animals not only eat more, but the intervals between meals becomes shorter such that they eat more meals. Thus they begin to gain weight. In part this is also due to changes in the sympathetic nervous system which increases vagal activity, thus signalling the need for more food. As noted, the ST is bidirectional.

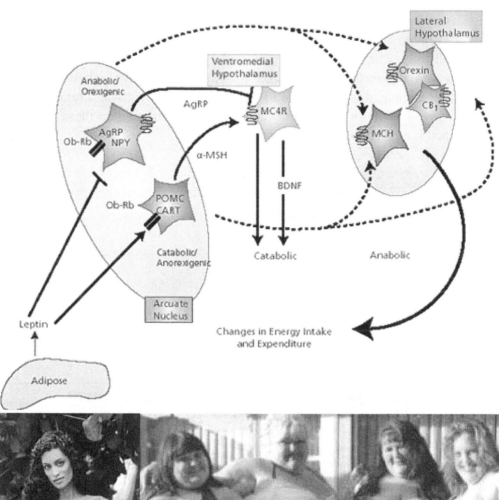

Normally the hypothalamus can act via the ST and thus the vagal complex and can signal satiation. However, with medial destruction, the ST becomes hyperactive thus inducing parasympathetic over activity which induces more rapid gastric emptying and the rapid storage of ingested calories. Because these calories are rapidly stored, caloric blood levels are reduced and the lateral hypothalamus is stimulated to begin eating again--which explains the increased frequency of meals. In fact, if animals that have become obese following ventromedial lesions are starved back to their normal weight, once they are allowed free access to food, they again become obese (Hoebel & Tetelbaum, 1966).

Overall, it appears that the lateral hypothalamus is involved in the initiation of eating and acts to maintain a lower weight limit such that when the limit is reached the organism is stimulated to eat. Conversely, the medial regions seems to be involved in setting a higher weight limit such that when these levels are approached it triggers the cessation of eating.

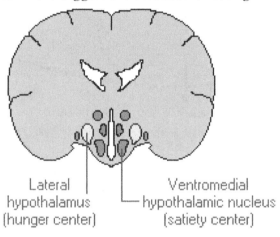

Lateral hypothalamus (hunger center)
Ventromedial hypothalamic nucleus (satiety center)

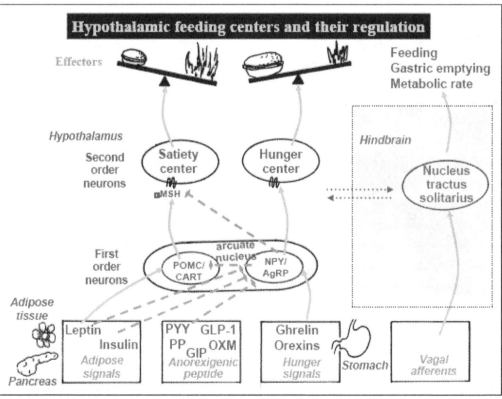

In part, these nuclei exert these differential influences on eating and drinking via motivational/emotional influences they exert on other brain nuclei (e.g. via reward or punishment). However, it should be stressed that there are a number of other structures and hormones and peptides involved, including the pancreatic islets, and insulin secretion.

PLEASURE & REWARD

In 1952, Heath (cited by Maclean, 1969) reported what was then considered remarkable. Electrical stimulation near the septal nuclei elicited feelings of pleasure in human subjects: "I have a glowing feeling. I feel good!" Subsequently, Olds and Milner (1954) reported that rats would tirelessly perform operants to receive electrical stimulation in this same region and concluded that stimulation "has an effect which is apparently equivalent to that of a conventional primary reward." Even hungry animals would demonstrate a preference for self-stimulation over food.

Feelings of pleasure (as demonstrated via self-stimulation) have been obtained following excitation to a number of diverse limbic areas including the olfactory bulbs, amygdala, hippocampus, cingulate, substantia nigra (a major source of dopamine), locus coeruleus (a major source of norepinephrine), raphe nucleus (serotonin), caudate, putamen, thalamus, reticular formation, medial forebrain bundle, and orbital frontal lobes (Brady, 1960; Lilly, 1960; Olds & Forbes, 1981; Stein & Ray, 1959; Waraczynski et al. 1987).

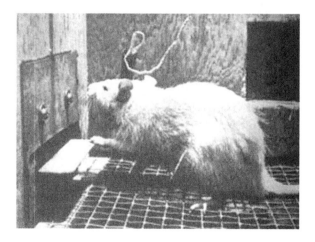

In mapping the brain for positive loci for self-stimulation, Olds (1956) found that the medial forebrain bundle (MFB) was a major pathway which supported this activity. Although the MFB interconnects the hippocampus, hypothalamus, septum, amygdala, orbital frontal lobes (areas which give rise to self-stimulation), Olds discovered in its course up to the lateral hypothalamus reward sites become more densely packed. Moreover, the greatest area of concentration and the highest rates of self-stimulatory activity were found to occur not in the MFB but in the lateral hypothalamus (Olds, 1956; Olds & Forbes, 1981). Indeed, animals "would continue to stimulate as rapidly as possible until physical fatigue forced them to slow or to sleep" (Olds, 1956).

Electrophysiological studies of single lateral hypothalamic neurons indicate that these cells become highly active in response to rewarding food items (Nakamura & Ono, 1986). In fact, many of these cells will become aroused by neutral stimuli repeatedly associated with reward such as a cue-tone --even in the absence of the actual reward (Nakamura & Ono, 1986; Ono et al. 1980). However, this ability to form associations appears to be secondary to amygdaloid activation (Fukuda et al. 1987) which in turn influences hypothalamic functioning.

Nevertheless, if the lateral region is destroyed the experience of pleasure and emotional responsiveness is almost completely attenuated. For example, in primates, faces become blank and expressionless, whereas if the lesion is unilateral, a marked neglect and indifference regarding all sensory events occurring on the contralateral side occurs (Marshall & Teitelbaum, 1974). Animals will in fact cease to eat and will die.

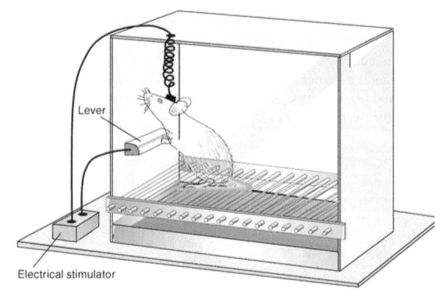

AVERSION

In contrast to the lateral hypothalamus and it's involvement in pleasurable self-stimulation, activation of the medial hypothalamus is apparently so aversive that subjects will work to reduce it (Olds & Forbes, 1981). Hence, electrical stimulation of the medial region leads to behavior which terminates the stimulation--apparently so as to obtain relief (e.g. active avoidance). When considering behavior such as eating, it might be postulated that when upper weight limits (or nutritional requirements) are met, the medial region becomes activated which in turn leads to behavior (e.g. cessation of eating) which terminates its activation.

It is possible, however, that medial hypothalamic activity may also lead to a state of quiescence such that the organism is motivated to simply cease to respond or to behave. In some instances this quiescent state may be physiologically neutral, whereas in other situations medial hypothalamic activity may be highly aversive. Quiescence is also associated with parasympathetic activity which is mediated by the medial area.

HYPOTHALAMIC DAMAGE & EMOTIONAL INCONTINENCE:

LAUGHTER & RAGE

When electrically stimulated, the hypothalamus responds by triggering two seemly oppositional feeling states, i.e. pleasure and unpleasure/aversion. The generation of these emotional reactions in turn influences the organism to respond so as to increase or decrease what is being experienced.

The hypothalamus, via it's rich interconnections with other limbic regions including the neocortex and frontal lobes, it able to mobilize and motivate the organism to either cease or continue to behave. Nevertheless, at the level of the hypothalamus, the emotional states elicited are very primitive, diffuse, undirected and unrefined.

The organism feels pleasure in general, or aversion/unpleasure in general. Higher order emotional reactions (e.g. desire, love, hate, etc.) require the involvement of other limbic regions as well as neocortical participation.

Emotional functioning at the level of the hypothalamus is not only quite limited and primitive, it is also largely reflexive. For example, when induced via stimulation, the moment the electrical stimulus is turned off the emotion elicited is immediately abolished. In contrast, true emotions (which require other limbic interactions) are not simply turned on or off but can last from minutes to hours to days and weeks before completely dissipating.

Nevertheless, in humans, disturbances of hypothalamic functioning (e.g. due to an irritating lesion such as tumor) can give rise to seemingly complex, higher order behavioral-emotional reactions, such as pathological laughter and crying which occurs uncontrollably. However, in some cases when patients are questioned, they may deny having any feelings which correspond to the emotion displayed (Davison & Kelman, 1939; Ironside, 1956; Martin, 1950). In part, these reactions are sometimes due to disinhibitory release of brainstem structures involved in respiration, whereas in other instances the resulting behavior is caused by hypothalamic triggering of other limbic nuclei (Siegel et al., 2010).

UNCONTROLLED LAUGHTER

Pathological laughter has frequently been reported to occur with hypophyseal and midline tumors involving the hypothalamus, aneurysm in this vicinity, hemorrhage, astrocytoma or papilloma of the 3rd ventricle (resulting in hypothalamic compression), as well as surgical manipulation of this nucleus (Davison & Kelman, 1939; Dott, 1938; Foerster & Gabel, 1933; Martin, 1950; Money & Hosta, 2007; Ironside, 1956; List et al, 1958).

For example, Martin (1950, p.455) describes a man who while "attending his mother's funeral was seized at the grave side with an attack of uncontrollable laughter which embarrassed and distressed him considerably." Although this particular attack dissipated, it was soon accompanied by several further fits of laughter and he died soon thereafter. Post-mortem a large ruptured aneurysm was found, compressing the mammillary bodies and hypothalamus.

In a similar case (Anderson, 1936; Cited by Martin, 1950), a patient literally died laughing following the eruption of the posterior communicating artery which resulted in compression (via hemorrhage) of the hypothalamus. "She was shaken by laughter and could not stop: short expirations followed each other in spasms, without the patient being able to make an adequate inspiration of air, she became cyanosed and nothing could stop the spasm of laughter which eventually became noiseless and little more than a grimace. After 24 hours of profound coma she died."

Because laughter in these instances has not been accompanied by corresponding feeling states, this pseudo-emotional condition has been referred to as "sham mirth" (Martin, 1950). However, in some cases, abnormal stimulation in this region (such as due to compression effects from neoplasm) has triggered corresponding emotions and behaviors -- presumably due to activation of other limbic nuclei.

For example, laughter has been noted to occur with hilarious or obscene speech--usually as a prelude to stupor or death--in cases where tumor has infiltrated the hypothalamus (Ironside, 1956). In several instances it has been reported by one group of neurosurgeons (Foerster & Gagel, 1933) that while swabbing the blood from the floor of the 3rd ventricle, patients "became lively, talkative, joking, and whistling each time the infundibular region of the hypothalamus was manipulated." In one case, the patient became excited and began to sing.

HYPOTHALAMIC RAGE

Stimulation of the lateral hypothalamus can induce extremes in emotionality, including intense attacks of rage accompanied by biting and attack upon any moving object (Flynn et al. 1971; Gunne & Lewander, 1966; Wasman & Flynn, 1962). If this nucleus is destroyed, aggressive and attack behavior is abolished (Karli & Vergness, 1969). Hence, the lateral hypothalamus is responsible for rage and aggressive behavior.

As noted, the lateral maintains an oppositional relationship with the medial hypothalamus. Hence, stimulation of the medial region counters the lateral area such that rage reactions are reduced or eliminated (Ingram, 1952; Wheately, 1944), whereas if the medial is destroyed there results lateral hypothalamic release and the triggering of extreme savagery.

In man, inflammation, neoplasm, and compression of the hypothalamus have also been noted to give rise to rage attacks (Pilleri & Poeck, 1965), and surgical manipulations or tumors within the hypothalamus have been observed to elicit manic and rage-like outbursts (Alpers, 1940). These appear to be release phenomenon, however. That is, rage, attack, aggressive, and related behaviors associated with the hypothalamus appears to be under the inhibitory influence of higher order limbic nuclei such as the amygdala and septum (Siegel & Skog, 1970). When the controlling pathways between these areas are damaged (i.e. disconnection) sometimes these behaviors are elicited.

For example, Pilleri and Poeck (1965) described a man with severe damage throughout the cerebrum including the amygdala, hippocampus, cingulate, but with complete sparing of the hypothalamus who continually reacted with howling, growling, and baring of teeth in response to noise, a slight touch, or if approached. Hence, the hypothalamus being released responds reflexively in an aggressive-like non-specific manner to any stimulus. Lesions of the frontal-hypothalamic pathways have been noted to result in severe rage reactions as well (Fulton & Ingraham, 1929; Kennard, 1945).

Nevertheless, like "sham mirth", rage reactions elicited in response to direct electrical activation of the hypothalamus immediately and completely dissipate when the stimulation is removed. As such, these outbursts have been referred to as "sham rage".

CIRCADIAN RHYTHM GENERATION & SEASONAL AFFECTIVE DISORDER

During the initial stages of cerebral evolution, the dorsal hypothalamus (like the dorsal thalamus, dorsal hippocampus, dorsal midbrain) was fashioned, at least in part, from photosensitive cells located in the anterior head region. Given the daily and seasonal changes in light vs darkness, nuclei in the midbrain-pons, and in the hypothalamus, became sensitive to and capable of generating rhythmic hormonal, neurotransmitter, and motoric activities. It is the hypothalamus, however, the suprachiasmatic nucleus (SCN) in particular, which appears to be the "master clock" for the generation of circadian rhythms which have a period length of 24 hours (Aronson et al. 1993; Morin 2014).

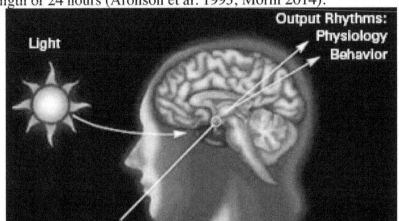

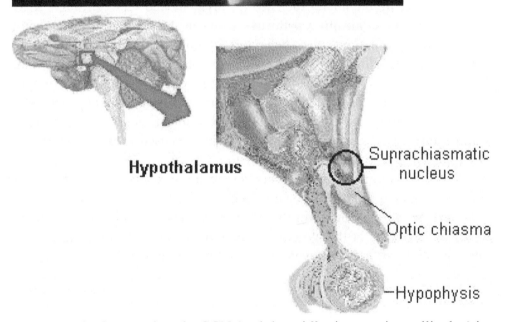

In humans and other species, the SCN (and the midbrain superior colliculus) is a direct recipient of retinal axons. It also receives indirect visual projections from the lateral geniculate nucleus of the thalamus (see Morin 2014). In this regard, the visual system appears to act to synchronize the SCN (and probably the midbrain-pons) to function in accordance with seasonal and day to day variations in the light/dark ratio. However, the SCN does not "see" per se, nor can it detect visual features, as its main concern is adjusting mood, and activity in regard to light intensity as related to rhythm generation.

There is thus some evidence which suggests that when the SCN of the hypothalamus is deprived of (or unable to effectively respond to) sufficient light, although rhythm generation is not grossly effected (Morin 2014), individuals may become depressed; a condition referred to as Seasonal Affective Disorder (SAD). That is, the hypothalamus (and midbrain-pons) appear to decrease those hormonal and neurochemical activities normally associated with activation and high (daytime) activity thus resulting in depression.

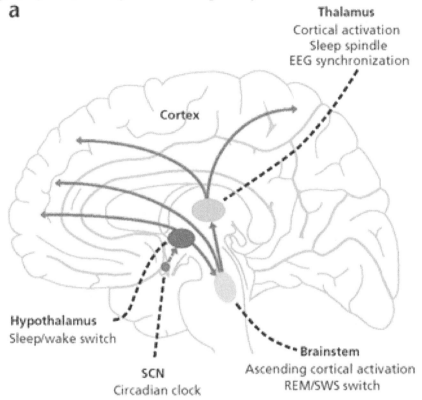

For example, the hypothalamic-pituitary axis secretes melatonin in phase with the circadian rhythm. Phase-delayed rhythms in plasma melatonin secretion have been repeatedly noted in most studies of individuals with SADs (Wirz-Justice et al. 1993). However, with light therapy, not only is the depression relieved but the melatonin secretions return to normal. This is significant for melatonin is derived from tryptophan via serotonin and low serotonin levels have been directly linked to depression (e.g. Van Pragg 1982).

There is some evidence which suggests that the hypothalamus (and the midbrain) may act to regulate serotonin release within the brainstem (Chaouloff 1993; however, see Morin 2014), which in turn may explain why serotonin levels rhythmically fluctuate (e.g. such as during the sleep cycle), or become abnormal when denied sufficient light; i.e. the production of serotonin by the raphe nucleus (in the pons) is abnormally effected.

On the other hand, numerous studies have reported that SADs and major

A. Serotonin Pathways in the Brain

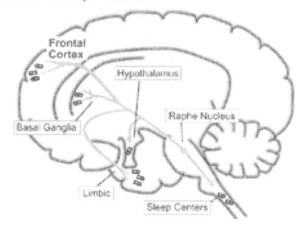

B. Norepinephrine Pathways in the Brain

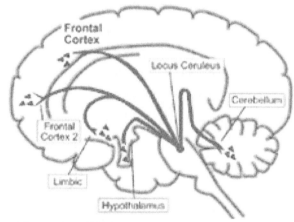

C. Symptoms Associated With
Serotonin and Norepinephrine Pathways

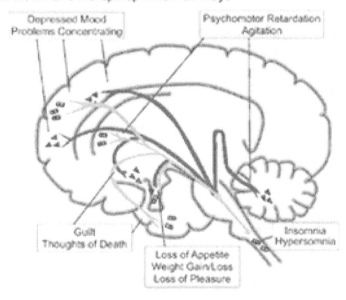

depression occurs most often during the Spring and not the winter, and is not influenced by latitude (e.g. Margnusson & Stefansson 1993; Wirz-Justice et al. 1993). There is also some suggestion that abnormal temperature perception, or aging within the SCN may be responsible for the genesis of SADs and related depressive disorders. For example, age related changes in the SCN have been noted to adversely effect circadian rhythm generation as well as metabolic and peptide activity (Aronson et al. 1993). In consequence, rest vs active cycles also become abnormal, with reductions in arousal and activity; i.e. the patient becomes depressed.

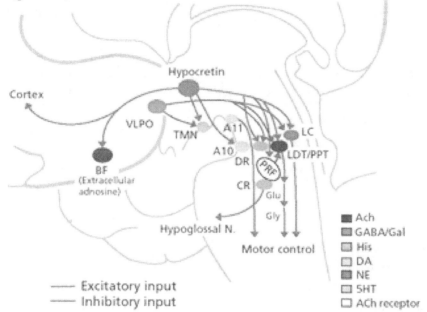

It is also possible, however, that although light therapy can assist in alleviating depressive symptoms associated with SADs, that the deregulation of the SCN (and melatonin/serotonin) might be unrelated to light, temperature, or aging, but may be a consequence of stress on the hypothalamus (Chauloff 1993) or other abnormalities involving this structure (Vandewalle et al., 2011). For example, the hypothalamic-pituitary axis is tightly linked with and in fact mediates stress induced alterations in serotonin; as well as norepinephrine (Swann et al. 2014) which has also been repeatedly implicated in the genesis of depression.

THE HYPOTHALAMUS-PITUITARY-ADRENAL AXIS

The hypothalamic, pituitary, adrenal system (HPA) is critically involved in the adaptation to stressful changes in the external or internal environment (Bao & Swaab, 2010; Foley & Kirschbaum 2010; Kudielka & Wust, 2010). For example, in response to fear, anger, anxiety, disappointment, and even hope, the hypothalamus begins to release corticotropin releasing factor (CRF) which

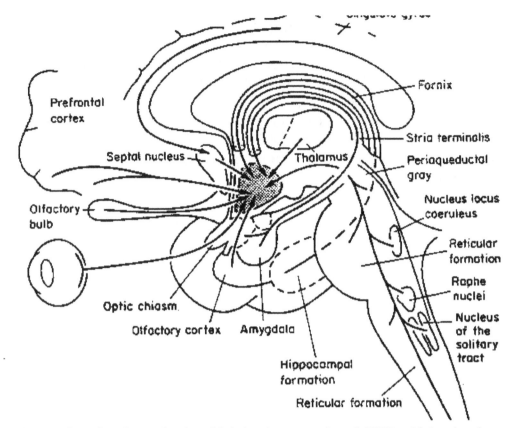

activates the adenohypophysis which begins secreting ACTH which stimulates the adrenal cortex which secretes cortisol (Fink, 2016).

These events in turn appear to be under the modulating influences of norepinephrine. That is, as stress increases, NE levels decrease, which triggers the activation of the HPA axis. As is well known, low levels of NE are associated with depression.

Normally, cortisol secretion is subject to the tonic influences of NE; whereas cortisol can indirectly reduce NE synthesis. Thus a feedback system is maintained via the interaction of these substances (in conjunction with ACTH). Moreover, cortisol and NE levels fluctuate in reverse, and thus maintain a reciprocal relationship with the circadian rhythm; i.e. in oppositional fashion they increase and then decrease throughout the day and evening.

Among certain subgroups suffering from depression, it appears that this entire feedback regulatory system and thus the HPA axis is disrupted ((Bao & Swaab, 2010; Carrol et al. 1976; Sachar et al. 1973). This results in the hyper secretion of ACTH and cortisol with a corresponding decrease in NE; which results in NE induced depression. It was these findings which led to the development of the Dexamethasone suppression test over 25 years ago.

Via the administration of Dexamethasone (a synthetic corticosteroid) it was determined that many depressed individuals have excess cortisol, and an increased frequency of cortisol secretory episodes (Carrol et al. 1976; Sachar et al. 1973;

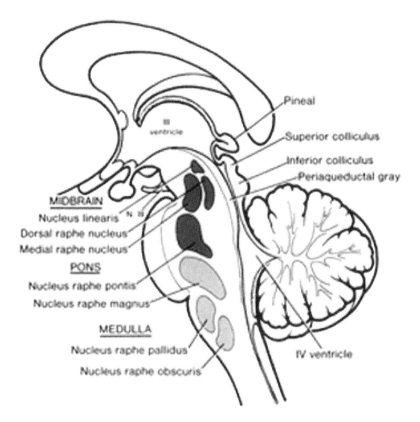

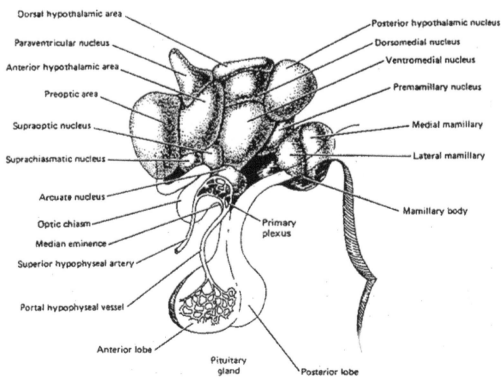

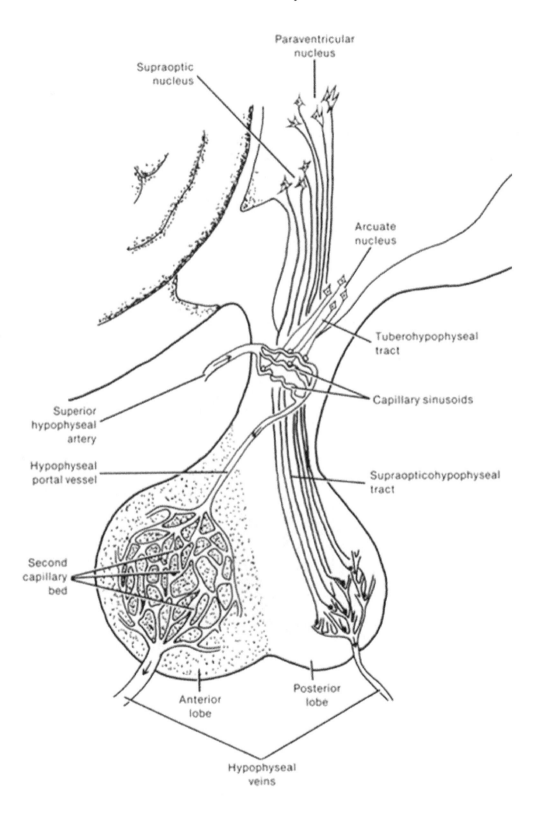

Swann et al. 2014). Moreover, those who demonstrate excess cortisol were found to respond to NE potentiating agents, whereas those who were depressed but with normal cortisol, responded best to serotonin potentiating compounds (Van Pragg 1982).

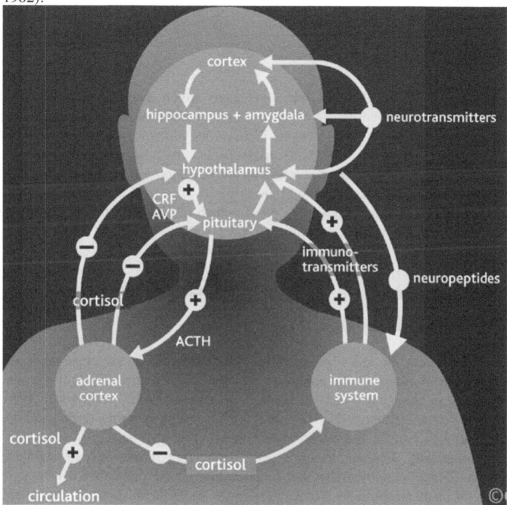

It is also noteworthy that dexamethasone non suppression rates are increased in mania; specifically "mixed manic" states which consist of lability, grandiosity, and lability superimposed over depression (Swann et al. 2014). These "mixed manic" individuals also display elevated NE levels but respond poorly to lithium and show higher levels of cortisol during the depressed phase of their illness (Swann et al. 2014).

As noted, the hypothalamus may greatly influence circadian activities within the midbrain and pons, and thus the rhythmical secretion of various neurotransmitters. For example, corticotropin-releasing factor acts directly on the locus coeruleus (Valentino et al. 2003) which manufactures NE, and on the raphe thereby influencing serotonin release. These findings suggest a disturbance in circadian or rhythmical control of hypothalamic and midbrain-pontine activity can give rise to depression, or mixed mania in some individuals; women in particular.

Lateralization

Although scant, there is some evidence which suggests that the right hypothalamus may be more heavily involved in the control of neuroendocrine functioning, particularly in females. Females are also far more likely to suffer from depression and from SADs. Moreover, right cerebral dysfunction can reduce NE levels in both the right and left hemisphere (Robinson 1979). Greater right hypothalamic concentration of substances such as LHRH (lutetinizing hormone) has also been reported (Gerendai, 1984), which in turn is a "female" hormone involved in lactation and pregnancy.

PSYCHIC MANIFESTATIONS OF HYPOTHALAMIC ACTIVITY: THE ID

Phylogenetically and from an evolutionary perspective, the appearance and development of the hypothalamus predates the differentiation of all other limbic nuclei, e.g., amygdala, septal nucleus, hippocampus (Andy & Stephan, 1961; Brown, 2003; Herrick, 1925; Humphrey, 1972). It constitutes the most primitive, archaic, reflexive, and purely biological aspect of the psyche.

Biologically the hypothalamus serves the body tissues by attempting to maintain internal homeostasis and by providing for the immediate discharge of tensions in an almost reflexive manner. Hence, as based on studies of lateral and medial hypothalamic functioning, it appears to act reflexively, in an almost on/off manner so as to seek or maintain the experience of pleasure and escape or avoid unpleasant, noxious conditions.

Emotions elicited by the hypothalamus are largely undirected, short-lived, being triggered reflexively and without concern or understanding regarding consequences; that is, unless chronically stressed or aroused. Nevertheless, direct contact with the real world is quite limited and almost entirely indirect as the hypothalamus is largely concerned with the internal environment of the organism. Although it receives and responds to light, it cannot "see." It has no sense of morals, danger, values, logic, etc., and cannot feel or express love or hate. Although quite powerful, hypothalamic emotions are largely undifferentiated, consisting of feelings such as pleasure, unpleasure, aversion, rage, hunger, thirst, etc.

As the hypothalamus is concerned with the internal environment much of it's activity occurs outside conscious-awareness. Moreover, being involved in maintaining internal homeostasis, via, for example, it's ability to reward or punish the organism with feelings of pleasure or aversion, it tends to serve what Freud (1911) has described as the pleasure principle.

THE PLEASURE PRINCIPLE

The lateral and medial nuclei exert counterbalancing influences which serve to modulate activity occurring in the other. As described by Freud (1911), the pleasure principal not only serves to maximize pleasant experiences, but acts to keep the psyche as a whole free from high levels of excitation (be they pleasurable or unpleasant).

Like the hypothalamus, the pleasure principle is present from birth and for some time thereafter the search for pleasure is manifested in an unrestricted manner and with a great deal of intensity as there are no oppositional forces (except those between the lateral and medial regions) to counter it's strivings. Indeed, higher order limbic nuclei have yet to mature.

Functionally isolated, the hypothalamus at birth has no way of reducing tension or mobilizing the organism for any form of effective action. It is helpless. When tensions associated with immediate needs (e.g. hunger or thirst) become unpleasant the only response available to the hypothalamus is to cry and make rage-like vocalizations. When satiated, the hypothalamus can only respond with a feeling state suggesting pleasure or at least quiescence. Indeed, as is well known, for the first few months of life the infants awareness largely consists of a very restricted matrix involving tactile, visceral (hunger) and kinesthetic sensations, where emotionally the infant is capable of screaming, crying, or demonstrating very rudimentary features of pleasure, i.e. an attitude of acceptance of quiescence (Bremner & Slater 2003; McGraw, 1969; Milner, 2007; Piaget, 1952; Snow & McGaha 2002; Spitz & Wolf, 1946; Tronic, E. (2007).

It is only with the further differentiation and maturation of higher order limbic nuclei (e.g. amygdala, septal nucleus, hippocampus) that the infant begins to achieve some awareness of external reality and begins to form memories as well as differentiate and associate externally occurring events and individuals.

AMYGDALA

In contrast to the primitive hypothalamus, the more recently developed amygdala (the "almond") is preeminent in the control and mediation of all higher order emotional and motivational activities. Via it's rich interconnections with various neocortical and subcortical regions, amygdaloid neurons are able to monitor and abstract from the sensory array stimuli that are of motivational significance to the organism (Blackford et al. 2009; Gaffan 1992; Gloor 1997; LeDoux 1992; Morris et al., 1996; Pessoa & Adolphs 2010; Rolls 1992; Rule et al., 2010; Steklis & Kling, 2005; Kling & Brothers 1992; Whalen & Phelps 2009). This includes the ability to discern and express even subtle social-emotional nuances such as friendliness, fear, love, affection, distrust, anger, etc., and at a more basic level, determine if something might be good to eat (Nitschke et al., 2009; Pape & Pare 2010; Pessoa & Adolphs 2010; Zhang et al., 2011).

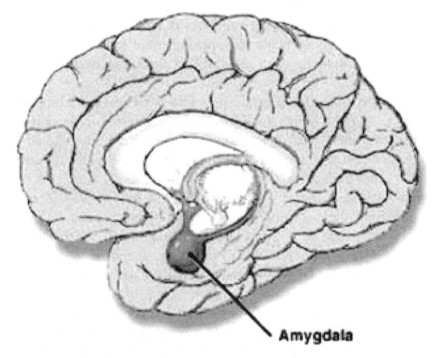

Amygdala

In fact, amygdaloid neurons respond selectively to the flavor of certain preferred foods, as well as to the sight or sound of something that might be especially desirable to eat (Fukuda et al. 1987; Gaffan et al. 1992; O'Keefe & Bouma, 1969; Ono et al. 1980; Ono & Nishijo, 1992) including even the sight of drugs that induce extreme pleasure. For example, it has been shown, using positron emission tomography, that detoxified cocaine users not only respond to a cocaine video with cocaine craving, but with increased amygdala (and anterior cingulate) activity (Childress, et al., 2016).

Belying its involvement in emotion, including the pleasure associated with cocaine usage, is the unique chemical anatomy of the amygdala, which is rich in a variety of neuropetides including enkephalins and beta-endorphins as well as opiate receptors (Atweh & Kuhar, 1977; Fallon & Ciofi, 1992; Uhl et al. 2014).

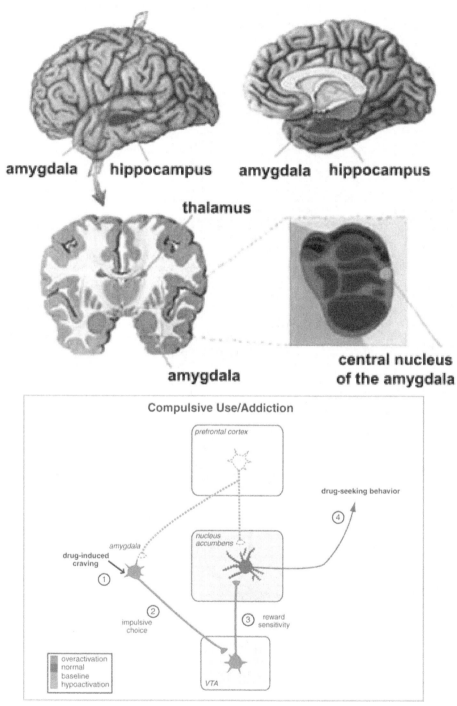

In fact, of all brain regions, the greatest concentration of opiate receptors is found within the human amygdala. Other chemical systems include lutenizing hormone, vasopressin, somatostatin, and corticotropin releasing factor (Fallon & Ciofi, 1992) --indications of its involvement in stress and sexuality, especially female sexuality. The primate amygdala is sexually differentiated with male and female patterns of dendritic organization and steroid activity (Bubenik & Brown, 1973; Nishizuka & Arai, 1981; Simerly, 1990).

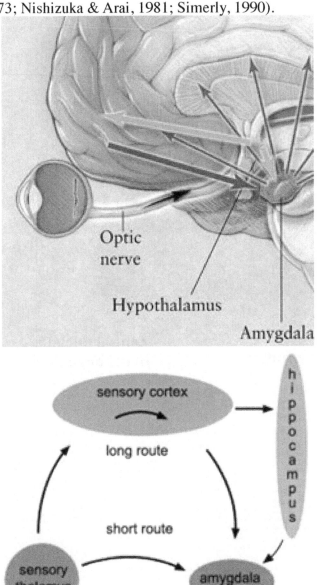

The amygdala is exceedingly responsive to social and emotional stimuli as conveyed vocally, through touch, sight, and via the expressions of the face (Gloor, 1992; Halgren, 1992; Kling & Brothers 1992; Morris et al., 1996; N'Diaye et al., (2009; Rolls, 1984, 1992; Rule et al., 2010). In fact, the amygdala, as well as the overlying (and partly coextensive) temporal lobe, contains neurons which respond selectively to smiles and to the eyes, and which can differentiate between male and female faces and the emotions they convey (Hasselmo et al., 1989, Heit et al., 1988; Kawashima, et al., 2016; Rolls, 1984). For example, the left amygdala acts to discriminate the direction of another person's gaze, whereas the right amygdala becomes activated while making eye-to-eye contact (Kawashima, et al., 2016).

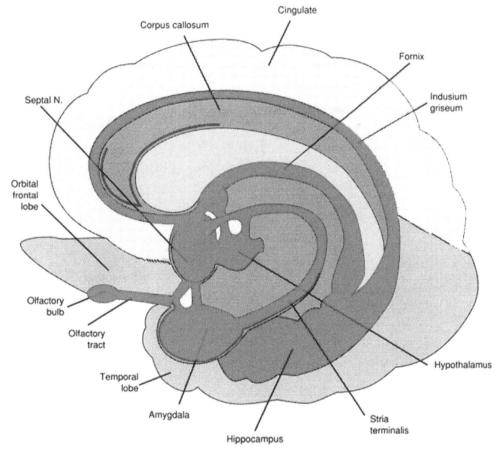

Moreover, the normal human amygdala typically responds to frightened faces by altering its activity (Morris et al., 1996), whereas injury to the amygdala disrupts the ability to recognize faces (Young, Aggleton, & Hellawell,1995). With bilateral destruction, emotional speech production and the capacity to respond appropriately to social emotionally stimuli is abolished (Lilly, Cummings, Benson, & Frankel, 2003; LeDoux, 1996; Marlowe, Mancall, Thomas,2015; Scott et al., 1997; Terzian & Ore, 1955).

Single amygdaloid neurons receive a considerable degree of topographic input, and are predominantly polymodal, responding to a variety of stimuli from different modalities simultaneously (Amaral et al. 1992; O'Keefe & Bouma, 1969; Ono & Nishijo, 1992; Perryman et al. 1987; Rolls 1992; Sawa & Delgado, 1963; Schutze et al. 1987; Turner et al. 1980; Van Hoesen, 1981; Whalen & Phelps

2009). The amygdala is also very sensitive to somesthetic input and physical contact such that even a slight touch in a very circumscribed area of the body can produce amygdaloid excitation. Overall, because emotional, motivational, and multimodal assimilation of various sensory impressions occurs in this region, it is also involved in attention, learning, and memory (Gloor, 1997; Halgren, 1992; Kensinger et al., 2011; Lang et al., 2009; Whalen & Phelps 2009).

Moreover, through the massive interconnections maintained with the lateral and medial (ventromedial) hypothalamus, the amygdala is able to act directly on this structure, driving the hypothalamus, so to speak, and thus tapping into its emotional reservoir so that its ends may be met. Indeed, it is able to modulate hypothalamic activity through inhibitory and excitatory projections to this structure (Dreifuss, et al., 1968).

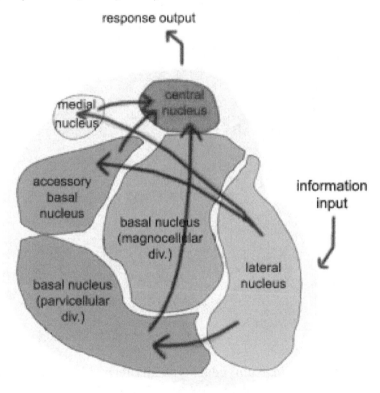

AMYGDALA

Direct stimulation of the basolateral amygdala and the ventral amydalofugal pathway excites the principle neurons of the medial hypothalamus (Dreifuss, et al., 1968). By contrast, stimulation of the ventro-medial amygdala and the stria terminalis pathway, inhibits these same hypothalamic neurons (Dreifuss, et al., 1968). Hence, whereas the lateral amygdala exerts excitatory influences on the hypothalamus, the medial amygdala exerts inhibitory influences, and can thus control, or at least exert excitatory/inhibitory and thus modulatory influences on

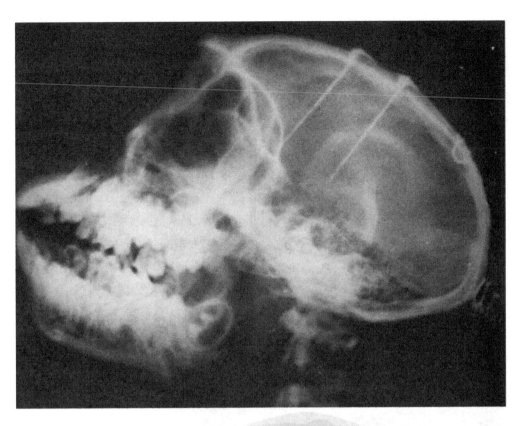

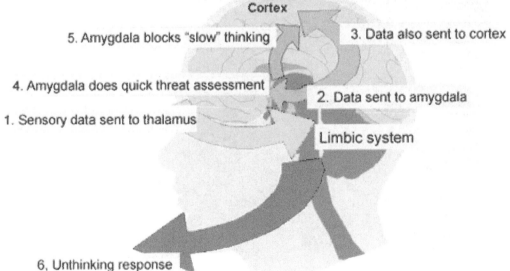

Cortex

5. Amygdala blocks "slow" thinking

3. Data also sent to cortex

4. Amygdala does quick threat assessment

2. Data sent to amygdala

1. Sensory data sent to thalamus

Limbic system

6. Unthinking response

hunger, thirst, sexual arousal, rage, etc., as well as hormonal, endocrine, and other functions associated with the hypothalamic nucleus (Gloor, 1997). Indeed, the amygdala can be likened to the chief executive of the limbic system and weilds enormous power via its control over the hypothalamus.

For example, in the cat and monkey, stimulation of the border area between the lateral and medial hypothalamus can trigger aggressive defensive reactions (De vito & Smith, 1982; Hess, 1949). As indicated by radioactive tracers, both the lateral and medial amygdala projection to this area (De vito & Smith, 1982). And, when the amygdala is electrically activated, the hypothalamus becomes activated (Dreifuss, et al., 1968), and defensive and aggressive reactions can be triggered.

However, this system is also interactional, especially in regard to sexual activity, fear, anger, hunger, and stress. For example, the hypothalamus can stimulate the amygdala which may then survey the environment so that internal needs may be met, and/or they may act in concert regarding sexual behavior, the stress response, and so on.

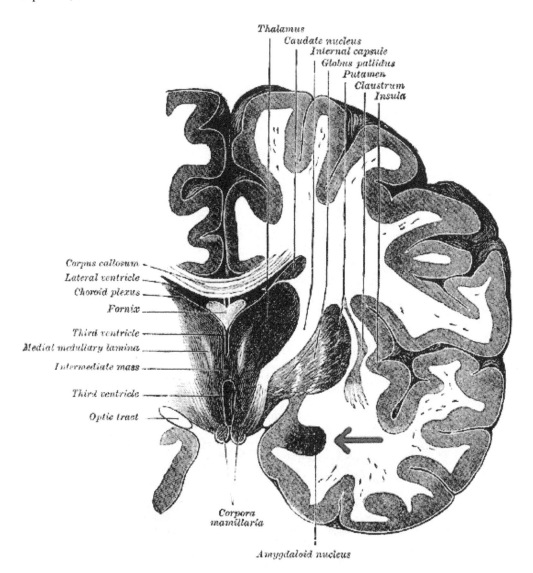

Thalamus
Caudate nucleus
Internal capsule
Globus pallidus
Putamen
Claustrum
Insula

Corpus callosum
Lateral ventricle
Choroid plexus
Fornix
Third ventricle
Medial medullary lamina
Intermediate mass
Third ventricle
Optic tract
Corpora mamillaria
Amygdaloid nucleus

AMYGDALA STRUCTURAL FUNCTIONAL ORGANIZATION: OVERVIEW

The amygdala is buried within the depths of the anterior-inferior temporal lobe and consists of several major nuclear groups including what has been referred to as the "extended amygdala." These include the cortical-medial, central, paralaminar, lateral, basal, and accessory basal nucleus (Amaral et al., 1992; Stephan & Andy, 1977; Whalen & Phelps,2009). Different authors propose different divisions and link them differently. For example, Stephan and Andy (1977) assign the cortical division to the basolateral amygdala, and the central division to the medial division. Price et al., (1977) subdivided the amygdala into basolateral, corticomedial and central amygdaloid nuclei. Others propose yet different schemes.

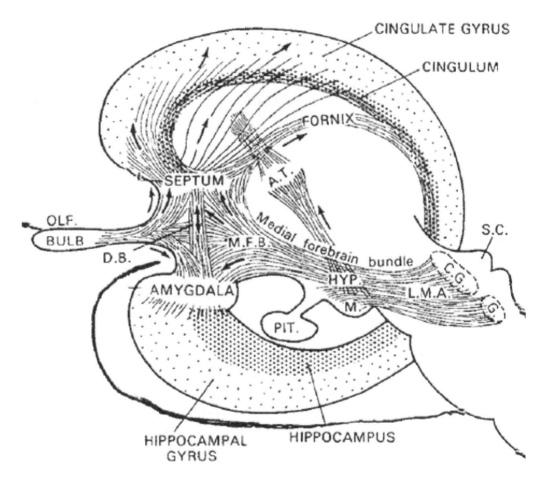

For our purposes we will primarily focus on the "medial" and the basolateral subdivisions. The phylogenetically ancient medial group (or cortico-medial amygdala) is involved in olfaction, sexual, and motor activity (via its interconnections with the striatum), and the relatively newer basolateral division (lateral amygdala) is most fully developed in primates and humans (Amaral et al. 1992; Herrick, 1925; Humphrey, 1972; McDonald 1992; Stephan & Andy, 1977). Of its various subdivisions, the basolateral amygdala is the most "cortex-like. However, being allocortex it contains three layers (vs 6 for the neocortex) with layer 2 containing pyramidal neurons which rely on excitatory neurotransmitters, e.g., glutamate--whereas the local-circuit (interneurons) rely on the inhibitory transmitters, e.g., GABA (Fallon & Ciofi, 1992).

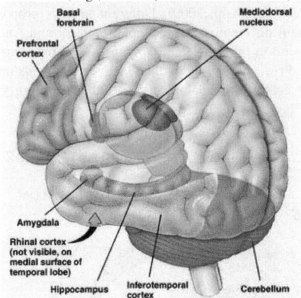

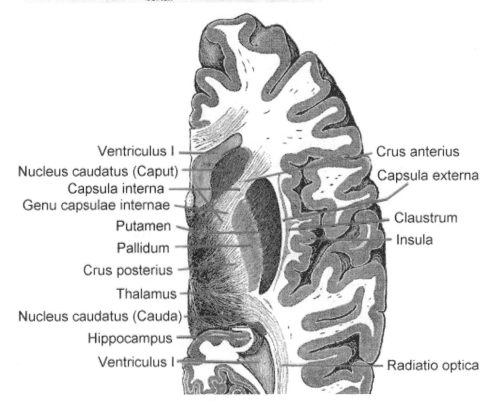

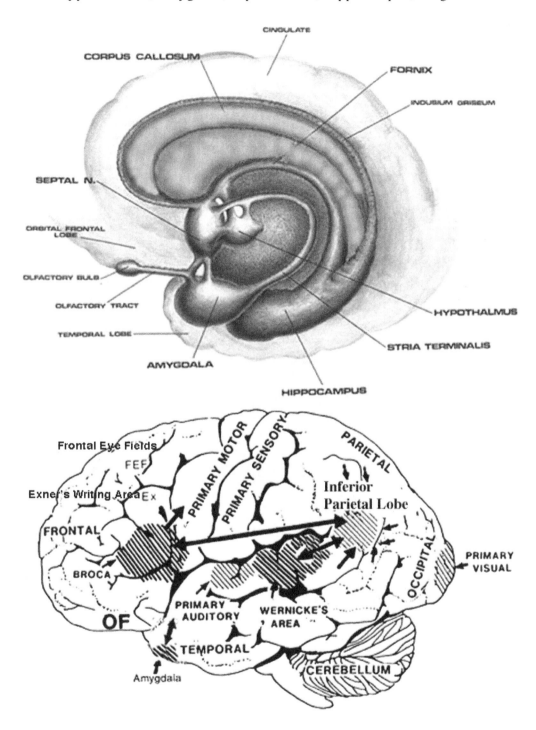

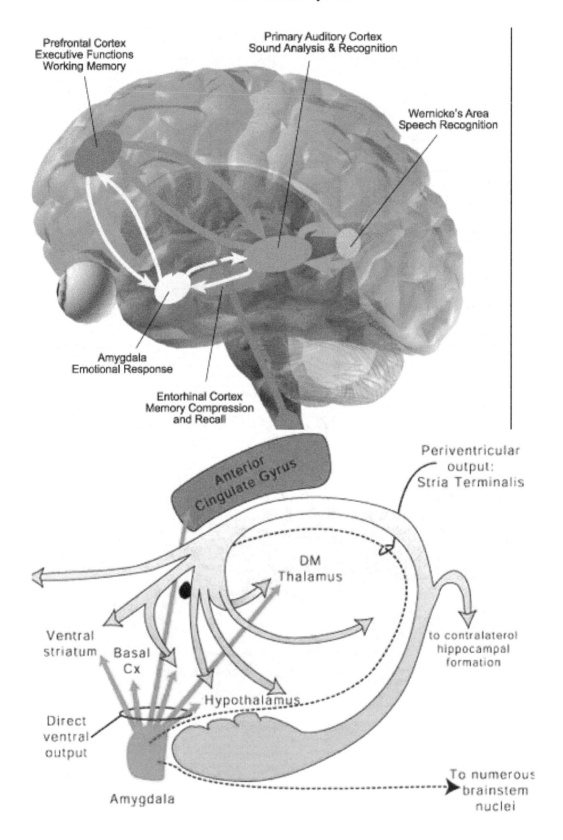

The lateral amygdala utilizes the ventral amygdalofugal pathway and less so the stria terminalis to influence the hypothalamus. The lateral amygdala also relies on the medial forebrain bundle which is the pathway subserving the pleasure circuit (Olds & Forbes, 1981). By contrast, the medial amygdala relies on the stria terminalis, and less so the amygdalofugal pathway to influences the hypothalamus. Through these pathways, these different subdivisions of the amygdala can act to modulate activity in the hypothalamus, septal nuclei, and other subcortical structures (Amaral et al. 1992; Stephan & Andy, 1977; Whalen & Phelps, 2009).

Evolution & Embryology

In humans, the right amygdala is also larger than the left amygdala, with the basolateral portion contributing to most of this asymmetry (Murphy et al., 1987). Moreover, over the course of evolution, and in the transition from amphibians to reptiles, to mammals and then humans, the basolateral amygdala appears to have grown the most in size as compared to other amygdaloid nuclei (Stephan & Andy, 1977)--that is, when considered only in regard to its subtemporal dimensions. However, it also appears that the medial amygdala may have contributed to the evolution of the piriform cortex, and then the evolution of the 4 to 5 layered mesocortex, which when layered upon the 3-layered allocortical piriform cortex, gave rise to the neocortex of the temporal lobe. Moreover, it appears that the medial group was broken up over the course of evolution such that structures such as the claustrum (Gilles et al., 2003), became separated and is now situated beneath the auditory cortex of the superior temporal lobe. Indeed, the claustrum which is very cortical in organization, may well act as an interface between the auditory cortex and the amygdala, processing and relaying auditory impulses to and fro, and may have, in addition to the medial amygdala, contributed to the evolution of the auditory cortex.

The amygdala, therefore, has definitely increased in size over the course of evolution (Stephan & Andy, 1977), and has become increasingly cortical, has contributed to the evolution of mesocortex and neocortex (which is thus a cortical extension of the neocortex, maintaining extensive interconnections). In addition, the right amygdala is larger than the left (Murphy et al., 1987) which in turn may contribute to right hemisphere dominance for emotion.

Intrinsic & Extrinsic Organization: The Flow of Information

Like the lateral and medial hypothalamus, the medial and basolateral (hereafter referred to as the lateral) amygdaloid nuclei subserve different functions and maintain different anatomical interconnections (Amaral et al., 1992; Stephan & Andy, 1977; Whalen & Phelps 2009). And, they can be subdivided into additional subnuclei. As noted, they also contain pyramidal neurons which are excitatory (Rolls, 1992) and use glutamate (Fallon & Ciofi, 1992) and which project throughout the neocortex as well as to the hippocampus (Whalen & Phelps 2009).

Local circuit neurons are mostly stellate-like and chandelier cells, which account for about 30% of the amygdala's neurons and which use the inhibitory transmitter GABA (Fallon & Ciofi, 1992). Considered rather broadly and simplistically, these local circuit neurons are organized in such a fashion that they appear to project information from the lateral to the basal amygdala, and from the lateral basal to the medial and central amygdala which transmits, via pyramid and local-circuit neurons to the uncus, piriform cortex, medial temporal cortex, entorhinal cortex, anterior hippocampus, and via pyramidal neurons to the striatum, the septal nuclei, hypothalamus, cingulate, medial dorsal nucleus of the thalamus, brainstem, and throughout the frontal and temporal lobes. However, the lateral amygdala also projects to the septal nuclei, hypothalamus, corpus striatum, dorsal medial thalamus, brainstem, and throughout the neocortex via pyramidal axons (Amaral et al, 1992).

It appears that much of the input from the neocortex is directed at the lateral amygdala (the exception being auditory cortex which also projects to the medial amygdala). Hence, in certain respects, at least at the level of the neocortex, it appears that there is an almost circular stream of activity, from lateral/basal to medial/central to neocortex to lateral/basal. However, subcortically, both the lateral and medial project to many of the same exact structures, often providing counterbalancing excitatory/inhibitory influences.

Moreover, the amygdala receives significant projections directly from the olfactory bulb. In act, "the olfactory system is the only sensory system in which first- and second-order central sensory neurons project directly to the amygdala" (Goor, 1997). Moreover, it receives projections from the gustatory system. Smell and taste thus converge in the amygdala, which may explain why some patients with temporal lobe epilepsy experience terrible odors and tastes as part of the aura which announces the onset of a seizure.

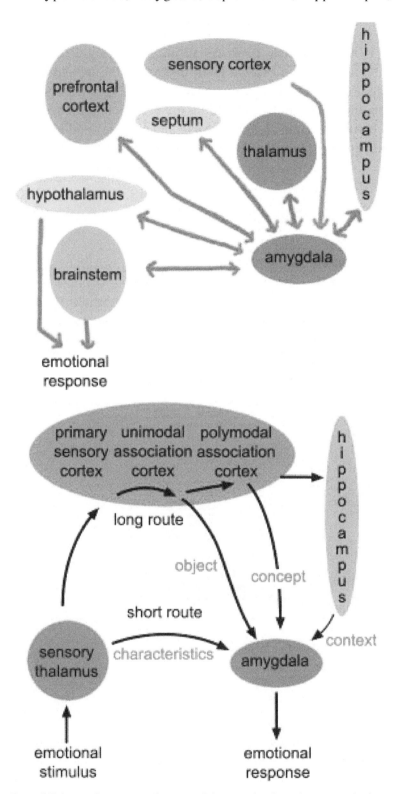

In addition, the secondary and in particular the association and multi-modal assimilation areas, including the orbital frontal lobe, project directly to the amygdala (Amaral et al, 1992; Carlsen et al. 1982; Gloor, 1955; Krettek & Price, 2014; McDonald 1992; Russchen, 1982; Swanson & Cowan, 1979; Stephan & Andy, 1977). In addition, as is evident from dissecting the human brain, the amygdala maintains significant reciprocal connections with the primary auditory area and Wernicke's area--and similar projections are evident in primates (Amaral et al., 1992). Hence, this structure receives simple and complex auditory, as well as fully formed perceptions from the neocortex which feeds the amygdala this information which it then analyzes for social, sexual, gustatory, and emotional significance.

The Amygdala-Striatum

Embryologically, the medial amygdala is the first portion of the basal ganglia (limbic) striatal complex to appear during development, being formed via neuroblast migration from the epithelium of the lateral ventricle (Humphrey, 1972). Specifically, around the sixth week of fetal development immature neuroblasts migrate in massive numbers from the ventricular lining, and congregate in the more caudal portion of the emerging forebrain, thus forming an arc shaped "striatal ridge" from which the primordial amygdala and striatum will emerge (Gilles et al., 2003; Humphrey, 1968).

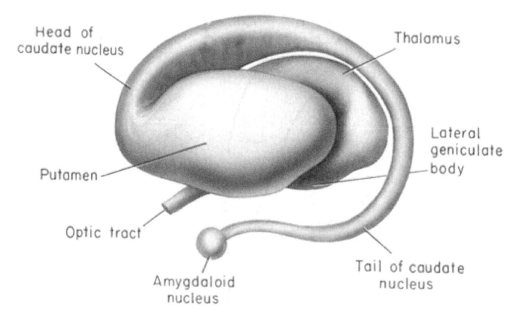

Approximately one week after the formation of the amygdala, this primordial amygdala-striatum begins to differentiate and balloon outward to also create the striatum. That is, both the striatum and amygdala are derived from the arc shaped "striatal ridge," the caudal portion giving rise to the primordial amgydala at about the 6th week of gestation, and the basal portion later giving rise to the primordial striatum which initially overlies and is contiguous with the amygdala (Gilles et al., 2003; Humphrey, 1968).

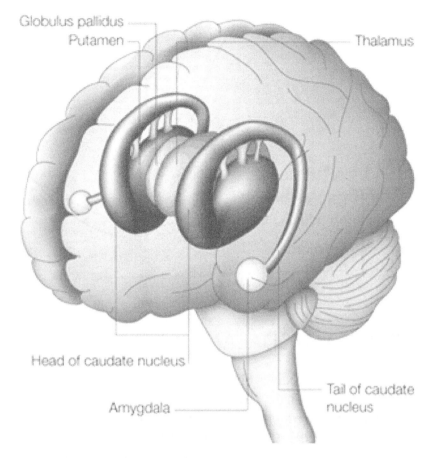

Thus initially these structures are contiguous. However, over the ensuing weeks, these structures are pushed apart as the forebrain and its interconnections form. However, although they are pushed apart and may even break up into semi-separate islands (or rather, peninsulas) the amgydala maintains connections with what is referred to as the "extended amygdala," i.e., the limbic striatum (Heimer & Alheid, 1991) and through what is called the "tail of the caudate" maintains massive interconnections with the corpus striatum.

Specifically, the tail of the caudate nucleus (as it circles in an arc from the frontal to temporal lobe) terminates and merges with the medial and in particular, the lateral amygdala. Hence, the lateral amygdala has also been referred to the "striatum limitans, and the "striatum accessorium" (Gloor, 1997).

By contrast, the medial amygdala (or rather, the central division of the medial amygdala, central-medial amygdala) extends almost imperceptibly around the fundus of the entorhinal sulcus, and merges with the substantia innominata of the limbic striatum. The amygdala, therefore, is in fact part of the basal ganglia and is heavily involved in motivating and coordinating gross, or whole body motor activity via the striatum (Heimer & Alheid, 1991; Mogenson & Yang, 1991).

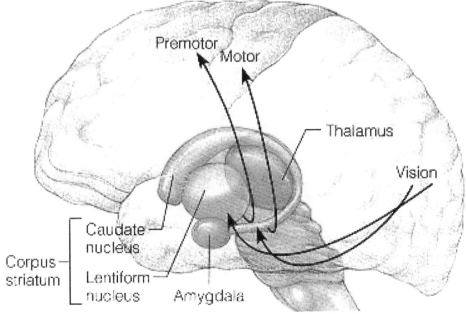

THE MEDIAL AMYGDALA

The medial amygdala receives fibers from the olfactory tract, and via a rope of fibers called the stria terminalis projects directly to and receives fibers from the medial hypothalamus (via which it exerts inhibitory influences) as well as the septal nucleus (Amaral et al, 1992; Carlsen et al. 1982; Gloor, 1955; McDonald 1992; Russchen, 1982; Swanson & Cowan, 1979). The stria terminals is significantly larger and thicker in males vs females (Allen & Gorksi 1992) which suggests that information and impulse exchange (or inhibition) between the hypothalamus and amygdala is different in men vs women. Moreover, in humans, the amygdala in general is large in males than in females, and in primates, the medial amygdala is sexually differentiated (Nishizuka & Arai, 1981; see also Simerly, 1990), such that the male amygdala contains a greater number of synaptic connections and shows different patterns of steroidal activity (Nishizuka & Arai, 1981; Simerly, 1990). In fact, the human amygdala is 16% larger in the male in total volume (Filipek, et al., 2014) whereas in male rats, the medial amygdala is 65% larger than the female amygdala and grows or shrinks in the presence of testosterone (Breedlove & Cooke, 2016).

The female medial amygdala is a principle site for uptake of the female sex hormone, estrogen, and contains a high concentration of lutenizing hormones (Stopa et al., 1991) which are important during pregnancy and nursing. In fact, the female medial amygdala fluctuates immunoreactive activity during estrus cycle, being highest during proestrus (Simerly, 1990). Moreover, the medial amygdala projects directly to the ventromedial hypothalamus and the preoptic area of the hypothalamus which, as noted above, are sexually differentiated (e.g. Allen et al., 1989; Gorski, et al., 2014; Le Vay, 1991; Raisman & Field, 1971), and which when activated produce sex specific behaviors (Hart et al., 2005; Lisk, 2007, 1971; MacLean, 1973) and, in primates, even maternal behavior (Numan, 2005). These amygdala to hypothalamic synapses are excitatory.

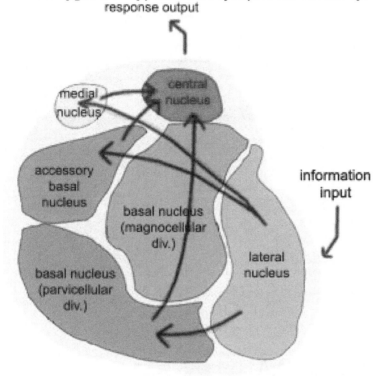

AMYGDALA

Because the medial amygdala is sexually differentiated, and through its massive connections with the hypothalamus and preoptic area, as well as the striatum which controls gross motor and limb movements, when activated, male vs female sexual behavior can be triggered. These amygdala-induced sexual behaviors include sexual posturing, penile erection and clitoral tumescence (Kling and Brothers, 1992; MacLean, 1990; Robinson and Mishkin, 1968; Stoffels et al., 1980), thrusting, sexual moaning, ejaculation, as well as ovulation, uterine contractions, lactogenetic responses, and orgasm (Backman and Rossel, 1984; Currier, Little, Suess and Andy, 1971; Freemon and Nevis,1969; Warneke, 1976; Remillard et al., 2003; Shealy and Peel, 1957).

In addition, the medial (and lateral) regions are rich in cells containing enkephalins, and opiate receptors can be found throughout the amygdala (Atweh & Kuhar, 1977; Fallon & Ciofi, 1992; Uhl et al. 2014) and the amygdala becomes exceedingly active when experiencing a craving for pleasure inducing drugs, such as cocaine (Childress et al., 2016). In this regard, the amygdala is capable of inducing extreme feelings of pleasure as well as motivating the individual to engage in pleasure-seeking behaviors such as sexual activity.

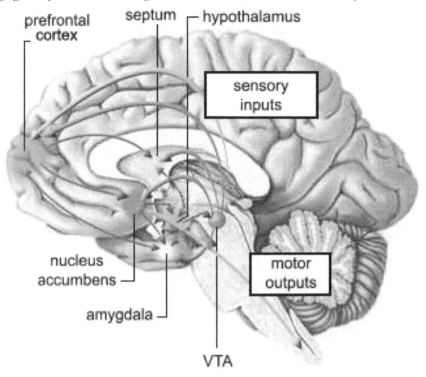

LATERAL AMYGDALA

With the evolutionary ascent of primates the lateral division of the amygdala progressively expands and differentiates. The lateral amygdala contributes fibers to the stria terminalis and gives rise to the amygdalofugal pathway via which it projects to the lateral and medial hypothalamus (upon which it exerts inhibitory and excitatory influences respectively), the dorsal medial thalamus (which is involved in memory, attention and arousal), the limbic and corpus striatum, as well as other subcortical regions including the brainstem (Aggleton et al. 1980; Amaral et al. 1992; Carlsen et al. 1982; Dreifuss et al., 1968; Gloor, 1955, 1960, 1997; Klinger & Gloor, 1960; McDonald 1992; Mehler, 1980; Russchen, 1982; Whalen & Phelps 2009). Lateral amygdala brainstem projection pathways include the dopamine producing substantia nigra, the vocalizing periaqueductal gray, the pontine tegmentum which includes and area that triggers the startle response (Amaral et al., 1992; Davis et al., 1997) as well as visceral nuclei such as those controlling blood pressure, respiration, vosodilation and constriction and so on. It also sends some fibers into the spinal cord, where they travel along with those of the pyramidal tract (Amaral et al., 1992; Whalen & Phelps 2009). It also receives fibers from the medial forebrain bundle which in turn has it's site of origin in the lateral hypothalamus (Mehler, 1980).

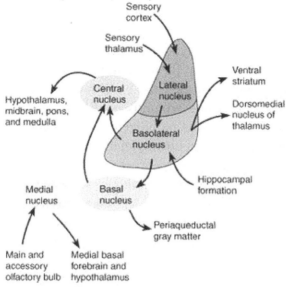

In general, whereas the medial amygdala is highly involved in motor, olfactory and sexual functioning, the lateral division is intimately involved in all aspects of emotional activity. Hence, it's rich interconnections with the lateral and medial hypothalamus, and the neocortex and those brainstem centers controlling the visceral aspects of affective-motor behavior.

The lateral amygdala maintains rich interconnections with the inferior, middle, and superior temporal lobes, as well as the insular temporal region, which in turn allows it to sample and influence the auditory, somesthetic, and visual information being received and processed in these areas, as well as scrutinize this information for motivational and emotional significance (Gloor 1992; Herzog & Van Hoesen 1976; Kling et al., 1987; Machne & Segundo, 1956; Mesulam & Mufson, 1982; O'Keefe & Bouma, 1969; Rolls 1992; Steklis & Kling, 2005; Turner et al., 1980; Van Hoesen, 1981). Gustatory and respiratory sense are also re-represented in this vicinity (Amaral et al. 1992; Fukuda et al., 1987; Maclean, 1949; Ono et al., 1980) as is the capacity to influence (via sensory analysis) food and water intake. The lateral division also maintains rich interconnections with cingulate gyrus, orbital and medial frontal lobes and the parietal cortex (Amaral et al. 1992; McDonald 1992; O'Keefe & Bouma, 1969; Pandya et al. 1973; Whalen & Phelps 2009) through which it able to influence emotional expression and receive complex somesthetic information.

The lateral amygdala is highly important in analyzing information received and transferring information back to the neocortex so that further elaboration may be carried out at the neocortical level. It is through the lateral division that emotional meaning and significance can be assigned to as well as extracted from that which is experienced.

The amygdala, overall, maintains a functionally interdependent relationship with the hypothalamus. It is able to modulate and even control rudimentary emotional forces governed by the hypothalamic nucleus. However, it also acts as the behest of hypothalamically induced drives. For example, if certain nutritional requirements need to be meet, the hypothalamus signals the amygdala which then surveys the external environment for something good to eat or drink.

On the other hand, if the amygdala via environmental surveillance were to discover a potentially threatening stimulus, it acts to excite and drive the hypothalamus so that the organism is mobilized to take appropriate action. as noted, direct stimulation of the basolateral amygdala and the ventral amydalofugal pathway excites the principle neurons of the ventromedial hypothalamus (Dreifuss, et al., 1968). When the hypothalamus is activated by the amygdala, instead of responding in an on/off manner, cellular activity continues for an appreciably longer time period (Dreifuss et. al. 1968; Rolls 1992). The amygdala can tap into the reservoir of emotional energy mediated by the hypothalamus so that certain ends may be attained.

ATTENTION

The amygdala acts to perform environmental surveillance and can trigger orienting responses as well as mediate the maintenance of attention if something of interest or importance were to appear (Gloor, 1955, 1960, 1992; Kaada, 1951; Kapp et al., 1992; Rolls 1992; Ursin & Kaada, 1960; Whalen & Phelps 2009).

In part, the attention response can be triggered by amygdala activation of the brainstem, frontal lobes, and the dorsal medial nucleus (DMN) of the thalamus, each of which is implicated in arousal (see chapter 19). The DMN, for example, in conjunction with the frontal lobe, acts to gate and regulate the flow of information destined for the neocortex (Joseph, 2016a). The amygdala, being provided thalamic, brainstem, as well as neocortical input (as well as projecting to these nuclei), is therefore able to directly influence the DMN so that attention can be directed to particular percepts (and emotional significance attached). In fact, the projections of the amygdala to extend well beyond the DMN, but extends throughout the thalamus (Aggleton et al., 1980; LeDoux, 1996; McDonald, 1992; Russchen, 1982; Whalen & Phelps 2009), as well as throughout the neocortex .

Electrical stimulation of the lateral amygdala, therefore, can initiate quick and/or anxious glancing and searching movements of the eyes and head such that the organism appears aroused and highly alert as if in expectation of something that is going to happen (Halgren 1992; Kapp et al., 1992; Ursin & Kaada, 1960). The EEG becomes desynchronized (indicating arousal), heart rate becomes depressed, respiration patterns change, and the galvanic skin response significantly alters (Bagshaw & Benzies, 1968; Kapp et al. 2014; Ursin & Kaada, 1960) and the animal may freeze (Gloor, 1960; Kapp et al., 1992) -- reactions which characteristically accompany the orienting response of most species.

Once a stimulus of potential interest is detected, the amygdala then acts to analyze its emotional-motivational importance and will act to alert other nuclei such as the hypothalamus, brainstem, and striatum, so that appropriate action may take place.

FEAR, RAGE & AGGRESSION

Initially, electrical stimulation of the amygdala produces sustained attention and orienting reactions. If the stimulation continues the subject may begin to experience, wariness, fear and/or rage (Cendes et al. 2014; Davis et al., 1997; Gloor 1992; Halgren 1992; LeDoux, 1996; Rosen & Schulkin, 1998; Ursin & Kaada, 1960). When fear follows the attention response, the pupils dilate and the subject will cringe, withdraw, and cower. This cowering reaction in turn may give way to extreme fear and/or panic such that the animal will attempt to take flight.

Among humans, the fear response is one of the most common manifestations of amygdaloid electrical stimulation and abnormal activation (Davis et al., 1997; Gloor, 1992, Halgren, 1992; LeDoux, 1996; Rosen & Schulkin, 1998). Moreover, unlike hypothalamic on/off emotional reactions, attention and fear reactions can last up to several minutes after the stimulation is withdrawn.

In addition to behavioral manifestations of heightened emotionality, amygdaloid stimulation can result in intense changes in emotional facial expression. This includes crying and facial contortions such as baring of the teeth, dilation of the pupils, widening or narrowing of the eye-lids, flaring of the nostrils, as well as sniffing, licking, and chewing (Anand & Dua, 1955; Ursin & Kaada, 1960). Indeed, some of the behavioral manifestations of a seizure in this vicinity (i.e. temporal lobe epilepsy) typically include throat and mouth movements, including chewing, smacking of the lips, licking, and swallowing--a consequence, perhaps of amygdala activation of the brainstem periaqueductal gray and nuclei subserving mastication.

In many instances patients or animals will react defensively and with anger, irritation, and rage which seems to gradually build up until finally the animal or human will attack (Egger & Flynn, 1963; Gunne & Lewander, 1966; Mark et al., 1972 Ursin & Kaada, 1960; Zbrozyna, 1963). Unlike hypothalamic "sham rage", amygdaloid activation results in attacks directed at something real, or, in the absence of an actual stimulus, at something imaginary. There have been reported instances of patient's suddenly lashing out and even attempting to attack those close by, while in the midst of a temporal lobe seizure (Saint-Hilaire et al., 1980), and/or attacking, kicking, and destroying furniture and other objects (Ashford et al., 1980). Moreover, rage and attack will persist well beyond the termination of the electrical stimulation of the amygdala. In fact, the amygdala remains electrophysiologically active for long time periods even after a stimulus has been removed (be it external-perceptual, or internal-electrical) such that is appears to continue to process--in the abstract--information even when that information is no longer observable (O'Keefe & Bouma, 1969).

The amygdala, in addition to sustained electrophysiological activity, has been shown to be heavily involved in the maintenance of behavioral responsiveness even in the absence of an immediately tangible or visible objective or stimulus (O'Keefe & Bouma, 1969). This includes motivating the organism to engage in the seeking of hidden objects or continuing a certain activity in anticipation of achieving some particular long term goal. At a more immediate level, the amygdala is probably very important in object permanence (i.e. the keeping of an object in mind when it is no longer visible) and concrete or abstract anticipation. Anticipation is, of course, very important in the prolongation of emotional states such as fear or anger, as well as the generation of more complex emotions such as anxiety (Nitschke et al., (2009). In this regard, the amygdala is probably important not only in regard to emotion, but in the maintenance of mood states.

Fear and rage reactions have also been triggered in humans following depth electrode stimulation of the amygdala (Chapman, 1960; Heath et al. 1955). Mark et al. (1972) describe one female patient who following amygdaloid stimulation became irritable and angry, and then enraged. Her lips retracted, there was extreme facial grimacing, threatening behavior, and then rage and attack-- all of which persisted well beyond stimulus termination. Similarly, Schiff et al. (1982) describe a man who developed intractable aggression following a head injury and damage (determined via depth electrode) to the amygdala (i.e. abnormal electrical activity). Subsequently, he became easily enraged, sexually preoccupied (although sexually hypoactive), and developed hyper-religiosity and psuedo-mystical ideas. Tumors invading the amygdala have been reported to trigger rage attacks (Sweet et al. 1960; Vonderache, 1940).

The amygdala appears capable of not only triggering and steering hypothalamic activity but acting on higher level neocortical processes so that individuals form emotional ideas . Indeed, the amygdala is able to overwhelm the neocortex and the rest of the brain so that the person not only forms emotional ideas but responds to them, sometimes with vicious, horrifying results. A famous example of this is Charles Whitman, who in 1966 climbed a tower at the University of Texas and began to indiscriminately kill people with a rifle (Whitman Case File # M968150. Austin Police Department, Texas, The Texas Department of Public Safety, File #4-38).

Case Study in Amygdala-Aggression: Charles Whitman

Charles Whitman was born on June 24, 1941 and even before entering grade school had shown exceptional intellectual promise, was well liked by neighbors and had already shown some mastery of the piano, which he "loved to play." At the age of six he was administered the Stanford Binet tests of intellectual ability and obtained an IQ of 138; thus scoring at the 99.9% rank. He also became enamored by guns; his father being described as a gun fanatic. According to his father, "Charlie could plug a squirrel in the eye by the time he was sixteen." However, Charlie loved animals, was somewhat religiously oriented as a child, was very athletic, was described as "handsome" and "fun" and "high spirited" and was in many respects the "all American boy." He became an Eagle Scout at age 12, and receiving national recognition as being the youngest Eagle Scout in the world. Within 15 months he had earned 21 merit badges. While in high school he continued these activities, also pitching for the baseball team and managing the football team. After high school he joined the Marines and was described as "the kind of guy you would want around if you went into combat." It was while in the Marines that he got married, and it was during this period that began to show the first subtle signs that something might be amiss.

He began having occasional bursts of anger. He threatened to "kick the teeth out" of another Marine, was court marshalled, consigned to the brig for 30 days, and reduced in rank. He also began taking copious notes, and developed what is referred to as "hypergraphia" excessive writing--a disturbance associated with the amygdala.

Incessantly he began to write and leave himself notes, ranging from the mundane, to the tremendous love he felt for his wife. "Received a call from Kathy... it was fabulous, she sounds so wonderful. I love her so much... I will love her to the day I die. She is the best thing I have in life. My Most Precious Possession."

Increasingly, however, he was having trouble with his temper and composed notes offering self-advice as to how to control his growing temper and rage attacks. "CONTROL your anger" he wrote, "Don't let it prove you the fool. SMILE--Its contagious. DON'T be belligerent. STOP cursing. CONTROL your passion; DON'T LET IT lead YOU."

On February 4, 1964, he purchased a diary. According to Charles: "I opened this diary of my daily events as a result of the peace of mind or release of feelings that I experienced when I started making notes of my daily events...."

Nevertheless, he also continued to excel and although he had been Court marshalled, he also won a scholarship to attend the University of Texas and to attend classes while still in the Marines. He also became increasingly religious and would often have discussions with his school mates about the nature of God-

71

-hyper religiousness also being associated with an abnormality involving the amygdala (see chapter 9). And, although he was attending classes, he also began to perform volunteer work, while simultaneously holding a part time job, and at times felt overwhelmed with energy, almost manic--mania also being associated with the amygdala (Strakowski et al., 2016) as well as the frontal lobes (Joseph, 1986a, 1988a, 2016a). And, he continued to be well liked and admired. His supervisor at the bank, E. R. Hendricks, described Charles "as a truly outstanding person. Very likeable. Neat. Nice looking... A great guy."

However, Charles also began suffering terrible headaches, and one day lost his temper in class, pulling a male student bodily from his chair and tossing him from the classroom. Apparently he felt considerable remorse. He also continued to have frequent bouts of anger and on occasion, difficulty concentrating, and was beginning to over eat--increased food consumption being associated with a disturbance of the hypothalamus. Moreover, he began having periods where he couldn't sleep for days at a time--yet another disturbance associated with the hypothalamus, a major sleep center. Charles also realized that something was wrong, and continued writing copious notes to himself, reminding himself to be nice, to control his appetite, and especially to control temper. But his temper was getting out of control and Charles was gaining weight.

A close friend, Elaine Fuess, also noticed that something was amiss. "Even when he looked perfectly normal, he gave you the feeling of trying to control something in himself. He knew he had a temper, and he hated this in himself. He hated the idea of cruelty in himself and tried to suppress it."

Charles Whitman finally sought professional help and consulted a staff psychiatrist, at the University of Texas Health Center about his periodic and uncontrollable violent impulses. Charles was referred to Dr. Heatly. According to the report written by Dr. Heatly about his session with Whitman, a report which was distributed to the media: "This massive, muscular youth seemed to be oozing with hostility as he initiated the hour with the statement that something was happening to him and he didn't seem to be himself...." Whitman "could talk for long periods of time and develop overt hostility while talking, and then during the same narration show signs of weeping.... Past history revealed a youth who... grew up in Florida where his father was a very successful plumbing contractor... who achieved considerable wealth. He identified his father as being brutal, domineering, and extremely demanding of the other three members of the family." Whitman "married four or five years ago, and served a hitch in the Marines.... He referred to several commendable achievements during his Marine service, but also made reference to a court martial for fighting which resulted in being reduced several grades to private. In spite of this he received a scholarship to attend the University for two years and remained a Marine at the same time... He expressed himself as being very fond of his wife, but admitted that he had on two occasions assaulted his wife physically. He said he has made an intense effort to avoid losing his temper with her... His real concern is with himself at the present moment. He readily admits having overwhelming periods of hostility with a very minimum of provocation... he... also... made vivid reference to thinking about going up on the tower with a deer rifle and start shooting people. ....He was told to make an appointment for the same day next week."

Instead, Charles apparently decided to climb the tower and to begin killing people. But not before first contacting the police and asking to be arrested. As Charles had not committed a crime, the desk sergeant instead suggested that he see a psychiatrist.

Several days prior to climbing the tower, Charles Whitman wrote himself a letter:

"I don't quite understand what it is that compels me to type this letter.... I don't really understand myself these days... Lately I have been a victim of many unusual and irrational thoughts. These thoughts constantly recur, and it requires a tremendous mental effort to concentrate. I consulted Dr. Cochrum at the University Health Center and asked him to recommend someone that I could consult with about some psychiatric disorders I felt I had.... I talked to a doctor once for about two hours and tried to convey to him my fears that I felt overcome by overwhelming violent impulses. After one session I never saw the Doctor again, and since then I have been fighting my mental turmoil alone, and seemingly to no avail. After my death I wish that an autopsy would be performed to see if there is any visible physical disorder. I have had tremendous headaches in the past and have consumed two large bottles of Excedrin in the past three months."

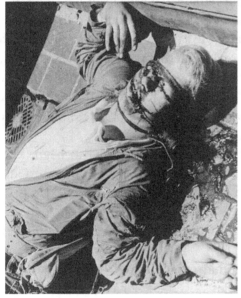

On August 1, 1966, one day before climbing the tower at the University of Texas, Charles Whitman paid a visit to his mother, who greeted him outside her penthouse and introduced him to the night watchman who noticed that Charles was carrying a big black attache case. According to police reports, Charles must have immediately attacked his mother after they entered the penthouse, and then brutally beat, strangled, and stabbed her to death, crushing the back of her head, smashing her hands, and stabbing her in the chest with a huge hunting knife.

Later, neighbors told police that the only sounds they heard were that of a "child crying and whimpering," which they found puzzling as no child lived in the penthouse.

After brutally murdering his mother, Charles cleaned up the mess, and placed her in bed with a note pad laying across and covering up the massive wound in her chest. Charles had left a note. It read: "To Whom It May Concern: I have just taken my mother's life. I am very upset over having done it. However, I feel that if there is a heaven she is definitely there now... I am truly sorry... Let there be no doubt in your mind that I loved this woman with all my heart."

After killing his mother, Charles returned home, planning on killing his wife "as painlessly as possible.," as he explained in yet another note:

"It was after much thought that I decided to kill my wife, Kathy, tonight....I love her dearly, and she has been a fine wife to me as any man could ever hope to have. I cannot rationally pinpoint any specific reason for doing this..."

Apparently she was sleeping, and after removing the blankets to expose her nude body, he viciously stabbed her repeatedly with his huge hunting knife, leaving five gaping holes in her chest. She died instantly.

Charles wrote another note which he left with the body: "I imagine it appears that I brutally killed both of my loved ones. I was only trying to do a quick thorough job... If my life insurance policy is valid please pay off my debts... donate the rest anonymously to a mental health foundation. Maybe research can prevent further tragedies of this type."

And then he added a post script beneath his signature: "Give our dog to my in-laws. Tell them Kathy loved "Schoci" very much."

The next morning Charles Whitman climbed the University tower carrying several guns, a sawed off shotgun, and a high powered hunting rifle, and for the next 90 minutes he shot at everything that moved, killing 14, wounding 38, He was finally killed by a police sharp shooter.

Post-mortem autopsy revealed a glioblastoma multiforme tumor the size of a walnut, erupting from the hypothalamus, extending into the temporal lobe and compressing the amygdaloid nucleus (Charles J. Whitman Catastrophe, Medical Aspects. Report to Governor, 9/8/66).

DOCILITY & AMYGDALOID DESTRUCTION

Bilateral destruction of the amygdala usually results in increased tameness, docility, and reduced aggressiveness in cats, monkeys and other animals (Schreiner & Kling, 1956; Weiskrantz, 1956; Vochteloo & Koolhaas, 1987), including purportedly ferocious creatures such as the agoutie and lynxe (Schreiner & Kling, 1956). In man, bilateral amygdala destruction (via neurosurgery) has been reported to reduce and/or eliminate paroxysmal aggressive and violent behavior (Terzian & Ore, 1955).

In some creatures, however, bilateral ablation of the amygdala has been reported to al least initially result in increased aggressive responding (Bard & Mountcastle, 1948), and if sufficiently aroused or irritated, even the most placid of amygdalectomized animals can be induced to fiercely fight (Fuller et al. 1957).

However, these aggressive responses are very short-lived and appear to be reflexively mediated by the hypothalamus. Hence, these findings (and the data reviewed above) suggests that true aggressive feelings including violent moods, are dependent upon activation of the amygdala.

SOCIAL-EMOTIONAL AGNOSIA

Among primates and mammals, bilateral destruction of the amygdala significantly disturbs the ability to determine and identify the motivational and emotional significance of externally occurring events, to discern social-emotional nuances conveyed by others, or to select what behavior is appropriate given a specific social context (Bunnel, 1966; Fuller et al. 1957; Gloor, 1960; Kling & Brothers 1992; Kluver & Bucy, 1939; Lilly et al., 2003; Marlowe et al., 2015; Scott et al., 1997; Terzian & Ore, 1955; Weiskrantz, 1956). Bilateral lesions lower responsiveness to aversive and social stimuli, reduce aggressiveness, fearfulness, competitiveness, dominance, and social interest (Rosvold et al. 1954). This condition is so pervasive that subjects have tremendous difficulty discerning the meaning or recognizing the significance of even common objects -- a condition sometimes referred to as "psychic blindness", or, the "Kluver-Bucy syndrome" (Lilly et al., 2003; Marlowe et al., 2015; Terzian & Ore, 1955).

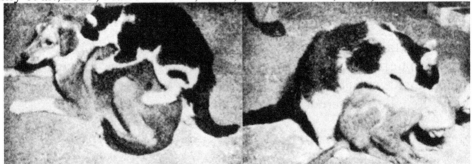

Thus, animals with bilateral amygdaloid destruction, although able to see and interact with their environment, may respond in an emotionally blunted manner, and seem unable to recognize what they see, feel, and experience. Things seem stripped of meaning. Like an infant (who similarly is without a fully functional amygdala), individuals with this condition engage in extreme orality and will indiscriminately pick up various objects and place them in their mouth regardless of its appropriateness. There is a repetitive quality to this behavior, for once they put it down they seem to have forgotten that they had just explored it, and will immediately pick it up and place it again in their mouth as if it were a completely unfamiliar object.

Although ostensibly exploratory, there is thus a failure to learn, to remember, to discern motivational significance, to habituate with repeated contact, or to discriminate between appropriate vs inappropriate stimuli. Rather, when the amygdala has been removed bilaterally the organism reverts to the most basic and primitive modes of object and social-emotional interaction (Brown & Schaffer, 1888; Gloor, 1960; Kluver & Bucy, 1939; Weiskrantz, 1956) such that even the ability to appropriately interact with loved ones is impaired (Lilly et al., 2003; Marlowe et al., 2015; Terzian & Ore, 1955).

For example, Terzian & Ore (1955) described a young man who following bilateral removal of the amygdala subsequently demonstrated an inability to recognize anyone, including close friends, relatives and his mother. He ceased to respond in an emotional manner to his environment and seemed unable to recognize feelings expressed by others. He also demonstrated many features of the Kluver-Bucy syndrome (perseverative oral "exploratory" behavior and psychic blindness), as well as an insatiable appetite. In addition, he became extremely socially unresponsive such that he preferred to sit in isolation, well away from others.

Among primates who have undergone bilateral amygdaloid removal, once they are released from captivity and allowed to return to their social group, a social-emotional agnosia becomes readily apparent as they no longer respond to or seem able to appreciate or understand emotional or social nuances. Indeed, they appear to have little or no interest in social activity and persistently attempt to avoid contact with others (Dicks et al. 1969; Jonason & Enloe, 1971; Kling & Brothers 1992; Jonason et al. 1973). If approached they withdraw, and if followed they flee.

Indeed, they behave as if they have no understanding of what is expected of them or what others intend or are attempting to convey, even when the behavior is quite friendly and concerned. Among adults with bilateral lesions, total isolation seems to be preferred.

In addition, they no longer display appropriate social or emotional behaviors, and if kept in captivity will fall in dominance in a group or competitive situation -- even when formerly dominant (Bunnel, 1966; Dicks et al., 1969; Fuller et al., 1957; Jonason & Enloe, 1971; Jonason et al., 1973; Rosvold et al. 1954). However, they may also engage in inappropriate sexual behavior, including attempts to have sex with other species of inanimate objects.

As might be expected, maternal behavior is severely affected. According to Kling (1972), mothers will behave as if their "infant were a strange object be mouthed, bitten and tossed around as though it were a rubber ball".

EMOTIONAL LANGUAGE & THE AMYGDALA

Although cries and vocalizations indicative of rage or pleasure have been elicited via hypothalamic stimulation, of all limbic nuclei the amygdala is the most vocally active--particularly the lateral division (Robinson, 2007). In humans and animals a wide range of emotional sounds have been evoked through amygdala activation, such as sounds indicative of pleasure, sadness, happiness, and anger (Hage 2010; Jurgens 2009; Robinson, 2007; Ursin & Kaada, 1960). The human amygdala can produce as well as perceive emotional vocalizations (Halgren, 1992; Heit, Smith, & Halgren, 1988).

Conversely, in humans, destruction limited to the amygdala (Freeman & Williams 1952, 1963), the right amygdala in particular, has abolished the ability to sing, convey melodic information or to properly enunciate via vocal inflection. Similar disturbances occur with right hemisphere damage (Joseph 1982, 1988a). Indeed, when the right temporal region (including the amygdala) has been grossly damaged or surgically removed, the ability to perceive, process, or even vocally reproduce most aspects of musical and emotional auditory input is significantly curtailed.

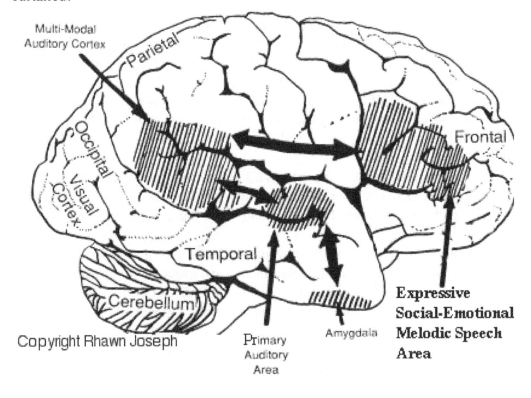

AMYGDALA, THE ANTERIOR COMMISSURE, SEXUALITY & EMOTION

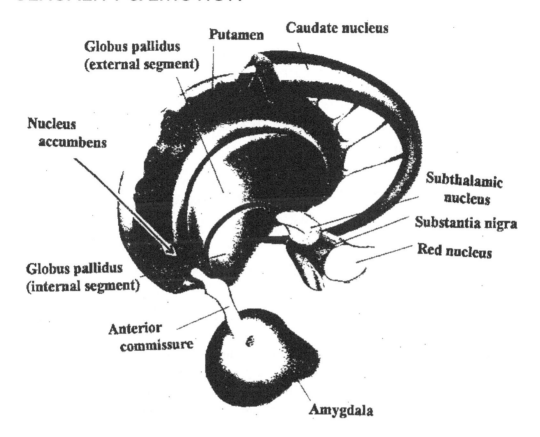

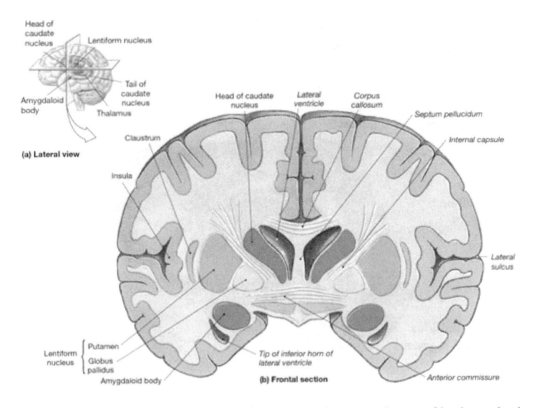

(a) Lateral view

(b) Frontal section

When the amygdala or the bed nuclei for the anterior commissure of both cerebral hemispheres are damaged, hyperactivated, or completely inhibited a striking disturbance in sexual and social behavior is evident (Brown & Schaffer, 1888; Gloor, 1960; Kluver & Bucy, 1939; Terzian & Ore, 1955; Schriner & Kling, 1953). Specifically, humans, non-human primates, and felines who have undergone bilateral amygdalectomies will engage in prolonged, repeated, and inappropriate sexual behavior and masturbation including repeated sexual acts with members of different species (e.g. a cat with a dog, a dog with a turtle, etc.).

When activated from seizures, patients may involuntarily behave in a sexual manner and even engage in what appears to be intercourse with an imaginary partner. This abnormality is one aspect of a complex of symptoms sometimes referred to as the Kluver-Bucy syndrome.

As noted, portions of the hypothalamus and amygdala are sexually dimorphic; i.e. there are male and female amygdaloid nuclei (Bubenik & Brown, 1973; Nishizuka & Arai, 1981; Rubinow, et al., 2009). In humans the male amygdala is 16% larger (Filipek, et al., 2014), and in male rats the medial amygdala is 65% larger than the female amygdala (Breedlove & Cooke, 2016), and the male amygdala grows or shrinks in the presence of testosterone--findings which may be related to sex differences in sexuality and aggression. Moreover, female amygdala neurons are smaller and more numerous, and densely packed than those of the male (Bubenik & Brown, 1973; Nishizuka & Arai, 1981), and smaller, densely packed neurons fire more easily and frequently than larger ones--which may contribute to the fact that females are more emotional and more easily frightened than males, as the amygdala is a principle structure involved in evoking feelings of fear.

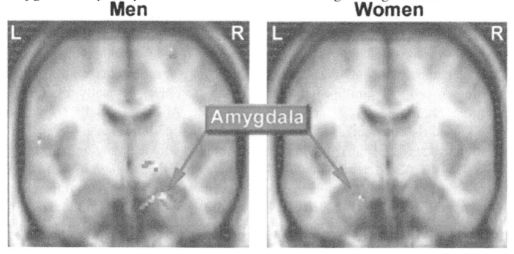

Moreover, despite myths to the contrary, females, regardless of species, are more sexually active than males, on average--that is, when they are in estrus-- and the human female is capable of experiencing multiple orgasms of increasing intensity--which may also be a function of sex differences in the amygdala. That is, since female primate amygdala neurons are more numerous and packed more closely together (Bubenik & Brown, 1973; Nishizuka & Arai, 1981), and as smaller, tightly packed neurons demonstrate enhanced electrical excitability, lower response thresholds, and increase susceptibility to kindling and thus hyper-excitation, the amygdala therefore is likely largely responsible for sex differences in emotionality and sexuality.

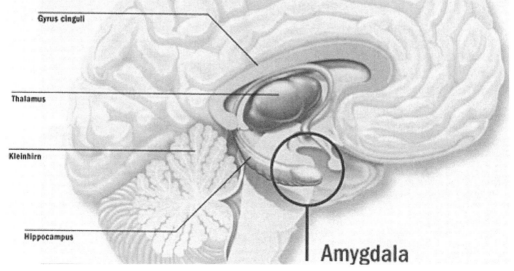

Electrical stimulation of the medial amygdala results in sex related behavior and activity. In females this includes ovulation, uterine contractions and lactogenetic responses, and in males penile erections (Robinson & Mishkin, 1968; Shealy & Peele, 1957). Moreover, in rats and other animals, kindling induced in the amygdala can trigger estrus and produce prolonged female sexual behavior.

Moreover, the anterior commissure, the band of axonal fibers which interconnects the right and left amygdala/temporal lobe is sexually differentiated. Like the corpus callosum, the anterior commissure is responsible for information transfer as well as inhibition within the limbic system. Specifically, the female anterior commissure is 18% larger than in the male (Allen & Gorski 1992). It has been argued that the increased capacity of the right and left female amygdala to communicate (via the anterior commissure) coupled with the more numerous and more densely packed neurons within the female amygdala (which in turn would decrease firing thresholds and enhance communication), and the sex differences in the hypothalamus, would also predispose females to be more emotionally and socially sensitive, perceptive, and expressive (Joseph 1993). Hence, these limbic sex differences induces her to be less aggressive and more compassionate and maternal, and affects her sexuality, feelings of dependency and nurturence, and desire to maintain and form attachments in a manner different than males.

In contrast, whereas the right and left female amygdala are provided a communication advantage not shared by males, the "male" amygdala in turn may be more greatly influenced by the (medial) hypothalamus via the stria terminalis which is larger in men than women (Allen & Gorski 1992). As noted, the male medial amygdala is larger than its female counterpart (Breedlove & Cooke, 2016) and changes in size in response to testosterone, which is significant as the medial nuclei (and testosterone) is directly implicated in negative and aggressive behaviors (see above).

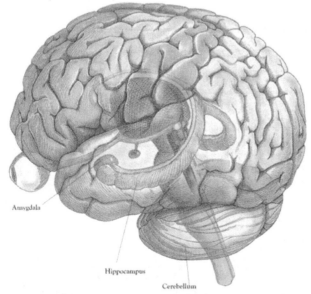

Although environmental influences can shape and sculpt behavior and the functional organization of the brain, most sex differences are innate and shared by other species; a direct consequence of the presence or absence of testosterone during adulthood and fetal development (Gerall et al. 1992; Joseph 1993, Joseph et al. 2014) and the sexual differentiation of the limbic system.

THE LIMBIC SYSTEM & TESTOSTERONE

In large part these and related sex differences in aggressiveness are also a consequence of the relatively higher concentrations of the activating hormone, testosterone flowing through male bodies and brains. The over arching influence of neurological and hormonal predispositions are also indicated by studies which have shown that females who have been prenatally exposed to high levels of masculinizing hormones (i.e. androgens) behave similar to males even in regard to spatial abilities (Joseph et al. 2014; Gerall et al. 1992). They are also more aggressive and engage in more rough and tumble play as compared to normal females (Money & Ehrhardt, 1972; Ehrhardt & Baker, 1974; Reinisch, 1974) and this is also true of other species such as dogs, wolves, gorillas, baboons, and chimpanzees.

Similarly, female primates and mammals who have been exposed to testosterone during neonatal development display an altered sexual orientation, as well as significantly higher levels of activity, competitiveness, combativeness and belligerence (Mitchell, 1979). Nevertheless, it is important to re-emphasize that it is generally the presence or absence of testosterone during the critical period of neuronal differentiation which determines if one is in possession of a "male" vs "female" limbic system.

SEXUAL ORIENTATION & HETEROSEXUAL DESIRE

As noted, the amygdala surveys the environment searching out stimuli, events, or individuals which are emotionally, sexually or motivationally significant. Moreover, it contains facial recognition neurons which are sensitive to different facial expressions and which are capable of determining the sex of the individual being viewed and which become excited when looking at a male vs female face (Leonard et al. 2005; Rolls 1984). In this regard, the amygdala can act to discern and detect potential sexual partners and then motivate sex-appropriate behavior culminating in sexual intercourse and orgasm.

That is, an individual who possess a "male" limbic system is likely to view the female face, body and genitalia as sexually arousing because the amygdala and limbic system responds with pleasure when stimulated by these particular features. Conversely, male physical features are likely to excite and sexually stimulate the limbic systems possessed by heterosexual females and homosexual males (Joseph, 1993). This is because, at a very basic level emotional, sexual, and motivational perceptual/behavioral functioning becomes influenced and guided by the anatomical sexual bias of the host.

OVERVIEW: THE AMYGDALA

Over the course of early evolutionary development, the hypothalamus reigned supreme in the control and expression of raw and reflexive emotionality, i.e., pleasure, displeasure, aversion, and rage. Largely, however, it has acted as an eye turned inward, monitoring internal homeostasis and concerned with basic needs. With the development of the amygdala, the organism was now equipped with an eye turned outward so that the external emotional features of reality could be tested and ascertained. When signalled by the hypothalamus the amygdala begins to search the sensory array for appropriate emotional-motivational stimuli until what is desired is discovered and attended to.

However, with the differentiation of the amygdala, emotional functioning also became differentiated and highly refined. The amygdala hierarchically wrested control of emotion from the hypothalamus.

The amygdala is primary in regard to the perception and expression of most aspects of emotionality, including fear, aggression, pleasure, happiness, sadness, etc., and in fact assigns emotional or motivational significance to that which is experienced. It can thus induce the organism to act on something seen, felt, heard, or anticipated. The integrity of the amygdala is essential in regard to the analysis of social-emotional nuances, the organization and mobilization of the persons internal motivational status regarding these cues, as well as the mediation of higher order emotional expression and impulse control. When damaged or functionally compromised, social-emotional functioning becomes grossly disturbed.

The amygdaloid nucleus via its rich interconnections with other brain regions is able to sample and influence activity occurring in other parts of the cerebrum and add emotional color to ones perceptions. As such it is highly involved in the assimilation and association of divergent emotional, motivational, somesthetic, visceral, auditory, visual, motor, olfactory and gustatory stimuli. Thus it is very concerned with learning, memory, and attention, and can generate reinforcement for certain behaviors. Moreover, via reward or punishment it can promote the encoding, storage and later retrieval of particular types of information. That is, learning often involved reward and it is via the amygdala (in concert with other nuclei) that emotional consequences can be attributed to certain events, actions, or experiences, as well as extracted from the world of possibility so that it can be attended to and remembered.

Lastly, as is evident from studies of individuals with abnormal activity or seizures originating in or involving this nuclei, the amygdala is able to overwhelm the neocortex and thus gain control over behavior. As based on electrophysiological studies, the amygdala seems capable of literally turning off the neocortex (such as occurs during a seizure) at least for brief time periods. That is, the amygdala can induce electrophysiological slow wave theta activity in the neocortex which indicates low levels of arousal (see below) as well as high voltage fast activity. In the normal brain it probably exerts similar influences such that at times individuals (i.e. their neocortex) "lose control" over themselves and respond in a highly emotionally charged manner.

In consequence, after they "explode" or respond "irrationally" they (that is, the neocortex of the left hemisphere) are likely to wonder aloud: "I don't know what came over me." But we know the answer: The Limbic System.

HIPPOCAMPUS

The hippocampus (Ammon's Horn" or the "sea horse") is an elongated structure located within the inferior medial wall of the temporal lobe (posterior to the amygdala) and surrounds, in part, the lateral ventricle. In humans it consists of an anterior and posterior region and depending on the angle at which it is viewed, could be construed as shaped somewhat like an old fashion telephone receiver, or a "sea horse."

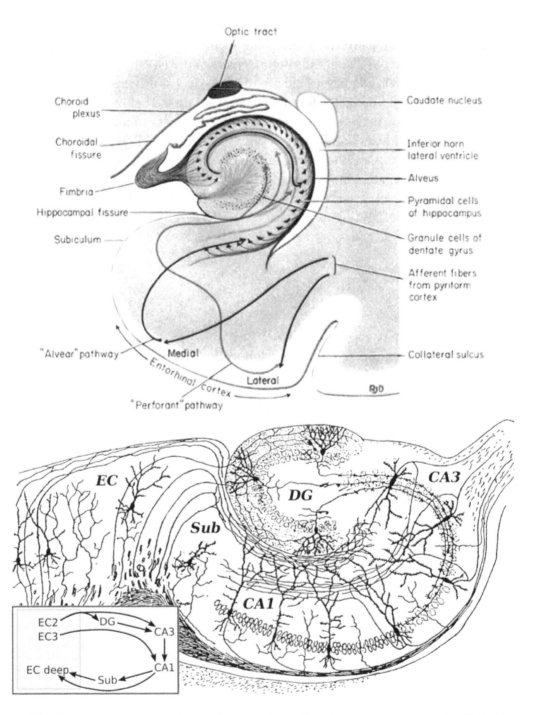

The hippocampus consists of a number of subcomponents, and adjoining structures, such as the parahippocampal gyrus, entorhinal and perirhinal cortex and the uncus (which it shares with the amygdala) are considered by some to be subdivisions, whereas the main body of the hippocampus consists of the dentate gyrus, the subiculum, and sectors referred to as CA1, CA2, CA3, CA4.

The uncus is a bulbar allocortical protrusion located in the anterior-inferior medial part of the temporal lobe, and consists of both the hippocampus and amygdala which become fused in forming this structure. That is the ventral-medial portion of the amygdala becomes fused with the head of the hippocampus, such that the uncus consists of both allocortex and mesocortex--the entorhinal cortex which shrouds the hippocampus.

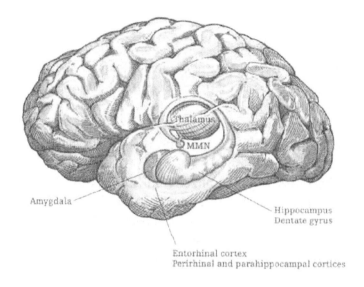

HIPPOCAMPAL AROUSAL, ATTENTION & INHIBITORY INFLUENCES

Various authors have assigned the hippocampus a major role in information processing, including memory, new learning, cognitive mapping of the environment, voluntary movement toward a goal, as well as attention, behavioral arousal, and orienting reactions (Andersen et al. 2006; Chadwick et al., 2010; Douglas, 2007; Eichenbaum et al. 2014; Enbert & Bonhoeffer, 2016; Frisk & Milner, 1990; Gartner & Frantz 2010; Isaacson, 1982; Milner, 1966, 1970, 1971; Nishitani, et al., 2016; Olton et al. 2014; Routtenberg, 1968; Squire, 1992; Victor & Agamanolis, 1990; Xu et al., 1998). For example, hippocampal cells greatly alter their activity in response to certain spatial correlates, particularly as an animal moves about in its environment (Nadel, 1991; O'Keefe, 1976; Olton et al., 2014; Wilson & McNaughton, 1993). It also develops slow wave theta activity during arousal (Green & Arduini, 1954) or when presented with noxious or novel stimuli (Adey et al. 1960)--at least in non-humans.

However, few studies have implicated this nucleus as important in emotional functioning per se, although responses such as "anxiety" or "bewilderment" have been observed when directly electrically stimulated (Kaada et al. 1953).

Indeed, in response to persistent and repeated instances of stress and unpleasant emotional arousal, the hippocampus appears to cease to participate in cognitive, emotional, or memory processing. Thus the role of the hippocampus in emotion is relatively minimal.

AROUSAL

Hippocampal-neocortical interactions. Desynchronization of the cortical EEG is associated with high levels of arousal and information input. As the level of input increases, the greater is the level of cortical arousal (Como et al. 1979; Joseph et al. 1981; Joseph, 1998b, 2016d). However, when arousal levels become too great, efficiently in information processing, memory, new learning, and attention become compromised as the brain becomes overwhelmed (Joseph, 1998b, 2016d; Joseph et al., 1981).

When the neocortex becomes desynchronized (indicating cortical arousal), the hippocampus often (but not always) develops slow wave theta activity (Grastyan et al., 1959; Green & Arduni, 1954) such that it appears to be functioning at a much lower level of arousal--as demonstrated in non-humans. Conversely, when cortical arousal is reduced to a low level (indicated by EEG synchrony), the hippocampal EEG often becomes desynchronized.

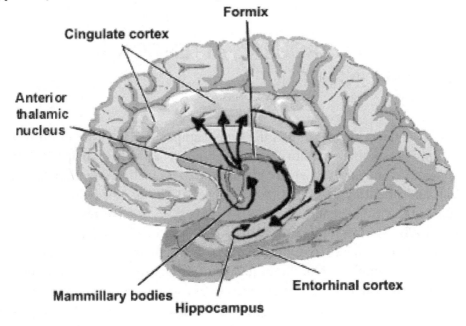

These findings suggest when the neocortex is highly stimulated the hippocampus, in order to monitor what is being received and processed, functions at a level much lower in order not to become overwhelmed. When the neocortex is not highly aroused, the hippocampus presumably compensates by increasing its own level of arousal so as to tune in to information that is being processed at a low level of intensity.

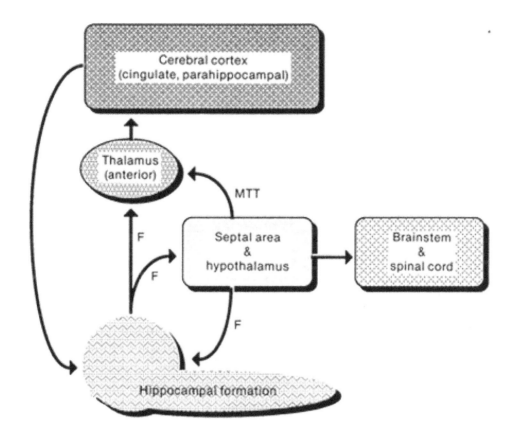

Hence, in situations where both the cortex and the hippocampus become desynchronized, there results distractibility and hyper responsiveness such that the subject becomes overwhelmed, confused, and may orient to and approach several stimuli (Grastyan et al., 1959). Attention, learning, and memory functioning are decreased. Situations such as this sometimes also occur when individuals are highly anxious or repetitively emotionally or physically traumatized.

The hippocampus consists of 3 layers, layer 2 consisting of pyramidal neurons which provide excitatory output and thus act to activate and arouse target tissues (Andersen et al., 2006; Duvernoy et al., 2005; Gartner & Frantz 2010); via the transmitters glutamate and aspartic acid. In addition, the entorhinal cortex provides excitatory input into the hippocampus--input which is derived from the neocortex (Andersen et al., 2006; Gartner & Frantz 2010); using aspartic and glutamate acid (reviewed in Gloor, 1997). Specifically, it appears that the hippocampus interacts with the neocortex is regard to arousal via the dorsal medial nucleus of the thalamus, the septal nuclei, the hypothalamus, amygdala and brainstem--structures with which it maintains direct interconnections. As per the neocortex, this sheet of tissue is also innervated by these structures, and by the entorhinal cortex.

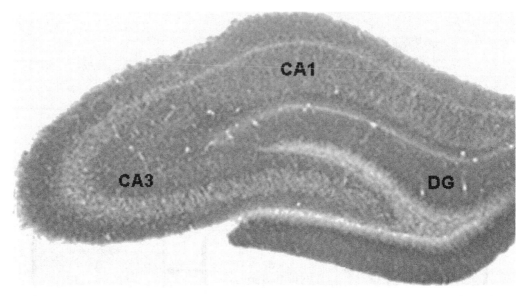

Hence, the hippocampus serves as a major component of an excitatory interface and can be aroused by neocortical activity (via the entorhinal cortex), and can provide excitatory input to directly to subcortical structures and indirectly to the neocortex (via the entorhinal cortex and dorsal medial nucleus). However, if the neocortex becomes excessively aroused, so to might the hippocampus, and vice versa. Under excessively arousing conditions, however, hippocampal pyramidal neurons may become inhibited or even damaged (Lupien & McEwen, 1997; Sapolsky, 1996), thus resulting in loss of memory.

There is also evidence to suggest that the hippocampus may act so as to reduce extremes in cortical arousal. For example, whereas stimulation of the reticular activating system augments cortical arousal and EEG evoked potentials, hippocampal stimulation reduces or inhibits these potentials such that cortical responsiveness and arousal is dampened (Feldman, 1962; Redding, 2007). On the other hand, if cortical arousal is at a low level, hippocampal stimulation often results in an augmentation of the cortical evoked potential (Redding, 2007).

The hippocampus also exerts desynchronizing or synchronizing influences on various thalamic nuclei (e.g., the dorsal medial thalamus) which in turn augments or decreases activity in this region (Green & Adey, 1956; Guillary, 1955; Nauta, 1956, 1958). As the dorsal medial thalamus is the major relay nucleus to the neocortex, the hippocampus therefore appears able to block or enhance information transfer to various neocortical areas (that is, in conjunction with the frontal lobe). It may be acting to insure that certain percepts are stored in memory at the level of the neocortex (Gloor, 1997; Squire 1992) by modulating cortical activity.

It is likely that the hippocampus may act to influence information reception and storage at the neocortical level as well as possibly reduce extremes in cortical arousal (be they too low or high) perhaps by activating inhibitory circuits in the dorsal medial nucleus, thus ensuring that the neocortex is not over or underwhelmed when engaged in the reception and processing of information. This is an important attribute since very high or very low states of excitation are incompatible with alertness and selective attention as well as the ability to learn and retain information (Joseph et al. 1981; Lupien & McEwen, 1997; Sapolsky, 2006).

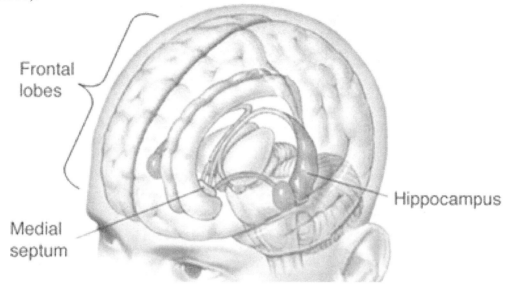

Aversion & Punishment.

In many ways, the hippocampus appears to act in concert with the medial hypothalamus and septal nuclei (with which it maintains rich interconnections) so as to also prevent extremes in emotional arousal and thus maintain a state of quiet alertness (or quiescence). Moreover, similar to the results following stimulation of the medial hypothalamus, it has been reported that the subjective components of aversive emotion in humans is correlated with electrophysiological alternations in the hippocampus and septal area (Heath, 1976).

The hippocampus also appears to be heavily involved in the modulation of reactions to frustrations or mild punishment (Gray, 1970, 1990), particularly in regard to single trial but not multiple trial learning. For example, the hippocampus responds with trains of slow theta waves when presented with noxious stimuli but habituates or ceases to respond with repeated presentation. It is likely, however, that these physiological responses are secondary to activity within the amygdala and hypothalamus which then effects hippocampal functioning.

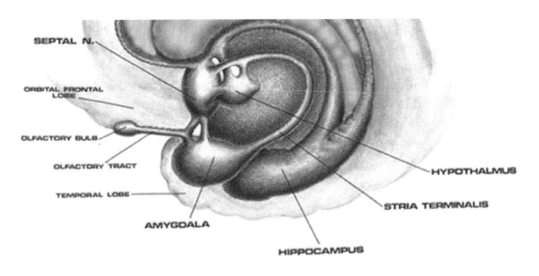

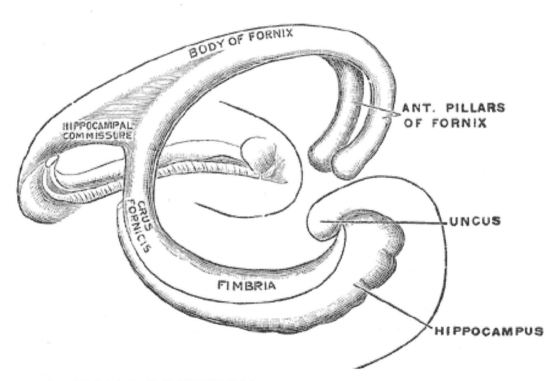

ATTENTION & INHIBITION

The hippocampus participates in the elicitation of orienting reactions and the maintenance of an aroused state of attention (Foreman & Stevens, 1987; Grastayan et al., 1959; Green & Arduini, 1954; Nishitani, et al., 2016; Routtenberg, 1968). When exposed to novel stimuli or when engaged in active searching of the environment, hippocampal theta appears (Adey, et al. 1960). However, with repeated presentations of a novel stimulus the hippocampus habituates and theta disappears (Adey et al. 1960). Thus, as information is attended to, recognized, and presumably learned and/or stored in memory, hippocampal participation diminishes. Theta also appears during the early stages of learning as well as when engaged in selective attention and the making of discriminant responses.

When the hippocampus is damaged or destroyed, animals have great difficulty inhibiting behavioral responsiveness or shifting attention. For example, Clark and Issacson (1965) found that animals with hippocampal lesions could not learn to wait 20 seconds between bar presses if first trained to respond to a continuous schedule. There is an inability to switch from a continuous to a discontinuous pattern, such that a marked degree of perseveration and inability to change sets or inhibit a pattern of behavior once initiated occurs (Douglas, 2007; Ellen, et al. 1964). Habituation is largely abolished and the ability to think or respond divergently is disrupted. Disinhibition due to hippocampal damage can even prevent the learning of a passive avoidance task, such as simple ceasing to move (Kimura, 1958).

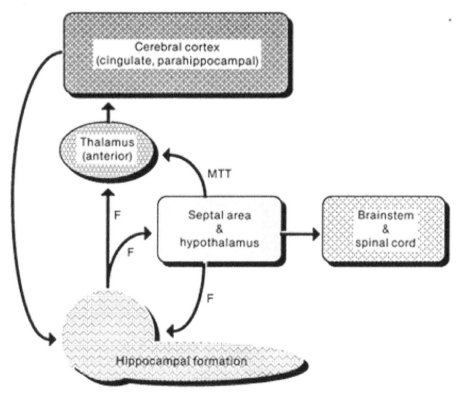

Hence, when coupled with the evidence presented above, it appears that the hippocampus acts to possibly selectively enhance or diminish areas of neural excitation which in turn allows for differential selective attention and differential responding, as well as the storage and consolidation of information into long term memory. When damaged, the ability to shift from one set of perceptions to another, or to change behavioral patterns is disrupted and the organism becomes overwhelmed by a particular mode of input. Learning, memory, as well as attention, are greatly compromised.

LEARNING & MEMORY: THE HIPPOCAMPUS

The hippocampus is most usually associated with learning and memory encoding, e.g. long term storage and retrieval of newly learned information (Andersen et al. 2006; Chadwick et al., 2010; Enbert & Bonhoeffer, 2016; Fedio & Van Buren, 1974; Frisk & Milner, 1990; Katche et al., 2010; Nunn et al., 2016; Penfield & Milner, 1958; Rawlins, 2005; Resteo et al., 2009; Squire, 1992; Victor & Agamanolis, 1990; Warburton & Brown 2009) particularly the anterior regions. Hence, if the hippocampus has been damaged the ability to convert short term memories into long term memories (i.e. anterograde amnesia), becomes significantly impaired in humans (MacKinnon & Squire, 1989; Nunn et al., 2016; Squire, 1992; Victor & Agamanolis, 1990) as well as primates (Zola-Morgan & Squire, 1986). In humans, memory for words, passages, conversations, and written material is also significantly impacted, particularly with left hippocampal destruction (Frisk & Milner, 1990; Squire, 1992).

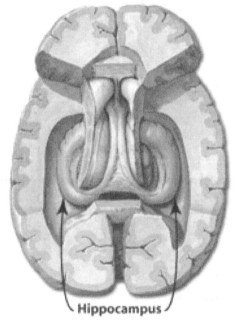

Hippocampus

Bilateral destruction of the anterior hippocampus results in striking and profound disturbances involving memory and new learning (i.e. anterograde amnesia). For example, one such individual who underwent bilateral destruction of this nuclei (H.M.), was subsequently found to have almost completely lost the ability to recall anything experienced after surgery. If you introduced yourself to him, left the room, and then returned a few minutes later he would have no recall of having met or spoken to you. Dr. Brenda Milner has worked with H.M. for almost 20 years and yet she was an utter stranger to him.

H.M. was in fact so amnesic for everything that had occurred since his surgery (although memory for events prior to his surgery is comparatively exceedingly well preserved), that every time he rediscovered that his favorite uncle died (actually a few years before his surgery) he suffered the same grief as if he had just been informed for the first time.

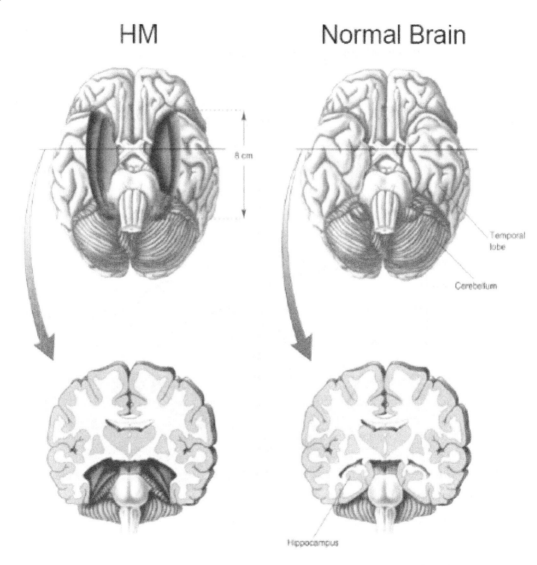

H.M., although without memory for new (non-motor) information, had adequate intelligence, was painfully aware of his deficit and constantly apologized for his problem. "Right now, I'm wondering" he once said, "Have I done or said anything amiss?" You see, at this moment everything looks clear to me, but what happened just before? That's what worries me. It's like waking from a dream. I just don't remember...Every day is alone in itself, whatever enjoyment I've had, and whatever sorrow I've had...I just don't remember" (Blakemore, 1977, p.96).

Presumably the hippocampus acts to protect memory and the encoding of new information during the storage and consolidation phase via the gating of afferent streams of information and the filtering/exclusion (or dampening) of irrelevant and interfering stimuli. When the hippocampus is damaged there results input overload, the neuroaxis is overwhelmed by neural noise, and the consolidation phase of memory is disrupted such that relevant information is not properly stored or even attended to. Consequently, the ability to form associations (e.g. between stimulus and response) or to alter preexisting schemas (such as occurs during learning) is attenuated (Douglas, 2007).

HIPPOCAMPAL & SEPTAL INTERACTIONS

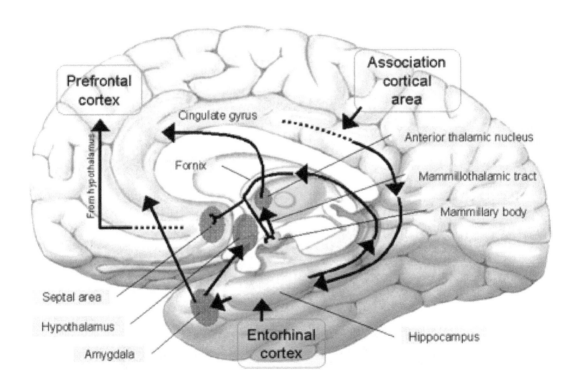

THE SEPTAL NUCLEI

The septal nuclei consists of medial and lateral nuclei, and can be further subdivided into several nuclear components (Ariens Kappers et al., 1936; Swanson & Cowan, 1979), such as the nucleus of the diagonal band of Broca. The septal nuclei is an evolutionary derivative of the hippocampus and the hypothalamus, and in the human brain is richly interconnected with both structures including the amygdala, and the substantia innomminata (SI) which is a major memory center, and which manufactures ACh--a transmitter directly implicated in memory (Gage et al., 2003; Olton, 1990). Andy and Stephan (1968) and Swanson and Cowan (1979) considered the bed nucleus of the stria terminals (which gives rise to a major pathway linking the septal nuclei, and amygdala and hypothalamus) as part of the septal nuclei, whereas others (Gloor, 1997) consider it to be part of the "extended amygdala." Likewise, some consider the nucleus accumbens as part of the septal nuclei, and others consider it part of the "extended amygdala;" i.e. the limbic striatum.

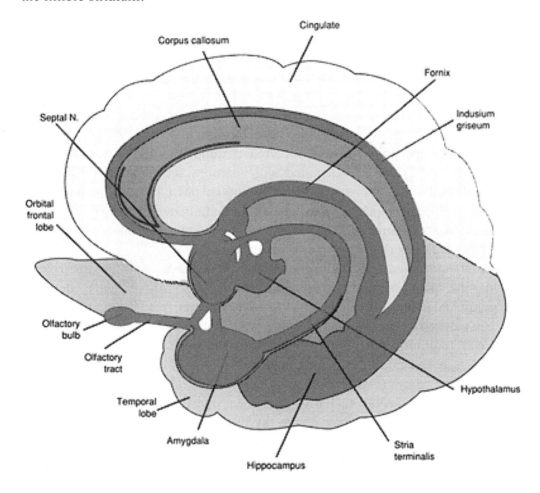

As noted the septal nuclei is massively interconnected with the hippocampus as well as with the entorhinal cortex (Andersen, et al. 2006; Swanson & Cowan, 1979) via a number of pathways, including the fornix. Directly implicating the septal nuclei in the memory functioning of the hippocampus (Bearer et al., 2007) is the finding that septal activation of this structure results in ACh secretion (Gage et al., 2003), whereas septal grafts into the hippocampus improves learning and memory (Gage et al., 1986). Conversely, lesions of the fimbria-fornix septal-hippocampal pathway results ACh depletion throughout the hippocampus (Gage et al., 2003; Olton, 1990), as well as loss of norepinephrine and serotonin coupled with memory loss (Olton, 1990).

The septal nucleus in part regulates hippocampal memory-related activity not only by stimulating ACh and other neurotransmitter production, but as it provides excitatory input and inhibitory-GABAnergic-- especially from the medial septal nuclei which in general exerts inhibitory influences not only on the hippocampus but the amygdala and hypothalamus. In general, it is supposed that the excitatory-inhibitory influences on the hippocampus (like those on the amygdala and hypothalamus) serve to modulate activity and prevent extremes in arousal (Joseph, 1992a, 2016d). This is accomplished in part not only through the interconnections maintained with the amygdala, hypothalamus and entorhinal cortex, but the brainstem reticular formation (Petsche et al., 1965)--with which the hippocampus is also connected directly and via the entorhinal cortex.

Septal influences on hippocampal/entorhinal arousal is also indicated by fluctuations in rhythmic slow activity (theta), which is generated by both the hippocampus and entorhinal cortex (Alonso & Garcia-Austt, 1987). Theta is an indication of hippocampal arousal (Green & Arduini, 1954; Petsche et al., 1965; Vanderwolf, 1992) and is associated with learning and memory (O'Keefe & Nadel, 2014). Theta is a robust electrophysiological phenomenon which has been found in the hippocampus of most species studied, including monkeys (Stewart & Fox, 1990) and humans (Sano et al., 1970); though in primates it seems to differ from the theta rhythm of non-primates (see Gloor, 1997).

O'Keefe and Nadel (2014) believe that theta plays an important role in creating the spatial maps that are maintained by hippocampal "place" neurons; i.e. pyramidal neurons which are attuned to specific environmental features and landmarks and the animals place in that environment as they move about. Moreover, long term potentiation (LTP) which is associated with learning and memory, is generated in those neurons demonstrating theta or activity that is at the "theta frequency" (Staubli & Lynch, 1987).

Neurons of the septal nucleus which innervate the hippocampus fluctuate in activity in parallel with changes in the theta rhythm (Petsche et al., 1965), whereas septal lesions abolish hippocampal theta (Green & Arduini, 1954). It has long been believed that septal neurons act as an interface between the reticular formation and the hippocampus (Petsche et al., 1965) and in conjunction with its connections with the amygdala and hypothalamus, therefore modulate hippocampal arousal as well as learning and memory (Bearer et al., 2007).

HIPPOCAMPAL & AMYGDALOID INTERACTIONS: MEMORY

It has been argued that significant impairments involving short-term memory and motor learning, cannot be produced by lesions supposedly restricted to the hippocampus (Horel, 2014; see also commentary in Eichenbaum et al. 2014); though in fact it is impossible to create such "restricted" lesions. Nevertheless, ignoring for the moment that inconvenient fact, in some instances with supposed restricted lesions, good recall of new information is possible for at least several minutes (Horel, 2014; Penfield & Milner, 1958; Squire 1992).

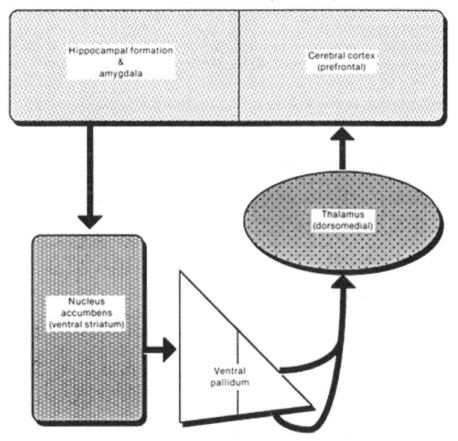

Moreover, there is considerable evidence which strongly suggests that the hippocampus plays an interdependent role with the amygdala in regard to memory (Gloor 1992, 1997; Halgren 1992; Kesner & Andrus, 1982; Lang et al., 2009; Mishkin, 2014; Murray 1992; Roozendaal et al., 2009; Sarter & Markowitsch, 2005); particularly in that they are richly interconnected, merge at the uncus, and exert mutual excitatory influences on one another. For example, it appears that the amygdala is responsible for storing the emotional aspects and personal reactions to events in memory (Kensinger et al., 2011; Lang et al. 2009; Pape & Pare, 2010; Poulos et al., 2009; Roozendaal et al., 2009), whereas the hippocampus acts to store the cognitive, visual, and contextual variables, whereas that the amygdala activates the hippocampus by providing excitatory input (Gloor, 1955, 1997).

Specifically, the amygdala plays a particularly important role in memory and learning when activities are related to reward and emotional arousal (Gaffan 1992; Gloor 1997; Halgren 1992; LeDoux 1996; Kesner 1992; Rolls 1992; Sarter & Markowitsch, 2005). Thus, if some event is associated with positive or negative emotional states it is more likely to be learned and remembered.

The amygdala becomes particularly active when recalling personal and emotional memories (Halgren, 1992; Heath, 1964; Penfield & Perot, 1963), and in response to cognitive and context determined stimuli regardless of their specific emotional qualities (Halgren, 1992). However, once these emotional memories are formed, it sometimes requires the specific emotional or associated visual context to trigger their recall (Rolls, 1992; Halgren, 1992). If those cues are not provided or ceased to be available, the original memory may not be triggered and may appear to be forgotten or repressed. However, even emotional context can trigger memory (Halgren, 1992) in the absence of specific cognitive cues.

Similarly, it is also possible for emotional and non-emotional memories to be activated in the absence of active search and retrieval, and thus without hippocampal or frontal lobe participation. Recognition memory which may be triggered by contextual or emotional cues. Indeed, there are a small group of neurons in the amygdala, as well as a larger group in the inferior temporal lobe which are involved in recognition memory (Murray, 1992; Rolls, 1992). Because of amygdaloid sensitivity to visual and emotional cues, even long forgotten memories may be evoked via recognition, even when search and retrieval repeatedly fail to activate the relevant memory store.

According to Gloor (1992), "a perceptual experience similar to a previous one can through activation of the isocortical population involved in the original experience recreate the entire matrix which corresponds to it and call forth the memory of the original event and an appropriate affective response through the activation of amygdaloid neurons." This can occur "at a relatively non-cognitive (affective) level, and thus lead to full or partial recall of the original perceptual message associated with the appropriate affect."

In this regard, it appears that the amygdala is responsible for emotional memory formation whereas the hippocampus is concerned with storing verbal-visual-spatial and contextual details in memory. Thus, in rats and primates damage to the hippocampus can impair retention of context, and contextual fear conditioning, but it has no effect on the retention of the fear itself or the fear reaction to the original cue (Kim & Fanselow 1992; Phillips & LeDoux 1992, 1996; Rudy & Morledge 2014). In these instances, fear-memory is retained due to preservation of the amygdala. However, when both the amygdala and hippocampus are damaged, striking and profound disturbances in memory functioning result (Kesner & Andrus, 1982; Mishkin, 2014).

Therefore, the role of the amygdala in memory and learning seems to involve activities related to reward, orientation, and attention, as well as emotional arousal and social-emotional recognition (Gloor, 1992, 1997; Rolls, 1992; Sarter & Markowitsch, 2005). If some event is associated with positive or negative emotional states it is more likely to be learned and remembered. That is, reward increases the probability of attention being paid to a particular stimulus or consequence as a function of its association with reinforcement (Gaffan 1992; Douglas, 2007; Kesner & Andrus, 1982).

Moreover, the amygdala appears to reinforce and maintain hippocampal activity via the identification of motivationally significant information and the generation of pleasurable rewards (through action on the lateral hypothalamus). However, the amygdala and hippocampus act differentially in regard to the effects of positive vs. negative reinforcement on learning and memory, particularly when highly stressed or repetitively aroused in a negative fashion. For example, whereas the hippocampus produces theta in response to noxious stimuli the amygdala increases its activity following the reception of a reward (Norton, 1970).

TEMPORAL LOBES & LATERALITY

It is now very well known that lesions involving the mesial-inferior temporal lobes (i.e. destruction or damage to the amygdala/hippocampus) of the left cerebral hemisphere typically produce significant disturbances involving verbal memory--particularly as contrasted with individuals with right sided destruction. Left sided damage disrupts the ability to recall simple sentences, complex verbal narrative passages, or to learn verbal paired-associates or a series of digits (Frisk & Milner 1990; Milner, 1966, 1970, 1971; Squire 1992).

In contract, right temporal destruction typically produces deficits involving visual memory, such as the learning and recall of geometric patterns, visual or tactile mazes, locations, objects, emotional sounds, or human faces (Corkin, 1965; Milner, 1965; Nunn et al., 2016; Kimura, 1963). Right sided damage also disrupts the ability to recognize (via recall) olfactory stimuli (Rausch et al. 1977), or recall emotional passages or personal memories (Cimino et al., 1991; Wechsler, 1973).

It appears, therefore, that the left amygdala and hippocampus are highly involved in processing and/or attending to verbal information, whereas the right amygdala/hippocampus is more involved in the learning, memory and recollection of non-verbal, visual-spatial, environmental, emotional, motivational, tactile, olfactory, and facial information.

THE PRIMARY PROCESS: AMYGDALA & PLEASURE

The amygdala maintains a functionally interdependent relationship with the hypothalamus in regard to emotional, sexual, autonomic, consummatory and motivational concerns. It is able to modulate and even control rudimentary emotional forces governed by the hypothalamic nucleus. However, the amygdala also acts at the behest of hypothalamically induced drives. For example, if certain nutritional requirements need to be meet, the hypothalamus signals the amygdala which then surveys the external environment for something good to eat (Joseph, 1982, 1992a). On the other hand, if the amygdala via environmental surveillance were to discover a potentially threatening stimulus, it acts to excite and drive the hypothalamus as well as the basal ganglia so that the organism is mobilized to take appropriate action.

When the hypothalamus is activated by the amygdala, instead of responding in an on/off manner, cellular activity continues for an appreciably longer time period (Dreifuss et. al., 1968). The amygdala can tap into the reservoir of emotional energy mediated by the hypothalamus so that certain ends may be attained (Joseph, 1982, 1992a)

AMYGDALA & HIPPOCAMPAL HALLUCINATIONS DURING INFANCY

The amygdala-hippocampal complex, particularly that of the right hemisphere, is very important in the production and recollection of non-linguistic and verbal-emotional images associated with past experience. In fact direct electrical stimulation of the temporal lobes, hippocampus and particularly the amygdala (Gloor, 1990, 1997) not only results in the recollection of images, but in the creation of fully formed visual and auditory hallucinations (Gloor 1992, 1997; Halgren 1992; Halgren et al., 2014; Horowitz et al., 1968; Malh et al., 1964; Penfield & Perot, 1963), as well as feelings of familiarity (e.g. deja vu).

Indeed, it has long been know that tumors invading specific regions of the brain can trigger the formation of hallucinations which range from the simple (flashing lights) to the complex. The most complex forms of hallucination, however, are associated with tumors within the most anterior portion of the temporal lobe (Critchley, 1939; Gibbs, 1951; Gloor 1992, 1997; Halgren 1992; Horowitz et al. 1968; Tarachow, 1941); i.e. the region containing the amygdala and anterior hippocampus.

Similarly, electrical stimulation of the anterior lateral temporal cortical surface results in visual hallucinations of people, objects, faces, and various sounds

(Gloor 1992, 1997; Halgren 1992; Horowitz et al., 1968)--particularly the right temporal lobe (Halgren et al. 2014). Depth electrode stimulation and thus direct activation of the amygdala and/or hippocampus is especially effective.

For example, stimulation of the right amygdala produces complex visual hallucinations, body sensations, deja vu, illusions, as well as gustatory and alimentary experiences (Weingarten et al. 1977), whereas Freeman and Williams (1963) have reported that the surgical removal of the right amygdala in one patient abolished hallucinations. Stimulation of the right hippocampus has also been associated with the production of memory- and dream-like hallucinations (Halgren et al. 2014; Horowitz et al. 1968).

The amygdala also becomes activated in response to bizarre stimuli (Halgren, 1992). Conversely, if activated to an abnormal degree, it may in turn produce bizarre memories and abnormal perceptual experiences. In fact, the amygdala contributes in large part to the production of very sexual as well as bizarre, unusual and fearful memories and mental phenomenon including dissociative states, feelings of depersonalization, and hallucinogenic and dream-like recollections (Bear, 1979; Gloor, 1986, 1992, 1997; Horowitz et al. 1968; Mesulam, 1981; Penfield & Perot, 1963; Weingarten et al. 1977; Williams, 1956). In addition, sexual feelings and related activity and behavior are often evoked by amygdala stimulation and temporal lobe seizures including memories of sexual intercourse or severe emotional trauma and abuse (Gloor, 1997).

Moreover, intense activation of the temporal lobe and amygdala has been reported to give rise to a host of sexual, religious and spiritual experiences; and chronic hyperstimulation (i.e. seizure activity) can induce some individuals to become hyper-religious or visualize and experience ghosts, demons, angels, and even God, as well as claim demonic and angelic possession or the sensation of having left their body (Bear 1979; Gloor 1986, 1992; Horowitz, Adams & Rutkin 1968; MacLean 1990; Mesulam 1981; Penfield & Perot 1963; Schenk, & Bear 1981; Weingarten, et al. 1977; Williams 1956).

LSD

As is well known, LSD can elicit profound hallucinations involving all spheres of experience. Following the administration of LSD high amplitude slow waves (theta) and bursts of paroxysmal spike discharges occurs in the hippocampus and amygdala (Chapman & Walter, 1965; Chapman et al. 1963), but with little cortical abnormal activity. In both humans and chimps, when the temporal lobes, amygdala and hippocampus are removed, LSD ceased to produce hallucinatory phenomena (Baldwin et al. 1959; Serafintides, 1965). Moreover, LSD induced hallucinations are significantly reduced when the right vs. left temporal lobe has been surgically ablated (Serafintides, 1965).

Overall, it appears that the amygdala, hippocampus, and the neocortex of the temporal lobe are highly interactionally involved in the production of hallucinatory experiences. Presumably, it is the neocortex of the temporal lobe which acts to interpret this material (Penfield & Perot, 1963) as perceptual phenomena. Indeed, it is the interrelated activity of the temporal lobes, hippocampus and amygdala which not only produce memories and hallucinations, but dreams. In fact, the amygdala's involvement in all aspects of emotion and sexual functioning, including associated memories, the production of overwhelming fear as well as bizarre and dream-like mental phenomenon, may well account for why this type of unusual stimuli, including personal and innocuous memories also appears in dreams.

DREAMING

When hallucinations follow depth electrode or cortical stimulation, much of the material experienced is very dream-like (Gloor 1990, 1992; Halgren et al., 2014; Malh et al., 1964; Penfield & Perot 1963) and consists of recent perceptions, ideas, feelings, and other emotions which are similarly illusionary and dream-like. Indeed, the right amygdala, hippocampus, and the right hemisphere in general (Broughton, 1982; Goldstein et al., 1972; Hodoba, 1986; Humphrey & Zangwill, 1961; Joseph 2011; Kerr & Foulkes, 2014; Meyer et al. 1987) also appear to be involved in the production of dream imagery as well as REM sleep. For example stimulation of the amygdala triggers and increases ponto-geniculo-occipital paradoxical activity during sleep (Calvo, et al. 1987), which in turn is associated with REM and dreaming. In addition, during REM, the hippocampus begins to produce slow wave, theta activity (Jouvet, 2007; Olmstead, Best, & Mays, 1973; Robinson et al. 1977), which is associated with long-term potentiation which is associated with learning and memory. Presumably, during REM, the hippocampus and amygdala act as a reservoir from which various images, emotions, words, and ideas are drawn and incorporated into the matrix of dream-like activity being woven by the right hemisphere. It is probably just as likely that the right hippocampus and amygdala serve as a source from which material is drawn during the course of a daydream.

The Right Hemisphere & Dreams

There have been reports of patients with right cerebral damage, hypoplasia and abnormalities in the corpus callosum who have ceased dreaming altogether, suffer a loss of hypnogogic imagery or tend to dream only in words (Botez et al.

2005; Humphrey & Zangwill, 1951; Kerr & Foulkes, 1981; Murri et al. 1984). However, there have also been some report that when the left hemisphere has been damaged, particularly the posterior portions (i.e. aphasic patients), the ability to verbally report and recall dreams also is greatly attenuated (e.g., Murri et al. 1984). Of course, aphasics have difficulty describing much of anything, let alone their dreams.

Electrophysiologically the right hemisphere also becomes highly active during REM, whereas, conversely, the left brain becomes more active during N-REM (Goldstein et al. 1972; Hodoba, 1986). Similarly, measurements of cerebral blood flow have shown an increase in the right temporal regions during REM sleep and in subjects who upon wakening report visual, hypnogogic, hallucinatory and auditory dreaming (Meyer et al. 1987). Interestingly, abnormal and enhanced activity in the right temporal and temporal-occipital area acts to increase dreaming and REM sleep for an atypically long time period (Hodoba, 1986). Hence, it appears that there is a specific complementary relationship between REM sleep and right temporal electrophysiological activity.

Interestingly, daydreams appear to follow the same 90-120 minute cycle that characterize the fluctuation between REM and NREM periods, as well as fluctuations in mental capabilities associated with the right and left hemisphere (Broughton, 1982; Kripke & Sonneschein 1973). That is, the cerebral hemisphere tend to oscillate in activity every 90-120 minutes -- a cycle which appears to correspond to the REM-NREM cycle and the appearance of day and night dreams.

Forgotten Dreams

Most individuals, however, have difficulty recalling their dreams. This may seem paradoxical considering that hippocampal theta is being produced. However, this is theta punctuated by high levels of desychronized activity, which is not conducive to learning. In this regard, theta activity may represent the reverberating activity of neural circuits formed during the day, such that the residue of day time memories come to be inserted into the dream. Conversely, due to the high level of desychronization occurring in the hippocampus (as it is so highly aroused), although it contributes images and the days memories, it does not participate in storing these dream-like experiences into memory.

Consider the results from temporal lobe, amygdala, and hippocampal electrical stimulation on memory recall and the production of hallucinations. Although personal memories are often activated at low intensities of stimulation (memories which are verified not only by the patient but family), if stimulation is sufficiently intense, the memory instead will become dreamlike and populated by hallucinated and cartoon like characters (Halgren, et al. 2014). That is, at low levels of stimulation memories are triggered but these memories become increasingly dream-like with high levels of activity. Moreover, once these high levels of stimulation are terminated, patients soon become verbally amnesic and fail to verbally recall having had these experiences (Gloor, 1992; Horowitz, et al. 1968). However, these memories can be later recalled if subjects are provided with specific contextual cues (Horowitz, et al. 1968). The same can occur during the course of the day when a fragment of a conversation, or some other experience, suddenly triggers the recall of a dream from the previous night which had otherwise been completely forgotten. Presumably it had seemingly been forgotten because the hippocampus did not participate in their storage and thus could not assist in their retrieval.

There is also some evidence to suggest that different regions of the hippocampus show different levels of arousal during paradoxical sleep. For example, it appears that the posterior hippocampus becomes activated during paradoxical sleep and shows theta activity, whereas the more anterior portions become inhibited (Olmstead et al. 1973). As the anterior portions are more involved in new learning (at least in humans), whereas the posterior hippocampus is more concerned with old and well established memories, this would suggest that the posterior hippocampus is contributing older or already established memories to the content of the dream--which explains why theta, which is associated with learning and memory, is also produced during the dream--that is, it is replaying various fragmentary memories. Conversely, the inhibition of the anterior region would prevent this dream material from becoming re memorized.

DREAMS & INFANCY

In the newborn, and up until approximately 6-9 months, there are two distinct stages of sleep which correspond to REM and N-REM periods demonstrated by adults (Berg & Berg, 2014; Dreyfus-Brisac & Monod, 2015; Parmelee et al. 2007). Among infants, however, REM occur during wakefullness as well as during sleep. In fact, REM can be observed when the eyes are open, when the infant is crying, fussing, eating, or sucking (Emde & Metcalf, 1970). Moreover, REM is also observed to occur within a few moments after an infant begins to engage in nutritional sucking and appears identical to that which occurs during sleep (Emde & Metcalf, 1970).

The production of REM during waking in some respects seems paradoxical. Nevertheless, it might be safe to assume that like an adult, when the infant is in REM, he or she is dreaming, or at least, in a dream-like state. Possibly, this state corresponds to what Freud has described as the Primary Process. That is, when produced when the infant is crying or fussing, it is dreaming of whatever relief it seeks. Correspondingly, REM which occurs while eating or sucking may have to do with the limbic structures which are involved not only in the production of dream-like activity, but the identification, learning and retention of motivationally significant information (i.e. the amygdala and hippocampus).

Presumably this relationship is a consequence of REM as well as eating and sucking being mediated, in part, by the amygdala as well as other limbic nuclei, which are also concerned with forming motivationally significant memories. Hence, when hungry, the hypothalamus becomes aroused which activates the amygdala which is responsible for the performing environmental surveillance so as to attend, orient to, identify and approach motivationally significant stimuli and eat. However, because the infants brain is so immature and as its resources for meeting its limbic needs are quite rudimentary, under certain conditions prolonged hypothalamus induced amygdala activation results in the formation and recall of relevant memories which may be experienced as hallucinations of the desired object. That is, previously formed neural networks become activated and the infant begins to dream and hallucinate food and will then suck and smack its lips as if eating or sucking when it is awake, in REM, and there is no food present.

THE PRIMARY PROCESS

The hypothalamus, our exceedingly ancient and primitive Id, has an eye that only sees inward. It can tell if the body needs nourishment but cannot determine what might be good to eat. It can feel thirst, but has no way of slacking this desire. The hypothalamus can only say: "I want", "I need", and can only signal pleasure and displeasure. However, being the seat of pleasure, the hypothalamus can be exceedingly gracious in rewarding the organism when its needs are met. Conversely, when its needs go unmet it can respond not only with displeasure and feelings of aversion, but with undirected fury and rage. It can cause the organism to cry out. Nevertheless, the cry does not produce the immediately desire relief or reduction in tension. There is thus a pressure on the limbic system and the organism to engage in environmental surveillance so as to meet the needs monitored by the hypothalamus.

Over the course of the first months of life, as the amygdala and then hippocampus develop, the organism begins to develop an eye that not only sees outward, but which can register and recall events, objects, people, etc., associated with tension reduction, pleasure and the satiaty of the infants internal needs (e.g. the taste, smell, feeling of mother's breast and milk, the experience of sucking and relief, etc.). This is called learning.

With the maturation of these two limbic nuclei the infant is increasingly able to differentiate what occurs in the external environment based on hypothalamically monitored needs and the emotional/motivational significance of that which is experienced. The infant can now orient, selectively attend, determine what brings satisfaction, and store this information in memory.

PRIMARY IMAGERY

Although admittedly we have no direct knowledge as to the psychic interactions in the neonate, it does seem reasonable to assume that as the neocortex and underlying structures and fiber pathways mature, neural "programs" are formed which correspond to the repeated registration of experiences which are deemed significant (e.g. pleasurable). That is, neural pathways which are repetitively fired, deactivated or activated in response to specific sensory and affective activities and experiences, become associated with that activity, such that an associated neural circuit is formed; i.e. a memory is created. Eventually, if this circuit is reactivated, the "learned" pattern is reexperienced; i.e. the organism remembers.

Infants as young as 2 days of age can learn to suck at the mere sight of a bottle and in order to receive milk as a reinforcement, infants can even modify their sucking response. Hence, they are susceptible to classical conditioning, although the possibility of operant conditioning has not been established. Nevertheless, the fact that they can recognize the bottle and suck (as well as cry and shed tears) indicates that various regions of the limbic system, especially that of the amygdala is functional and that learning and the creation of specific, context specific neural circuits have been formed very early in life. Thus, when the amygdala/hippocampus are stimulated by a hungry hypothalamus, the events and images associated with past experiences of pleasure can not only be searched out externally, but recalled in imaginal form. For example, as an infant experiences hunger and stomach contractions as well as it own cries of displeasure, these states become associated with the sound, smell, taste, etc. of mother and her associated movement and other stimuli which accompany being fed (cf Piaget, 1952). Repetitively experienced, the sequence from hunger to satiety becomes associated with the activation of certain neural pathways and the creation of a specific neural network subserving that memory.

Eventually, when the infant becomes hungry, if prolonged there is the possibility that the entire neural sequence associated with hunger and feeding (i.e. hunger, mother, food, satiaty), may become involuntarily triggered and activated (via association) such that an "image" of being fed is experienced. The activation of these rudimentary and infantile memory-images is probably what constitutes, at least in part, the primary process.

Behaviorally this is manifested by REM and via sucking and tongue movements as if eating, when in fact there is no food present (cf, Piaget, 1952). That is, when hungry, the infant will begin to cry, rapid eye movement (REM) might be observed, and then the infant will stop crying and smack its lips and make sucking movement (mediated by the amygdala) as if it were being fed. The infant experiences the experience of being fed in the form of a dream (Joseph, 1982) or hallucination, although it is awake.

In that the brain of the human infant is quite immature for in fact several years, which in turn restricts information reception and processing, and given the limited amount of reality contact infants are able to achieve, these rudimentary memories and images (even when occurring during waking, i.e. REM), are probably indistinguishable from actual experience simply because they are experience. Like a dream, when replayed, the infant presumably reexperiences to some degree the sensations, emotions, etc., originally linked to tension reduction. Thus, the young infant, as yet unable to distinguish between representation and reality, responds to the image as reality (Freud, 1900, 1911), even while awake--as manifested by REM. When hunger is prolonged the association linked to feeding are triggered and for a brief time period the infant behaves as if its hunger has been sated. Reality is replaced by an image, or rather, a "dream". This is the primary process.

Since the hypothalamus (which monitors internal homeostasis) is not conscious that the dream images experienced are not real, it initially accepts the memory/dream images transmitted from the amygdala and hippocampus and ceases to cry, i.e. it responds to the imagined sources of nourishment just as it responds to a cue-tone associated with a food reward (Nakamuar & Ono, 1986; Ono et al., 1980). However, the hypothalamus is not long fooled, for the primary process does not offer effective long lasting relief from tension. As the pain of hunger remains and increases, limbic activity is increased, and the image falls away to be replaced by a cry of hunger (Joseph, 1982). The amygdala and hippocampus are thus forced to renew their surveillance of the environment in search of sources of tension reduction. Cognitive development is thus promoted.

"Whatever was thought of (desired) was simply imagined in an hallucinatory form, as still happens today with our dream-thoughts every night. This attempt at satisfaction by means of hallucination was abandoned only in consequence of the absence of the expected gratification, because of the disappointment experienced. Instead, the mental apparatus had to decide to form a conception of the real circumstances in the outer world and to exert itself to alter them... The increased significance of external reality heightened the significance also of the sense-organs directed towards the outer word, and of the consciousness attached to them; the later now learned to comprehend the qualities of sense in addition to the qualities of pleasure and "pain" which hitherto had alone been of interest to it. A special function was instituted which had periodically to search the outer word in order that its data might be already familiar if an urgent need should arise; this function was attention. Its activity meets the sense-impressions halfway, instead of awaiting their appearance. At the same time there was probably introduced a system of notation, whose task was to deposit the results of this periodical activity of consciousness--a part of that which we call memory" (Freud, 1911, pp. 410-411).

Part II
Limbic Language & Social Emotional Development
Hypothalamus, Amygdala,
Septal Nuclei, Cingulate

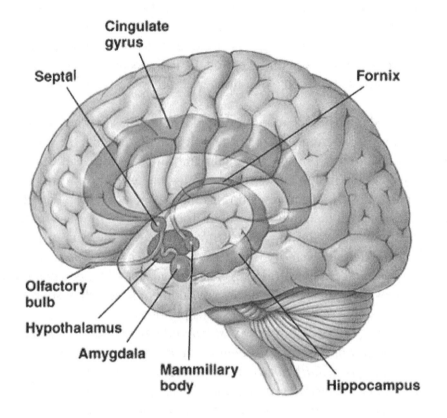

The core of our emotionality including the capacity to speak and comprehend emotional language is mediated by the sexually differentiated limbic system. Emotional and language development parallels the maturation of specific diencephalic and limbic forebrain structures, notably the brainstem and hypothalamus, followed by the medial amygdala and lateral amygdala, and then the septal nuclei and anterior cingulate (Joseph, 1992a, 2016b).

The brainstem and forebrain matures in a caudal to rostral and paramedian to lateral arc (Barkovich et al., 1988; Brody et al., 1987; Gibson, 1991; Harbord, et al., 1990; Holland, et al., 1986; Lee et al., 1986; Joseph 2000; Langworthy, 1937; Lee et al., 1986; Styles, 2008; Yakovlev & Lecours, 2007). Therefore, functions associated with earlier developing structures such as the brainstem, appear in advance of later maturing tissues, such as the hypothalamus, followed by the amygdala, septal nucleus, anterior cingulate and neocortex (Joseph 1992, 2000). Hence, for the first several weeks of postnatal life, much of human behavior, and the first rudimentary expressions of "emotion" and "cognition" including "smiling" and vocalization, are under the reflexive control of the brainstem with the still immature hypothalamus exerting increasing influences over the ensuing days and weeks (Joseph 2000). As based on physiological indices "the general rule appears to be that phylogenetically older structures (e.g. brainstem, cerebellum, thalamus) demonstrate considerable metabolic maturity compared to telencephalic structures in the neonatal period" (Chugani, 2014, p. 155).

Because the brainstem and then the forebrain matures in a caudal to rostral and paramedian to lateral arc, functions associated with the brainstem appear in advance of the hypothalamus which appears in advance of those associated with the amygdala which begin to emerge in advance of those associated with the septal nucleus and anterior cingulate, which appear in advance of those associated with the neocortex (Joseph 1996). These differential maturational gradients are evident not only neuroanatomically and physiologically, but behaviorally and functionally and also account for the emergence of sex differences even at this tender age. That is, the overlapping progressive maturation of these limbic structures corresponds to and parallels the development of complex emotions and affective behaviors, i.e., pleasure, joy, wariness, fear, separation anxiety and the establishment of loving attachments and social-emotional speech. Moreover, because these structures are sexually differentiated, as they mature, sex differences in affective and social behavior becomes more pronounced. In addition, because these structures mature at overlapping rates (Benes, 2014; Yakovlev & Lecours, 2007), the ability to perceive and express various social-emotional nuances behaviorally and through the expression of language also emerge and develop at different ages.

Consider for example, the development of separation anxiety and fear of strangers. Initially the infant welcomes attention from family and strangers. This stage of fearlessness and willingness to seek contact comfort even from strangers, is due, in part, to the immaturity of the amygdala (as well as the cingulate gyrus and septal nuclei), whereas the formation of specific attachments, and the development of separation anxiety and fear of strangers parallels the functional maturity of these same limbic structures (Joseph 1996).

Initially the infant is fearless. Fear is an emotion associated with the amygdala (Davis et al. 1997; Gloor, 1997; Halgren, 1992; Pessoa & Adolphs 2010; Poulos et al., 2009; LeDoux, 1996; Rosen & Schulkin, 1998; Whalen & Phelps, 2009). However, the human medial amygdala is exceedingly immature at birth and doesn't become well myelinated until around the 8th postnatal month (Gilles et al. 2003; Langworthy, 1937; Yakovlev & Lecours, 2007)--the development of axonal myelin insulation being one of many indicators of functional maturation and synaptic viability. Likewise, the infant does not begin to demonstrate fear until around the 8th postnatal month (Snow & McGaha 2002; Tronic 2007); an emotion that develops after the emergence of wariness at around 6 months (which is also an amygdala mediated emotion). Hence, paralleling the maturation and myelination of the medial amygdala, at 6 months the infant first experiences and expresses wariness, and at 8-months the infant first begins to experience and express feelings of fear, and then becomes progressively more fearful, such as in response to an approaching stranger (Bronson, 1972; Emde et al. 1976; Sroufe & Waters, 1976; Snow & McGaha 2002; Tronic 2007). This initial fearlessness (and amygdala immaturity) is exceedingly adaptive, for the generation of fear would interfere with the initial establishment of intimate emotional attachments, and the infant's need for considerable social-emotional and physical stimulation (Joseph 2016), which is initially and eagerly welcomed even from strangers.

Over the ensuing months, and due to increasing amygdala as well as septal and anterior cingulate influences, emotional perception and expression becomes increasingly complex, the infant demands considerable social and emotional stimulation, but then, around 8 to 12 months of age, begins to increasingly demonstrate fear and separation anxiety. It is also at this later age that males and females will begin vocalizing a separation cry and will begin forming specific and enduring attachments while avoiding contact with strangers.

Whereas fear is directly associated with amygdala maturation, separation anxiety, the separation cry, and the formation of specific emotional attachments are also associated with the maturation of the septal nuclei and anterior cingulate (Joseph, 1992, 1996). These limbic structures are also "experience-expectant" and require considerable social emotional and maternal input to develop normally. If subjected to sexual, physical, or emotional abuse, or other forms of traumatic stress, or if sufficient social, emotional, or maternal stimulation is not provided during each critical stage of structural development, the hypothalamus, amygdala, septal nuclei, or cingulate will abnormally develop and social emotional and even sexual functioning may become abnormal (Joseph 1996, 2016).

THE NEONATAL BRAINSTEM: FUNCTIONAL OVERVIEW

The brainstem consists of the medulla, pons, and midbrain. When specific brainstem nuclei are stimulated, involuntary, stereotyped and routine motor acts can be produced such as groping, grasping, opening and closing the mouth, touching the mouth or wiping the face with the hand, as well as visual tracking, head elevation, head turning, sucking, chewing, swallowing, screaming, and crying (Blessing, 1997; Cowie et al., 2014; Davidson & Bender, 1991; Larson et al., 2014; Skinner & Garcia-Rill, 1990; Zhang et al., 2014). Identical behaviors are demonstrated by the new born infant (Capute, 1986; Debakan, 1970; McGraw,

1969; Piper & Darrah, 2014; Piaget, 1952; Snow & McGaha 2002). Moreover, these same behaviors, including screaming, crying, rudimentary smiling, and involuntary grasping and groping, can be triggered in the complete absence of the forebrain, and are demonstrated by some anencepahlics who have only a functional brainstem (Emde et al., 1976; Lemire et al., 2014; Monnier, 1956). Given the immaturity of the forebrain and the fact that there are no myelinated fibers beyond the neonatal brainstem (Yakovlev & Lecours, 2007), it can thus be concluded that these behaviors are under the reflexive control of the brainstem.

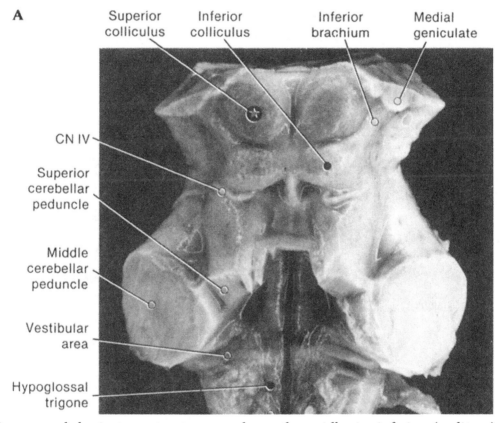

For example,brainstem structures such as the midbrain inferior (auditory) colliculi can perceive and discriminate between a wide variety of acoustic parameters, and can trigger head turning and eye movement (Aitkin, 1986; Merzenich & Reid, 1974). Likewise, the neonate is able to discriminate phonetic sounds within days after birth (Eimas, 2005) as well as turn the head and orient with the eyes or react with whole body movements to sudden or loud sounds; i.e. the Moro reflex (Capute et al 1986; Debakan, 1970; McGraw, 1969; Piper & Darrah, 2014; Snow & McGaha 2002). Similar behaviors are typical of some anencephalics (Lemire et al., 2014) and are thus brainstem reflexes. Likewise, because the superior (visual) colliculus is sensitive to and can trigger eye and head movements in reaction to visual motion but not stationary stimuli (Davidson & Bender, 1991), for the first several postnatal days the infant is almost completely unresponsive to stationary stimuli but may fixate on and briefly follow moving objects (Bronson, 1974; Piper & Darrah, 2014; Snow & McGaha 2002).

The neonate as well as anencephalics, however, are capable of screaming and crying, as well as turning up the corners of their mouths as if "smiling" (Lemire et al., 2014; Monnier, 1956). However, these too are brainstem reflexes. When directly stimulated, brainstem nuclei and associated oral-facial cranial nerves can produce a wide range of facial expressions such as smiling (Weinstein & Bender, 1943), as well as crying and screaming --vocalizations which are produced by the midbrain periaqueductal gray (Newman 2007, 2010; Jurgens 1990, 2009). The midbrain periaqueductal gray controls the oral-laryngeal musculature (Jurgens, 2014; Larson et al., 2014; Zhang et al., 2014) and via lower brainstem nuclei, can induce inspiration and respiration thus producing a variety of loud sounds including grunting, crying, and screaming.

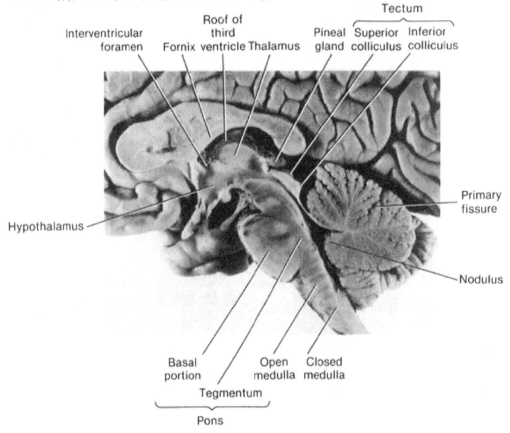

In the child and adult, brainstem nuclei, including the periaqueductal gray are subject to hierarchical forebrain and neocortical control. Hence, through forebrain influences, individuals can purposeful smile, laugh, crying, and so on, or at least pretend to do so. However, forebrain influences are only brought to bear later in development well after birth. Again, there is no evidence of myelinated fibers anterior to the midbrain during the first few days and weeks after birth (Langworthy, 1937; Yakovlev & Lecours, 2007). Given numerous indices which indicate little or no forebrain activity in the newborn (Chugani, 2014; Chugani,

Phelps, & Mazziotta, 1987; Kellaway, 1979; Langworthy, 1937; Ohtahara, 1981; McGraw, 1969), it appears that these behaviors are also innate brainstem reflexes. This is why some anencephalics--babies born without a forebrain--can also smile, grunt and cry out (Lemire et al., 2014; Monnier, 1956). Although conscious cognitive and meaningful emotional activity is implied, these vocalizations and facial expressions are brainstem reflexes.

SHAM EMOTIONS AND THE NEONATAL "SMILE"

Infants born with only a brainstem, i.e. anencephalics, are capable of crying, screaming, grunting, and make other sounds typical of infants (Lemire et al., 2014). Anencephalics can also "smile" and their "smile" is indistinguishable from that of a "normal" infant (Monnier, 1956). Likewise, stimulation of the brainstem can trigger a variety of facial expressions, including a wide grinned smile (Weinstein & Bender, 1943). However, these "smiles" are devoid of emotion, as they are brainstem reflexes.

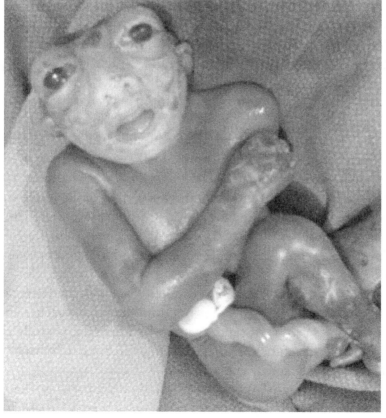

Like the anencephalic, the neonate can also "smile" (Izard, 1991; Sroufe, 1996; Snow & McGaha 2002; Tronic 2007). However, rather than a "true smile" the neonate and week-old infant (like the anencephalic), slightly lifts the corners of its mouth upward. However, there is little evidence that these "smiles" represent true emotions (Spitz et al. 1970; Sroufe, 1996; Wolff, 1963), as they instead appear to be brainstem reflexes. Some investigators (Bremner & Slater 2003), including Izard (1991), disagree with this view, and argue instead that the corresponding emotion is part of the infant's emotional repertoire regardless of the context in which the "smile" is produced. Thus, the infant "smiles" because it's happy and desirous of communicating these feelings. This view, however, is rather untenable, as it is the forebrain which experiences happiness or pleasure, and the forebrain of the week-old infant is exceedingly immature (Blinkov & Glezer, 1968; Conel, 1937) and there is almost no evidence of forebrain metabolic activity (Chugani et al., 1987). It is not until about one year of age that neocortical glucose activity begins to significantly increase (Chugani et al., 1987). Again, anencephalics are capable of "smiling" (Monnier, 1956). However, anencephalics do not possess an "emotional repertoire" as they do not possess a forebrain (Lemire et al., 2014). Hence, perhaps these "smiling" reactions should be considered "sham" emotions.

In fact, rather than indicating happiness, excitement or pleasure, neonatal smiles are often a prelude to immediately falling asleep and occur when the infant is tired and drowsy (Sroufe, 1996; Wolff, 1963). For example, although smiling can be triggered by feeding, as well as through vigorous visual and auditory stimulation, including the repetitive honking of a horn (Sroufe, 1996; Wolff, 1963), the infant will also immediately fall asleep and demonstrate REM-rapid eye movements (Emde & Koenig, 1969; Tennes, Emde, Kilsley, & Metcalf, 1972). Likewise, by the end of the first month smiling can be triggered by a nodding head or mother's voice (Wolff, 1963; Tronic 2007). Again, however, the infant not only "smiles" but it may immediately fall asleep and display REM (Emde & Koenig, 1969; Emde et al. 1976; Tennes et al., 1972); and REM as well as reflexive "smiling" are brainstem mediated activities (Steriade & McCarley, 1990; Weinstein & Bender, 1943). Moreover, for the first several months of life most "smiling" occurs during REM sleep (Emde et al., 1976; Sroufe & Waters, 1976). In addition, for the first two months, physical stimulation, such as jiggling the infant or blowing on the skin, can trigger a "smile" even while the infant is sleeping (Emde & Koenig, 1969).

If the infant were truly happy, these same smiles should occur even more frequently when alert and awake. However, it's not until the infant reaches about 3-months of age that smiles can be easily triggered when the infant is fully alert (Wolff, 1963; Tronic 2007); a function of increasing forebrain maturity (e.g. Hallett & Proctor, 1996; Herschkowitz et al., 1997).

Therefore, for the first several days and weeks, rather than feeling "happy" when the "smile" is produced, it appears the brainstem is merely aroused and triggering reflexive facial movements. That is, the brainstem activates the oral and facial musculature thus producing a "smiling" face in response to generalized and nonspecific tactile, visual and auditory stimulation and arousal, and while asleep and in REM. Thus, the brainstem appears to maintain the neural-musculature motor-memories for producing smiles, and these motor components are produced during the first few hours and days after birth.

Over the ensuing months, not only does true smiling gradually emerge, but reflexive smiling (as well as crying) declines (Herschkowitz et al., 1997); findings which suggest increasing forebrain control over the brainstem.

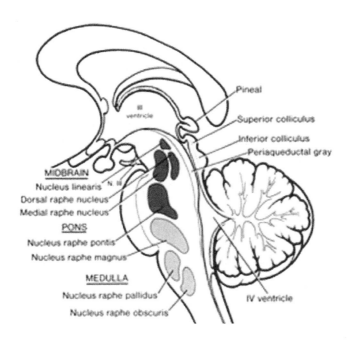

HYPOTHALAMUS, PERIAQUEDUCTAL GRAY, VOCALIZATION, QUIESCENCE, DISTRESS

For the first several postnatal weeks, other than quiescence, the infant displays only one behavioral state suggestive of emotion: displeasure --demonstrated by crying and screaming (McGraw, 1969; Piaget, 1952; Snow & McGaha 2002; Spitz & Wolf, 1946; Tronic 2007). As based on neuroanatomical, metabolic, and physiological indices, these particular behaviors appear to be triggered by the still immature hypothalamus in conjunction with the midbrain periaqueductal gray which controls the oral-laryngeal musculature. When activated the periaqueductal gray acts on and coordinates the activity of the laryngeal, oral-facial, and principal and accessory muscles of respiration and inspiration and can thus vocalize a variety of sounds, including grunting, screaming, yelling, as well as crying in reaction to noxious stimuli (Jurgens, 2014; Gonzalez-Lima 2010; Larson et al., 2014; Newman 2010; Siegel et al., 2010; Zhang et al., 2014).

Specifically, the "motor engrams" for vocalization appear to be pre-programmed into the midbrain periaqueductal gray (Jurgens, 2014; Larson et al., 2014; Zhang et al., 2014). Hence, if the periaqueductal gray is disconnected from the limbic system and neocortex (such as by a midbrain transection), although language can no longer be produced, stimulation of this nuclei, or the immediately adjacent diencephalon (Davison & Kelman, 1939; Ironside, 1956; Martin, 1950) will continue to evoke vocalizations that are little different from a howling infant. This is why babies born without a forebrain can also grunt and cry out (Lemire et al., 2014; Monnier, 1956). Thus, initially, these infant vocalizations are brainstem reflexes.

The hypothalamus, which monitors hunger and thirst, and governs internal homeostasis, is immediately anterior to the brainstem, and is richly connected with the periaqueductal gray. Given that the medial hypothalamus begins to mature and has established its brainstem connections at birth (Gibson, 1991; Langworthy, 1937), this structure can also stimulate crying and screaming if the infant is experiencing hunger, thirst, or other internal noxious sensations.

Nuclei of the Hypothalamus

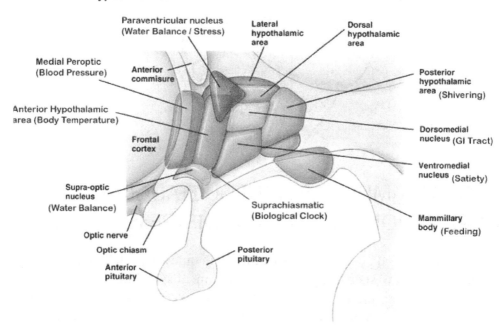

As noted, the brainstem generally matures in a caudal to rostral arc, and the forebrain in a paramedian to lateral direction. Thus, the medial hypothalamus matures in advance of the lateral hypothalamus (Joseph, 1992); though in fact the hypothalamus as a whole continues to grow in volume well into puberty (Jernigan et al., 1991). Nevertheless, the hypothalamus begins its cycle of maturation and myelination following the brainstem; and at birth, the fiber pathways linking the hypothalamus and the brainstem are well established (Debakan, 1970; Langworthy, 1937) and appear to be fully, or at least, semi-functional (Joseph, 1992 1996). Since the hypothalamus is directly implicated in the generation of noxious and unpleasant mood states (Borszcz, & Spuz 2010; MacLean, 1990; Olds

& Forbes, 1981; Siegel et al., 2010) it can be assumed that the hypothalamus, the medial hypothalamus in particular, which contributes and may be responsible for the infant's initial tendency to frequently cry as well as display displeasure. Depth electrode activation of the medial hypothalamus is so aversive subjects will work to reduce it (Olds & Forbes, 1981). Hence, at birth the medial hypothalamus appears fully capable of acting on the brainstem so as to reflexively trigger crying and distress, particularly in reaction to hunger and thirst as the hypothalamus also monitors internal homeostasis (Blouet et al., 2009; Milanski et al, 2009; Suzuki et al. 2010). And, it also appears to be responsible for generating quiescence such as following feeding.

The medial hypothalamus regulates the parasympathetic nervous system (e.g. reduction in heart rate, increased peripheral circulation) and exerts a dampening effect on certain forms of emotional/motivational arousal thereby producing quiescence. The parasympathetic nervous system also matures in advance of the (SNS) sympathetic nervous system (Schore, 2014) which controls and promotes extremes in emotionality including positive emotions. However, the SNS is governed by the later to mature lateral hypothalamus (MacLean, 1990; Smith, DeVito, Astley,1990).

Quiescence and distress, the two predominate behavioral states demonstrated by the infant (McGraw, 1969; Piaget, 1952; Snow & McGaha 2002; Spitz & Wolff, 1946; Tronic 2007), is thus associated with medial hypothalamic activity. Therefore, for the first several postnatal weeks it appears that the medial hypothalamus is responsible for and is able to reflexively activate the infant's brainstem so as to produce crying in response to hunger, or quiescence following feeding.

Over the ensuing weeks and months, the medial followed by the lateral hypothalamus continues to mature--a developmental process which continues until puberty (Yakovlev & Lecours, 2007). However, in contrast to the medial hypothalamus, the lateral nucleus is implicated in positive mood states (Olds, 1956; Olds & Forbes, 1981). Therefore, as the lateral hypothalamus matures, the infant begins to display genuine feelings of pleasure.

Thus, the infant's initial vocalizations and expression of *emotion* appear to be under the control of the brainstem and hypothalamus. As the brain continues to mature, these initial vocalizations will become increasingly complex and will parallel social and emotional behavioral and cognitive development--a function of the maturation of the amygdala followed by the septal nuclei and cingulate gyrus.

LIMBIC LANGUAGE

Human language, and the original impetus to vocalize, springs forth from roots buried within the depths of the ancient limbic lobes which is buried in the body of the brain. These vocalizing structures include the hypothalamus, amygdala, cingulate gyrus as well as brainstem structures such as the periaqueductal grey.

It is these ancient vocal-emotional centers which explain why non-human animals also vocalize to convey feeling and emotion. Thus, although non-humans and infants generally do not have the capacity to meaningfully communicate in grammatical word sequences, they still vocalize, and these vocalizations are often limbic and emotional in origin (Hauser, 1997; Joseph, 1982, 1992a; Hage, 2010; Jurgens, 2009; Jurgens and Muller-Preuss, 1977; MacLean, 1990; Meyer et al., 1973; Newman 2010; Ploog, 1992; Robinson, 2007, 1972).

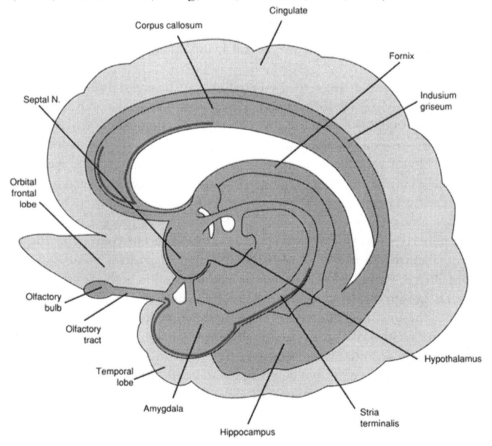

We know that language is evoked from the limbic system and not from the neocortical surface of the brain, since electrode stimulation of the neocortex does not provoke complex vocalization. Although the neocortex can segment, grammatically organized, and sequence the sounds of language, the source of speech belongs to the old limbic brain. Indeed, emotional cries and warning calls have been produced via stimulation of wide areas of the limbic system (Borszcz & Spuz 2010; Chang et al., 2007; Hage, 2010; Jurgens, 2009; Gonzalez-Lima 2010; MacLean, 1990; Manteuffel, et al., 2007; Newman 2007, 2010; Ploog, 1992; Robinson, 2007, 1972; Siegel et al 2010) including the human amygdala (Halgren, 1992; Heith, Smith and Halgren, 1988) and the anterior cingulate gyrus (Meyer et al., 1973) which also becomes activated when speaking (Frith and Dolan, 1997; Passingham, 1997; Paulesu et al., 1997). And these and other limbic structures often become activated in response to certain emotional sounds (Kuraoka & Nakamura 2006; Lorberbaum et al. 2002; Sander et al., 2007; Seifritz et al., 2003). In fact, the limbic system is more vocal than any other part of the brain (Jurgens, 1990, 2009; Robinson, 2007).

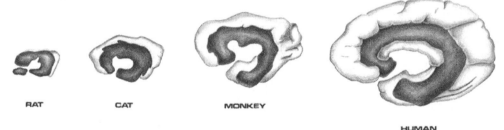

Characteristically, limbic vocalizations are evoked in situations involving sexual arousal, terror, anger, rage and extreme fear and fright and are similarly expressed by a wide range of species (MacLean 1990; Newman 2004). They are also expressed by infants such as when separated from the primary caretaker when young. Some of these limbic vocalizations are emitted soon after birth.

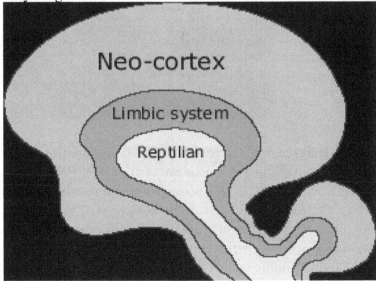

In fact, because these vocalizations are mediated by the limbic system, human infants and apes and monkeys reared in isolation or (in the case of non-human primates) with surgically muted mothers and thus with little or no "language"

experience or training, are able to produce complex and appropriate emotional calls and cries which accurately indicate fear or distress. They are also expressed by children born blind and deaf (Eibl-Eisbesfeldt, 2007).

In the case of non-human primates, they will react appropriately to these vocalizations the first time they are exposed to them (Herzog and Hopf, 1984; Winter et al., 1973). For example, squirrel monkeys reared in isolation respond appropriately with fear and anxiety in response to warning "yapping" calls (signifying the presence of a predator) the very first time they are heard (Herzog and Hopf, 1984). They will also produce an appropriate "yapping" cry when they are first exposed to a potential predator.

The first vocalizations of human infants (McGraw, 1969; Milner, 2007; Piaget, 1952; Snow & McGaha 2002; Spitz and Wolf, 1946; Sroufe, 1996; Tronic 2007), including anencephalics (Barnet et al., 1966; Lemire et al., 2014; Monnier, 1956; Nielsen & Sedgwick 1949) and those born deaf and blind (Eibl-Eisbesfeldt, 2007) are similarly emotional in origin and limbically mediated.

Initially these sounds consist of grunts and sounds indicative of displeasure, and weeks then months later will include pleasure, fear and the separation cry. These vocalizations can also be produced by direct stimulation of the hypothalamus, amygdala, or anterior cingulate gyrus (Jurgens, 2014, 2009; MacLean, 1990; Meyer et al., 1973; Newman 2009; Ploog, 1992; Robinson, 2007, 1972).

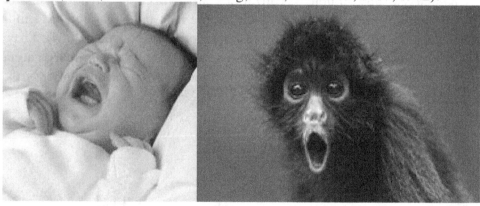

The human amygdala (Halgren, 1992; Heith et al., 1988) and anterior cingulate (Frith and Dolan, 1997; Passingham, 1997; Paulesu et al., 1997; Peterson et al., 1988) become activated when hearing or producing emotional words and sounds, whereas the medial hypothalamus (MacLean, 1990; Robinson, 2007, 1972) and the midbrain periaqueductal grey (Casey et al., 2014; Coghill et al., 2014; Zhang et al., 2014) become active when experiencing or vocally expressing negative mood states. Hence the term: "limbic language" (Joseph, 1982; Jurgens, 1990).

The normal pattern of maturational development, as is evident behaviorally and as based on myelination and metabolic activity, is that the brainstem and cerebellum begin to develop in advance of the forebrain, which in turn matures in a upward, rostral and paramedial to lateral arc, i.e. diencephalon (medial hypothalamus), limbic system (amygdala), striatum, cingulate, neocortex (Barkovich et al., 1988; Brody et al., 1987; Gibson, 1991; Harbord, et al., 1990; Holland, et al., 1986; Lee et al., 1986).

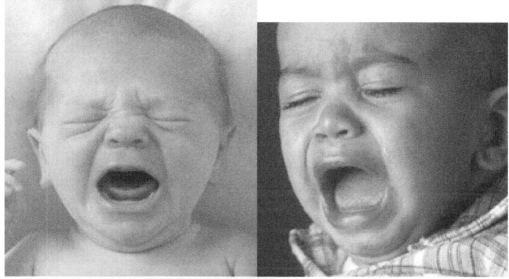

Because the maturation of the forebrain and neocortex are exceedingly prolonged (Benes, 2014; Blinkov and Glezer, 1968; Brody, et al.,, 1987; Conel, 1939, 1941; Debakan, 1970; Flechsig, 1901; Holcomb et al., 1992; Huttenlocher, 1990; Paus et al., 2016; Pfefferbaum, et al., 2014; Reiss, et al., 1996; Stiles 2008; Yakovlev and Lecours, 2007), and as the limbic system matures in advance of the neocortical speech areas, infants (and their mothers) are dependent on limbic language and the limbic system in order to communicate their needs and to discern the social-emotional intentions of others. This is why infants will react appropriately even if the speaker speaks a "foreign language" (Fernald, 1993).

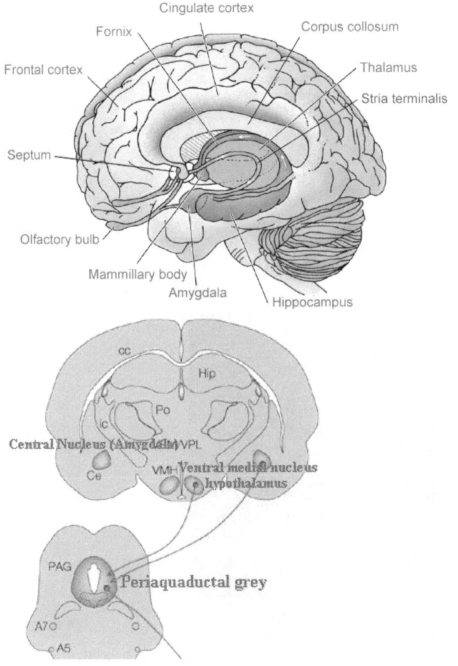

Since these emotional sounds are limbically produced and comprehended, and because these structures are common to all humans and mammals, these sounds are stereotypically vocalized and comprehended cross-culturally, and by infants and different animal species (Beier and Zautra, 1972; Eibl-Eibesfeldt 2007; Fernald, 1992; Fernald et al., 1989; Hauser, 1997; Joseph, 1988a, 1993; Kramer, 1964; Nakazima, 2015; Newman 2004). Hence, the famous aside: "I don't know what they are saying, but I sure don't like the sound of it!"

It is because of the commonality of the (social) mammalian limbic system, that social animals, such as dogs, are able to comprehend and respond to emotional inflections in the human voice; including recognizing sounds of sadness.

For example, be it human, primate, or social mammal, certain specific sounds arouse or convey fear, sadness, caution or alarm (e.g. thunder, growling, low tones), or conversely, pleasure, gaiety, or peaceful conditions (e.g., soft or higher rolling, and smoother pitched tones and melodies). It is because certain sounds can signify and arouse specific and universal mood states that movie and television programs are often accompanied by "mood" music.

As noted, despite neocortical immaturity, and although lacking denotative, grammatical language skills, infants are quite adept at distinguishing between different emotional vocalizations so as to determine the mood state and intentions of others (Fernald, 1993; Haviland and Lelwica, 1987).

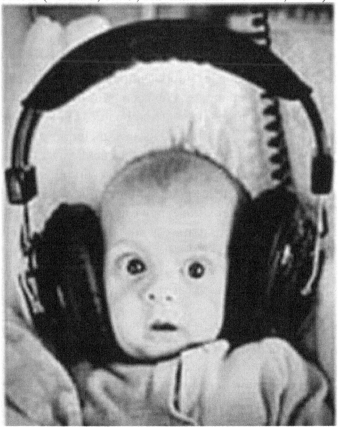

For example, it has been demonstrated that preverbal infants between the ages of 10 weeks and 5 months are capable of appropriately discerning, discriminating and responding to social-emotional vocalizations conveying approval, disproval, happiness, and anger (Fernald, 1993; Haviland and Lelwica, 1987). Moreover, 5 month old (American) infants are able to make these discriminations even in the absence of words and vocabulary, and in response to nonsense English, as well as to German and Italian vocalizations (Fernald, 1993). However, infants even younger are capable of producing these same limbic vocalizations (Joseph, 1982), and the same is true of those born deaf and blind, which again indicates that these abilities are innate.

LIMBIC LANGUAGE DEVELOPMENT

Be it infant H. sapiens, or non-human primates and mammals (hereafter referred to as "primates" and "mammals"), different structures within the limbic system produce different (as well as similar) vocalizations. The type of cry or vocalization elicited, in general, depends upon which limbic structure has been activated (Jurgens, 1990, 2009; Jurgens and Muller-Preuss, 1977; Newman 2007; Robinson, 2007, 1972). This is because different limbic structures, and in fact, different divisions within these nuclei, subserve unique functions, and maintain different anatomical interconnections with various regions of the brain.

For example, portions of the septal nuclei, hippocampus, anterior cingulate, medial amygdala, and medial hypothalamus have been repeatedly shown to generate negative and unpleasant mood states (MacLean, 1990; Olds and Forbes, 1981; Robinson, 2007, 1972). Other limbic tissues, including the lateral hypothalamus, lateral amygdala and portions of the septal nuclei, are associated with pleasurable feelings. Hence, areas associated with pleasurable sensations often give rise, when sufficiently stimulated, to pleasurable calls, whereas those linked to negative mood states, will trigger shrieks and cries of alarm.

However, because these limbic structures mature at somewhat different, albeit overlapping rates (Benes, 2014; Brody et al., 1987; Debakan, 1970; Holcomb et al., 1992; Paus et al., 2016; Pfefferbaum, et al., 2014; Reiss, et al., 1996; Yakovlev and Lecours, 2007) the infant's emotional vocal repertoire also develops in a stereotypical fashion in parallel.

For example, the midbrain periaqueductal gray and hypothalamus are almost fully functional at birth, and as will be detailed, these structures can produce crying, screaming, and grunting sounds (Borszcz & Spuz 2010; Gonzalez-Lima 2010; Siegel et al., 2010)--vocalizations characteristic of the human infant. It is the somewhat later to mature amygdala and cingulate gyrus which in turn are responsible for the increasing complexity and range of the infant's vocal-emotional repertoire, including the development of early and late babbling (Joseph 1982, 1992a, 1993).

Initially infant emotional sound production appears to convey generalized meanings, e.g. pleasure, displeasure. These sounds are associated with the hypothalamus and periaqueductal gray. Over the following weeks and months, these vocalizations become modified and more elaborate and produced in specific contexts, and are then increasingly shaped and tied to specific mood states or events and social-emotional phenomenon (Joseph, 1982, 1992a, 2016c; Milner, 1966; Piaget, 1952). That is, the increasing range of sounds produced and perceived become modulated, differentiated, more elaborate and complex, and specifically tied to sadness, joy, affection, sorrow, fear, and so on, rather than just pleasure and displeasure. These increases in vocal complexity in turn are associated with maturational events occurring within the amygdala and anterior cingulate.

Similar developmental alterations and elaborations in limbic vocalizations have been noted among primates. For example, vervet monkeys employ three distinct calls which they differentially produce in the presence of eagles, snakes and leopards (Cheney and Seyfarth, 1990). Experienced and normally reared monkeys respond to these calls by looking up ("eagle"), looking down ("snake"), or climbing up a tree ("Leopard") depending on which call is produced, even when played from a tape recorder (Seyfarth et al. 1980).

However, infants reared in isolation merely respond with generalized alarm when presented with these same calls, and are as likely to look up as down as climb a tree. That is, although they recognize the emotional significance of the call, they are not yet able to differentiate these sounds as signifying particular and specific social-emotional events or situations. These abilities are increasingly acquired over the course of the first few months as the limbic system matures, and in response to specific environmental experiences. In fact, these differential limbic maturational and vocalization events are also associated with and parallel social-emotional developmental behavioral changes which are mediated by these same limbic structures (Joseph, 1992a, 2016c).

LIMBIC LANGUAGE HIERARCHICAL DEVELOPMENT

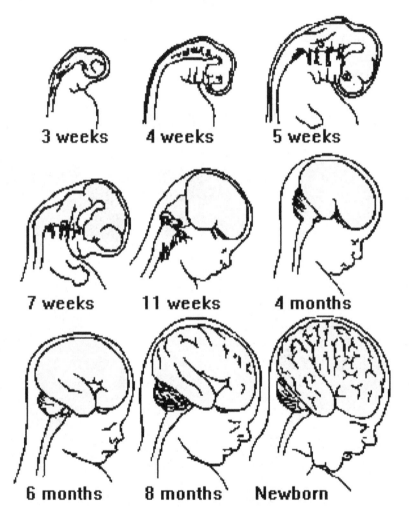

The brain develops and matures in a caudal to rostral and paramedial to lateral arc such that functions associated with the midbrain periaqueductal gray are soon followed by that of the medial hypothalamus which sits atop and is partly contiguous with the midbrain. At birth, the medial hypothalamus appears to be functionally active and/or at a state of semi-functional and anatomical maturity. An advanced state of (neonatal) hypothalamic maturity is indicated by the emergence of associated behaviors and vocalizations (Joseph, 1992a, 1993, 2016), myelination patterns and the establishment of its massive fiber interconnections with the midbrain and periaqueductal gray (Gilles et al., 2003; Debakan, 1970; Langworthy, 1937; Yakovlev and Lecours, 2007).

As noted the neonatal and infant neocortex is exceedingly immature and in the case of the neonate, displays almost no functional activity (Blinkov and Glezer, 1968; Chugani, 2014; Conel, 1939, 1941; Debakan, 1970; Flechsig, 1901; Holcomb et al., 1992; Huttenlocher, 1990; Paus et al., 2016; Pfefferbaum, et al., 2014; Reiss, et al., 1996; Yakovlev and Lecours, 2007). Hence, the behavior of the human neonate appears to be mediated by the brainstem and midbrain periaqueductal gray which mediate chewing, sucking, swallowing, phonating, and breathing, and reflexively vocalizes when aroused (Joseph, 2016c; Jurgens, 1992, 2014; Ploog, 1992), as well as the medial hypothalamus which appears to be functionally active at birth.

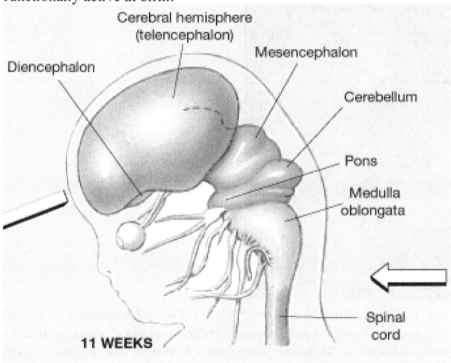

This explains why similar neonatal sounds can be vocalized by anencephalics who are generally devoid of neural tissue anterior to the diencephalon (Emde, Gaensbauer, and Harmon, 1976; Lemire et al., 2014; Monnier, 1956). With complete forebrain destruction, and following depth electrode activation of the brainstem periaqueductal gray (Jurgens, 2014; Larson et al., 2014; Zhang et al., 2014), or with stimulation of the hypothalamus (Gonzalez-Lima 2010; MacLean, 1990; Robinson, 2007, 1972) grunting, howling and crying can be reflexively triggered, including those similar to those produced by a howling infant or anencephalic.

Brainstem vocalization centers appear to be fully functional at birth, though they also continue to mature and myelinate over the course of the first 3-12 postnatal months (Debakan, 1970; Gilles, 1991; Yakovlev and Lecours, 2007), whereas the neocortex, including the neocortical speech areas can take well over 10 years to reach an advanced stage of maturation.

However, when the hypothalamus is stimulated, not just emotional vocalizations but complex and emotionally congruent behaviors can be elicited including facial displays of rage or pleasure. On the other hand, as with midbrain stimulation, once the stimulation is terminated, the behavior and vocalizations cease. Nevertheless, although the hypothalamus responds in an on/off fashion, so long as it is activated (such as by hunger or pain) and in the case of neonates (because it is so immature) it will continue to react and cry out for long time periods, even in the absence of an obvious external stimulating source.

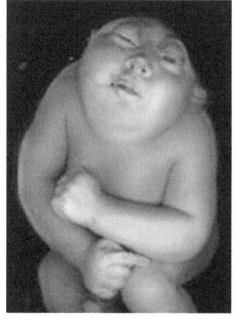

By contrast, activation of the more highly evolved amygdala and anterior cingulate produces complex and sustained feeling and mood states even after the stimulation is removed. Moreover, cingulate stimulation can produce emotional sounds that accurately reflect or which have no relation to the individual's mood. These latter structures, however, begin to functionally mature at a later age of development, which is why associated behaviors and emotions appear at later ages as well (Joseph, 2016b,c,).

Specifically, the later maturation of the amygdala is associated with the developing of cooing and other emotional sounds and the onset of "early babbling" (Joseph, 1982, 1992a, 2016b). "Early babbling," although not emotional per se, appears to be a function of the the amygdala's massive fiber pathway to the masticatory centers in the brainstem, which, at this age, are decidedly immature (see Takeuchi et al., 1988). That is, because of its immaturity, it induces rudimentary and repetitive reflexive jaw and lip movements including chewing, sucking, and swallowing--functions that many scientists believe are integral to speech development ((Hoff & Shatz, 2009; Moore and Ruark, 1996).

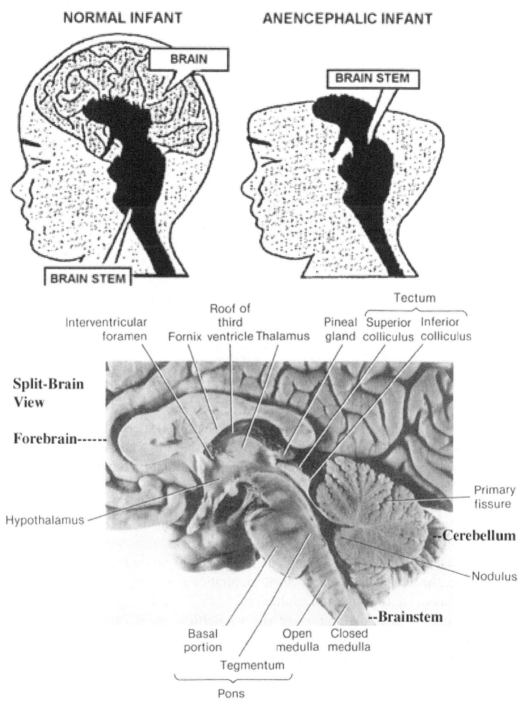

The much later to develop "late" (canonical) babbling, and other complex emotional vocalizations, are associated with the maturation of the anterior cingulate (Joseph, 1993, 2016b)--a structure which when electrically stimulated produces all manner of complex and repetitive sounds including "dadadada" (Dimmer and Luders, 1995; Penfield and Welch, 1951). The cingulate ("canonical") late babbling stage is followed by jargon babbling and then human speech, beginning with the first words, all of which are associated with increased neocortical maturity and the establishment of neocortical hierarchical control over limbic and brainstem nuclei.

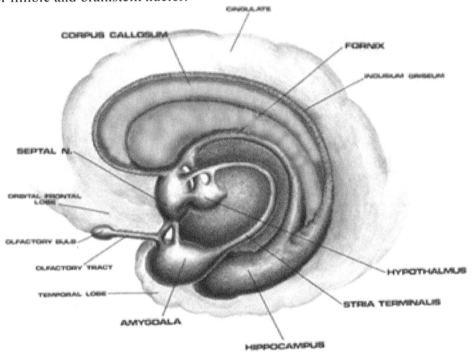

Thus, babbling and limbic language and emotional speech become increasingly complex as the hypothalamus, followed by the amygdala and cingulate gyrus mature--structures which myelinate and functionally develop following the myelination of the brainstem. Moreover, not just speech, but associated limbic behaviors also emerge in parallel. Again, the normal pattern of maturational development is that the brainstem develops in advance of the forebrain, which in turn matures in a caudal to rostral and paramedial to lateral arc, i.e. diencephalon (medial hypothalamus), limbic system (amygdala), striatum, cingulate, neocortex. Again, however, these neocortical maturational events continue well into late childhood, adolescence and adulthood.

With the later maturation of the neocortical speech areas, it appears that limbic language becomes hierarchically and sequentially reorganized, thereby giving rise, in children and adults, to segmented-prosodic, temporal sequential, grammatical, vocabulary-rich human speech (Joseph, 1982, 1992a, 2016a,e; Hallet and Proctor 1996; Herschkowitz, Kagan, and Zilles, 1997).

In this regard, a hierarchy of progressive complexity in emotional vocalization and feeling states could be said to begin with the periaqueductal gray and medial hypothalamus, and then progressively expands so as to incorporate the amygdala followed by the cingulate gyrus and finally the neocortical speech areas which hierarchically mediate and sequence limbic emotional vocalizations thereby producing complex, vocabulary-rich grammatical speech (Joseph, 2016a,e; 2000a).

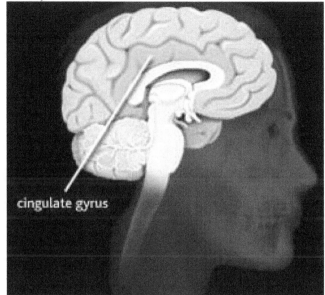

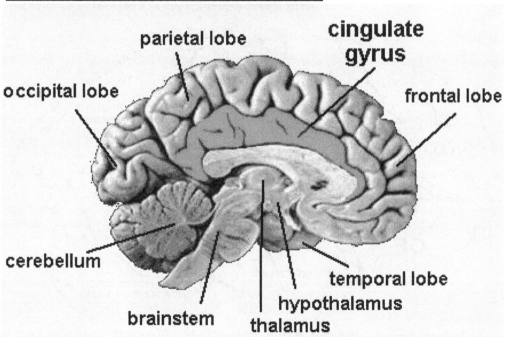

Specifically, with the maturation (and evolution) not only of the neocortical speech areas but the inferior parietal lobule, Broca's and Wernicke's areas become interlocked at the neocortical level thereby giving rise to the language axis, and modern human speech through the hierarchical representation of limbic speech which is punctuated and fractionated into words and temporal sequences (Joseph,

1982, 2016e, 2000a). However, even in the adult, these neocortical tissues remain dependent on the limbic system and the brainstem in order to vocalize and communicate as these tissues are directly connected. If these pathways are destroyed the patient may become mute.

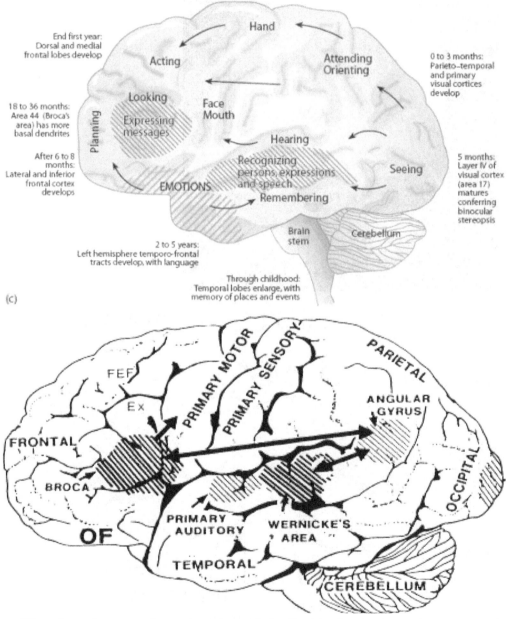

Therefore, because the maturation of the limbic forebrain and neocortex is exceedingly prolonged (Benes, 2014; Blinkov and Glezer, 1968; Brody et al., 1987; Conel, 1939, 1941; Debakan, 1970; Flechsig, 1901; Holcomb et al., 1992; Huttenlocher, 1990; Paus et al., 2016; Pfefferbaum, et al., 2014; Reiss, et al., 1996; Yakovlev and Lecours, 2007) so too is the development and acquisition of human language, the first sounds of which appear to be reflexively uttered by the

Hypothalamus, Amygdala, Septal Nuclei, Hippocampus, Cingulate

brainstem periaqueductal gray and the medial hypothalamus.

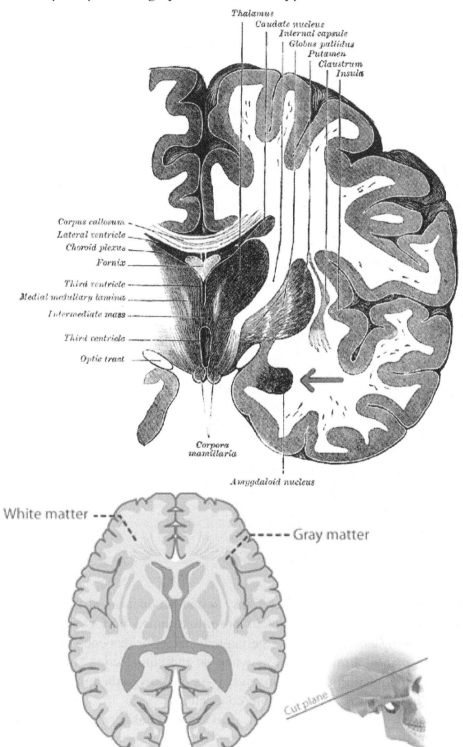

PERIAQUEDUCTAL GRAY AND VOCALIZATION

Activity within the midbrain periaqueductal gray (which receives extensive input from the amygdala, hypothalamus, and other limbic nuclei) can trigger the production of a variety of sounds that are suggestive of exceedingly negative feelings. The periaqueductal gray, in fact, becomes functionally active in response to noxious and painful stimuli as do other pontine-midbrain nuclei as demonstrated through functional imaging. However, if the periaqueductal gray is disconnected from the limbic system and neocortex (such as by a midbrain transection), stimulation of this nuclei will continue to evoke vocalization. Nevertheless, with the exception of facial contortions (produced by the fifth and 7th cranial nerves) and changes in breathing and thus vocalization, stimulation of the isolated periaqueductal gray is not accompanied by complex behavioral displays, and when the stimulation is removed, the vocalizations immediately cease. Moreover, patients with "bulbar palsy" (due to partial brainstem injury and disconnection), report that their vocalizations do not correspond to their actual feelings.

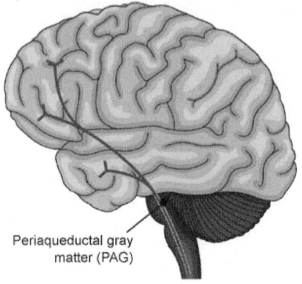

Periaqueductal gray
matter (PAG)

This suggests that periaqueductal gray sound production, at the level of the midbrain, is due to the activation of pre-programmed motor engrams stored within the brainstem. Moreover, periaqueductal gray responds reflexively in response to painful stimuli (such as when an individual cries "ouch"), and in reaction to emotional impulses transmitted via the amygdala and hypothalamus -nuclei with which it is intimately interconnected.

However, if denied forebrain input, or if provided abnormal input, although the periaqueductal gray may vocalize, the "emotions" conveyed may not have a corresponding feeling state but instead represents a reflexive motor program involving the vocalization centers. In fact, the coordinated activity of these

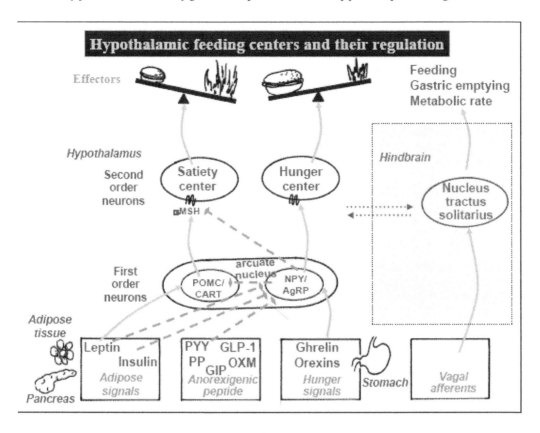

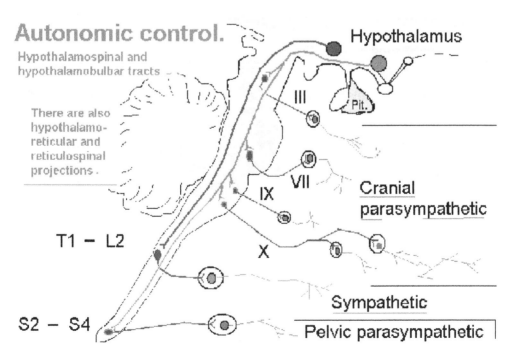

tissues and activation of these motor programs would enable an individual to laugh, cry, or howl, even if the brain anterior to the midbrain were dead and there was no evidence of consciousness. Hence, similar vocalizations are produced by anencephalics born with only a brainstem (Emde et al., 1976; Lemire et al., 2014; Monnier, 1956).

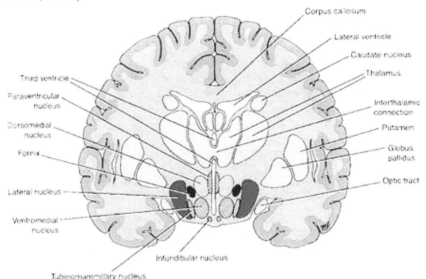

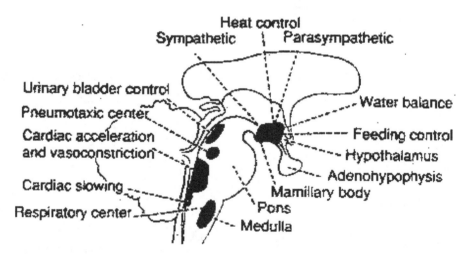

Specifically, the midbrain periaqueductal gray receives input from throughout the brainstem, spinal cord, as well as the hypothlamus, amygdala, cingulate, and the speech areas in the left and right frontal lobes, and is able to activate and coordinates the laryngeal, oral-facial, and principal and accessory muscles of respiration and inspiration thereby producing a wide range of vocalizations (Jurgens, 2014, 2007; Larson et al. 2014; Newman 2007, 2010; Zhang et al. 2014). The periaqueductal gray appears to be the site where particular vocalization motor patterns are stored.

When the periaqueductal gray is activated by impulses received from the limbic system or neocortex, it activates the appropriate motor program and then organizes and coordinates the oral-laryngeal and respiratory muscles so that the appropriate sounds can be produced (Jurgens, 2014; Newman 2007, 2010; Zhang et al, 2014). In this manner the felt aspects of emotion (as generated within the forebrain) are accompanied by appropriate sound production as released and mediated by the brainstem and cranial nerves.

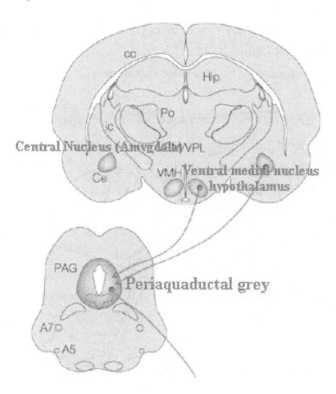

THE MEDIAL HYPOTHALAMUS: CRYING AND SCREAMING

By birth the hypothalamus has established massive fiber interconnections with the midbrain and periaqueductal gray (Gilles et al. 2003; Debakan, 1970; Langworthy, 1937; Yakovlev and Lecours, 2007) and is thus capable of reflexively activating this structure. That is, the infantile periaqueductal gray reflexively vocalizes in response to hypothalamic influences and thus may cry in reaction to hunger or thirst. The hypothalamus is involved in all aspects of endocrine, hormonal, visceral and autonomic nervous system functioning and contains lipostatic, glucose, and osmoreceptors which are sensitive to the body's fat content and fluctuations in circulating metabolites and water levels. The hypothalamus also becomes exceedingly active when hungry and while eating or simply looking at food (Blouet et al., 2009; Milanski et al., 2009; Nakamura and Ono, 1986; Rolls et al. 1976; Suzuki et al. 2010). Thus, the monitoring of internal homeostasis is a major function of the hypothalamus. As the remainder of the forebrain is exceedingly immature, the vocalizing behavior and auditory capabilities of the neonate appear to reflect brainstem-periaqueductal and medial hypothalamic influences. Thus, for example, when experiencing hunger or thirst, the infantile hypothalamus may activate the brainstem including the periaqueductal gray which reflexively reacts by crying. However, once sated, the medial hypothalamus becomes quiescent.

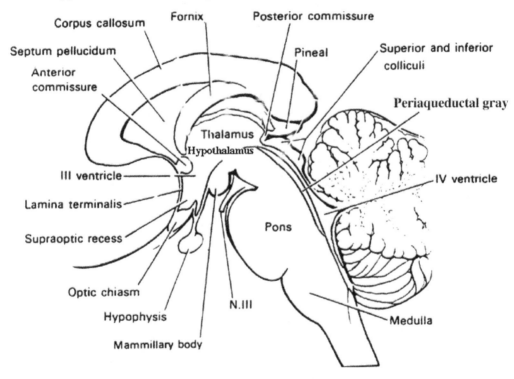

THE LATERAL HYPOTHALAMUS AND THE PLEASURE PRINCIPLE

The medial hypothalamus begins to mature before the lateral nucleus--a developmental process which may not be complete until late puberty (Yakovlev and Lecours, 2007). However, as the lateral hypothalamus (and other forebrain nuclei) mature, it increasingly exerts its own unique influences and the developing infant will increasingly demonstrate and vocalize feelings of pleasure (Joseph,

1992a; Hershkowitz et al. 1997).

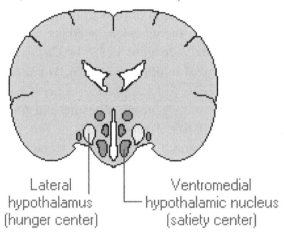

Lateral hypothalamic functional maturation, however, also overlaps with that of other forebrain structures, including the amygdala. And, feelings and vocalizations indicative of pleasure have been triggered following excitation of a number of diverse limbic areas including the amygdala, cingulate gyrus, and the medial forebrain bundle (Jurgens, 1990, 2007; Jurgens and Muller-Preuss, 1977; Olds and Forbes, 1981; Robinson, 2007, 1972). Following depth-electrode placement, animals will repeatedly engage in self-stimulatory activity to deliver electric impulses to these nuclei. However, the greatest area of concentration of reward sites, and the highest rates of self-stimulatory activity occur in the lateral hypothalamus. According to Olds (1956), animals "would contine to stimulate as rapidly as possible until physical fatigue forced them to slow or to sleep." By contrast, if the lateral region is destroyed the experience of pleasure and emotional responsiveness is almost completely attenuated (Marshall and Teitelbaum, 1974).

Thus, whereas the medial hypothalamus produces distress and quiescence, the later to mature lateral hypothalamus produces feelings of pleasure, such that by 3 months of age, infants will smile and vocalize with genuine pleasure (Sroufe, 1996). In this regard, it could be said that the hypothalamus mediates the pleasure principle (Joseph, 1992a). In fact, activation of the lateral hypothalamus produces vocalizations suggestive of extreme pleasure, and in humans can even trigger uncontrolled laughter (Davison and Kelman, 1939; Ironside, 1956; Martin, 1950. Hence, as the lateral hypothalamus (and other forebrain structures mature) infants also begin to laugh around 3-4 months of age.

Presumably the hypothalamus activates the periaqueductal gray and brainstem respiratory centers (e.g. Boliek et al. 1996) which reflexively produces facial expressions and respiration-related vocalizations suggestive of pleasure, including laughter, or conversely, cries of distress. By 3 months of age the amygdala is also significantly contributing to the infant's behavior and speech patterns.

Nevertheless, as forebrain maturity continues in a medial to lateral and a caudal to rostral arc, initially the hypothalamus matures at an earlier age than the amygdala (and forebrain), and exerts a more profound influence on neonatal behavior. Over the ensuing weeks, and as the lateral and medial hypothalamus mature, followed by the amygdala/forebrain, the vocal as well as emotional and behavioral repertoire of the infant expands (Joseph, 1982, 1992a), whereas crying begins to wane due to increased cortical inhibitory control (Hershkowitz et al. 1997).

By 3-4 months of age infants will smile with genuine pleasure and produce laughter similar to adult laughter (Sroufe, 1996; Tronic, 2007); a function of increasingy forebrain maturity (e.g. Hallett and Proctor, 1996; Herschkowitz et al., 1997). As the amygdala and the forebrain mature, the infant's ability to vocalize becomes increasingly differentiated and expressive of more complex emotions such as joy, wariness and fear.

THE AMYGDALA, HYPOTHALAMUS, AND PERIAQUEDUCTAL GRAY

The amygdala responds to and in turn, exerts inhibitory and excitatory influences on the brainstem and hypothalamus and thus emotional behavior, through the amygdalofugal fiber pathway and stria terminalis (Davis et al. 1997; Joseph, 1992a; Rosen and Schulkin, 1998). The stria terminalis and amygdalofugal pathways are bidirectional and interlink the medial and lateral amygdala with the medial and lateral hypothalamus and periaqueductal gray.

Through these same pathways the amygdala can activate the brainstem including the periaqueductal gray, and is able to modulate and even control rudimentary emotional forces governed by the hypothalamus as well as act at the behest of hypothalamically induced drives. For example, if certain nutritional requirements need to be meet, the hypothalamus signals the amygdala via the stria terminalis. The amygdala then surveys the external environment in search of an appropriate stimulus.

On the other hand, if presented with a potentially threatening or motivationally significant stimulus, the amygdala may stimulate hypothalamic activity (as well as the brainstem and striatum, e.g. Davis et al. 1997; LeDoux, 1996; Rosen and Schulkin, 1998) so that the organism is mobilized to take appropriate action. Hence, when the hypothalamus is activated and driven by the amygdala, instead of responding in an on/off manner which is typical of the hypothalamus, cellular activity continues for an appreciably longer time period (Dreifuss et al. 1968; Rolls 1992).

The amygdala also acts independently of the hypothalamus, and can, for example, generate extreme feelings of pleasure and corresponding facial expressions and vocalizations. Indeed, the lateral amygdala receives and contributes fibers to the medial forebrain bundle which in turn has its site of origin in the lateral hypothalamus (Mehler, 1980) and projects to the brainstem. Moreover, the amygdala is rich in cells containing enkephalins, and opiate receptors can be found throughout this nucleus (Atweh and Kuhar, 1977; Uhl, Kuhar, and Snyder, 2014). It is also a major pleasure center which promotes self-stimulatory activity (Olds and Forbes, 1981) and the vocalization of pleasure (e.g. cooing and gooing). Therefore, as the medial and then the lateral amygdala mature and gains hierarchical control over the hypothalamus and brainstem, the emotional repertoire expands as does the infant's ability to perceive and produce a variety of exceedingly complex social-emotional behaviors and vocalizations, including, as will be detailed later, the development of "early babbling."

THE AMYGDALA AND SOCIAL-EMOTIONAL VOCALIZATION

Although there is much debate as to the infant's emotional capabilities, or lack thereof (e.g. Bremner & Slater 2003; Hershkowitz et al. 1997; Izard, 1991; Sroufe, 1996), for the first several weeks of postnatal life the limbic forebrain is simply too immature to accurately perceive or vocalize emotional feelings other than displeasure. Likewise, although the newborn and week-old infant will lift the corners of its mouth, as if "smiling," these initial "smiles" do not appear to represent true emotions but are probably brainstem reflexes (Joseph, 2016c). It is only as the lateral hypothalamus, and medial and lateral amygdala (and other forebrain structures) begin to mature that the infant becomes capable of truly "smiling," laughing, and producing complex social-emotional vocalizations.

The amygdala is an exceedingly complex structure consisting of a variety of nuclei including the claustrum and the limbic and corpus striatum. It also maintains massive interconnections with the hypothalamus, cingulate, frontal and parietal lobes, and periaqueductal gray (Whalen & Phelps 2009). In addition, the amygdala receives direct input from the auditory areas in the temporal lobe via a thick neural pathway, the inferior arcuate fasciculus, and through the claustrum which is a "broken off" segment of the amygdala situated near and is connected with the auditory receiving areas in the temporal lobe. Hence the human amygdala responds to complex auditory-affective stimuli including words and sentences, and if electrically stimulated, patients report hearing voices which tend to be experienced as emotionally significant.

The medial amygdala (in conjunction with the hippocampus) forms a cortical bulbous protrusion in the anterior-medial temporal lobe (the uncus), and over the course of evolution gave rise to sheets of 3-layered allocortex, then 5-layered mesocortex, and finally neocortex and contributed to the formation of the auditory neocortex and Wernicke's area, which are thus, in part, evolutionary extensions of the amygdala. Immediately beneath the insula and approaching the auditory neocortex is a thick band of amygdala-cortex, the claustrum. Over the course of evolution the claustrum apparently split off from the amygdala due to the expansion of the temporal lobe and the passage of additional axons coursing throughout the white matter including the arcuate fasciculus.

Nevertheless, the claustrum maintains rich interconnections with the auditory cortex as well as the amygdala which in turn is linked directly with the neocortical auditory areas. This is evident from dissection of the human brain which reveals that the fibers of the arcuate fasciculus (and claustrum) project to and from the amygdala, leading not only to Wernicke's area, but continuing through the inferior parietal lobule and angular gyrus, projecting directly to Broca's area.

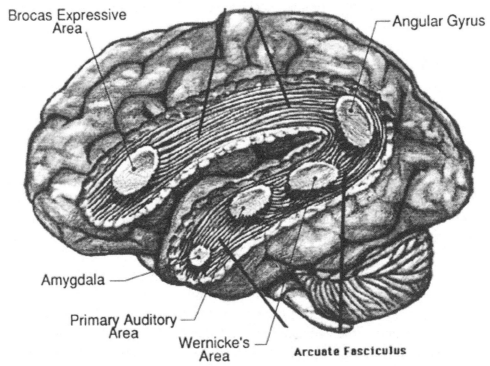

Hence, via these extensive interconnections with the auditory neocortex (and the midbrain inferior-auditory colliculus and medial geniculate of the thalamus) the amygdala is able to receive and analyze auditory input in order to discern and identify stimuli which are emotionally and motivationally significant (Gloor, 1997; Halgren, 1992). When emotional, sexual and motivationally relevant stimuli (e.g. food, sex partner) are detected the amygdala can organize appropriate behavioral and vocal responses and can trigger startle or defensive reactions, as in response to transient sounds, or those typically made by predators, prey, or potential mates (Edeline and Weinberger, 1991; Hitchock and Davis, 1991; Gloor, 1997; Hocherhman and Yirmiya, 1990; Rolls, 1992; Ursin and Kaada, 1960). These motor-behavioral reactions, in turn, are mediated by the limbic and corpus striatum, the periaqueductal gray, and lower brainstem, all at the behest of the amygdala.

Moreover, it can vocalize via the neocortical speech areas and pariaqueductal gray. In fact, in conjunction with the anterior cingulate the amygdala is one of the most vocally responsive structures of the brain (Jurgens, 1990, 1992; Robinson, 2007, 1972) and become activated in response to emotional sounds and emotional words (Gonzalez-Lima 2010; Halgren, 1992; Heit et al., 1988; Kuraoka & Nakamura 2006; Newman 2007). Moreover, the female human amygdala (and cingulate) responds to infant laughing and crying (Leibenluft et al., 2004; Sander et al., 2007; Seifritz et al., 2003).

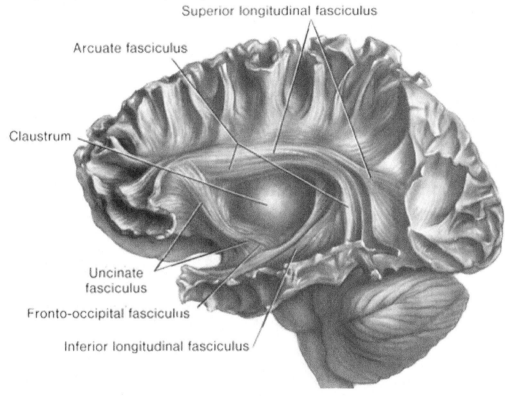

In humans, destruction limited to the normal amygdala, the right amygdala in particular, can severely disrupt the ability to sing, convey melodic information or to enunciate properly via vocal inflection, and can result in great changes in pitch and the timbre of speech (Freeman and Williams, 1952, 1963; Joseph, 1992a). With bilateral destruction of the normal (vs the diseased) amygdala, emotional speech production and the capacity to respond appropriately to emotionally significant visual or auditory stimuli is significantly disrupted (Lilly et al. 2003; LeDoux, 1996; Marlowe et al., 2015; Scott et al., 1997; Terzian and Ore, 1955).

The amygdala, therefore is primary in regard to the perception and expression of social and emotional nuances and in large part is responsible for the expression and comprehension of not just limbic language, but human speech, the sounds of which are shunted to and from the amygdala via the inferior fasciculus and the claustrum which is a "broken off" segment of the amygdala situated near the primary auditory receiving areas.

As noted (and described briefly below), portions of the auditory neocortex -which extends from the anterior and medial temporal lobe and beyond the insula to include the superior temporal lobe and the inferior parietal lobule- is in part, an evolutionary derivative of the amygdala. In this regard it could be argued that the primary, secondary and auditory association areas including Wernicke's area, have evolved (at least in part) from the amygdala, and in fact remain extensively interconnected with this nuclei via the inferior portions of the arcuate fasciculus as well as the claustrum.

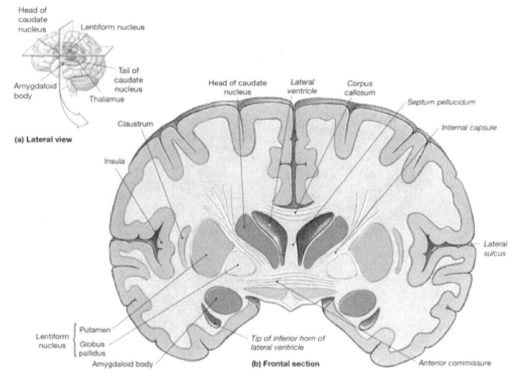

In consequence, when the neocortical auditory areas are injured, the amygdala is sometimes disconnected and can no longer extract or inpart emotional nuances to incoming or outgoing sounds. For example, with right superior temporal lobe lesions, patients may suffer from a receptive auditory affective agnosia, as well as an agnosia for environmental sounds. They may have difficulty ascertaining the feelings of others or perceiving social emotional nuances. Hence, emotional peception and expression may become grossly disorganized and inappropriate.

By contrast, if the left amygdala is disconnected from the left superior temporal lobe, patients may verbally complain that they consciously feel cut off from their emotions. Moreover, with left temporal lobe dysfunction, speech and thought processes may come to be abnormally invested or devoid of emotion, and patients may be diagnosed as psychotic and/or paranoid.

Hence, although the left and right amygdala are functionally lateralized, with the right amygdala significantly larger than the left, both contribute significantly to the perception and expression of language, and assist in maintaining the functional integrity of the neocortical auditory areas in the right and left temporal lobe. It is through these interconnections that limbic languages comes to be hierarchically organized at the level of the temporal neocortex.

AMYGDALA SOCIAL EMOTIONAL DEVELOPMENT

Activation of the amygdala can produce complex affective-motor displays (see below), social-emotional vocalizations (Gonzalez-Lima 2010; Jurgens 2009; Manteuffel et al. 2007; Robinson, 2007, 1972), including laughter, or conversely a dense depression, coupled with sadness and crying (e.g., Chen & Forster, 1973; Offen, Davidoff, Troost, & Richey, 1976; Sethi & Rao, 1976). However, initially the amygdala is so immature that its influences are negligible. The neonate initially behaves as if it has been amygdalectomized (Joseph, 1992a, 2016b). The newborn does not fixate, does not maintain attention, does not respond to visual threat, and appears incapable of experiencing fear, wariness, or anxiety--emotions and motoric reactions stereotypically associated with the amygdala. In fact, these emotional reactions and almost all aspects of social and emotional behavior are generally abolished following bilateral amygdalectomy (Kluver & Bucy, 1939; Lilly et al., 2003; Marlowe et al., 2015; Terzian & Ore, 1955; Toscano et al., 2009; Weiskrantz, 1956).

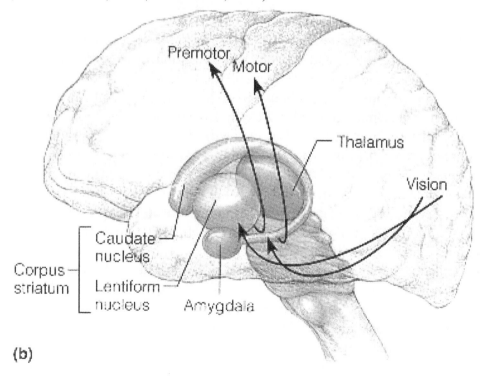

(b)

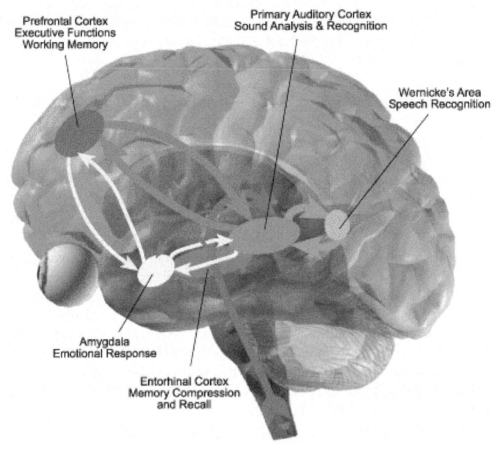

By 3-months of age infants will vigorously smile with an open mouth, laugh, coo, express pleasure, and crinkle their eyes, and these smiles can be easily triggered when the infant is fully alert (Snow & McGaha 2002; Sroufe, 1996; Tronic 2007; Wolff, 1963); affective behaviors associated with the amygdala and lateral hypothalamus, and which are indicative of increasingy forebrain maturity (e.g. Hallett & Proctor, 1996; Herschkowitz et al., 1997). Correspondingly, it is not until after 3-months that drowsy and REM-sleep-induced smiling begins to disappear (Emde et al., 1976; Sroufe & Waters, 1976). It is also around 3-months that infants begin to smile at stationary stimuli (Snow & McGaha 2002; Tronic 2007; Zelazo, 1972), such as mother's smiling face, or stimuli which can put into motion by the infant (Wolff, 1963; Spitz et al., 1970). In contrast to the initial reflexive smiles, these latter "smiles" often occur only after prolonged or repeated presentations of an engaging stimulus. Therefore, and as also argued by Sroufe (1996), it is not until 3-months that the infant displays "true emotions," and a true smile --a time period which corresponds to increased forebrain functional activity as demonstrated by changes in the EEG (Spitz et al., 1970), which are still actually rather random in organization (Kellaway, 1979; Ohtahara, 1981).

The development of these more complex emotional reactions implicates the amygdala and striatum, as together these structures begin to mature around 2-3 months of age, and produce complex affective motor movements, vocalizations, and facial displays of emotion including social smiling (Joseph, 2016b). Because the forebrain myelinates and matures in a caudal to rostral, paramedian to lateral arc, the paramedially located amygdala begins to functionally mature and myelinate in advance of anterior-medially located forebrain structures such as the septal nuclei and anterior cingulate (Joseph, 1992a, 2016b). Hence, given the role of the amygdala in generating, perceiving, remembering, and expressing a variety of complex emotions, including the experience and expression of anxiety, fear, joy, and the desire for social emotional contact (Gloor, 1997; Kensinger et al., 2011; LeDoux, 1996; Morris et al., 1996; Nitschke et al. 2009; Poulos et al 2009; Todd & Anderson 2009; Whalen & Phelps 2009), and as the amygdala is also responsive to facial stimuli, including direction of gaze and eye-to-eye contact (Blackford et al., 2009; Hasselmo et al. 1989, Heit et al., 1988; Kawashima et al., 2016; N'Diaye et al., 2009; Rule et al., 2010), the infant's emotional, vocal, and affective-motor repertoire becomes increasingly complex, and spends more time gazing as faces and making eye-to-eye contact, as the amygdala matures.

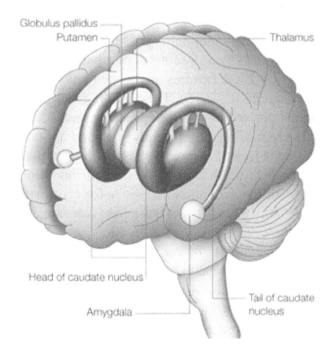

AMYGDALA, SOCIAL SMILE, AND THE HUMAN FACE

The amygdala is exceedingly responsive to social and emotional stimuli as conveyed vocally, through touch, and via the face and eyes (Blackford et al., 2009; Gloor, 1992; Halgren, 1992; Kawashima et al., 2016; Kling & Brothers 1992; Morris et al., 1996; N'Diaye et al., 2009; Rolls, 1984, 1992; Rule et al., 2010). In fact, in conjunction with the overlying (partly contiguous) temporal lobe, the amygdala contains neurons which selectively respond to smiles, to the eyes, the direction of gaze, and which differentiate between male and female faces and the emotions they convey (Hasselmo et al. 1989; Kawashima, et al., 2016; Morris et al. 1996; Rolls, 1984; Rule et al., 2010). For example, the normal human amygdala will respond to frightened faces by altering and increasing its activity (Morris et al. 1996); whereas injury to the amygdala disrupts the ability to recognize faces (Young et al. 1995). Moreover, the left amygdala acts to discriminate the direction of another person's gaze, whereas the right amygdala becomes activated while making eye-to-eye contact (Kawashima, et al., 2016). Likewise, the amygdala of human mothers becomes activated when gazing at their infants, and more so than when gazing at the infants of other mothers (Leibenluft et al., 2004; Ranote et al., 2004). Moreover, the right amydala of human mothers becomes highly active when listening to cries (Sander & Scheich 2001).

As the medial-uncal regions of the temporal lobe and medial and lateral amygdala mature, a broad range of feature-detecting neurons become functional and activated by specific stimuli, such as the human face. In fact, the human (female) infant will display semi-orienting responses toward faces, and even the outlines of the human face, as early as 9 minutes post partum--that is, so long as it contains all facial features. If the features are deleted this waxing and waning tendency disappears (Goren et al., 2015). These findings also indicate that the brain is genetically predetermined to respond to facial stimuli.

That these responses are mediated by the amygdala and not the visual cortex is also apparent based on the lack of responsiveness of the visual cortex to facial stimuli, and the fact that it is not until around the 4th month of age that the neurons and connections in the neocortex necessary for form perception begin to develop (Brukhalter et al., 1993). Hence, these behaviors appear to be largely mediated by the amygdala.

As the infant approaches 2-months of age it will orient toward a familiar face (Carpenter, 1974; Snow & McGaha 2002; Tronic 2007) and begins to display definite preferences for facial stimuli. As these structures and their facial-feature-detecting neurons mature, infants increasingly attend to and demonstrate an almost irresistible interest in facial stimuli (Bronson, 1972; Snow & McGaha 2002; Tronic 2007). If presented with a strange face, although the infant may look away, it will also quickly look back, "and will make eye-to-eye contact as though drawn by a magnet" (Sroufe, 1996, p. 103). By 6-months it can discriminate between male and female faces, and by 9 months it can easily discriminate between different facial expressions (Caron et al. 2005; Snow & McGaha 2002;

Sroufe, 1996; Tronic 2007)--functions associated with the temporal lobe and amygdala.

The maturation of temporal lobe-amygdala neurons which are selectively sensitive and drawn to human faces is an exceedingly adaptive development as it promotes social emotional, face-to-face interaction and the formation of emotional attachments. Moreover, these eye-to-eye and facial-detecting-neurons are richly interconnected with yet other amygdala-temporal lobe and striatal neurons concerned with social and emotional functioning, including those which can trigger a smiling, laughing, and even a crying and sobbing response (Chen & Forster, 1973; Offen et al., 1976; Sethi & Rao, 1976).

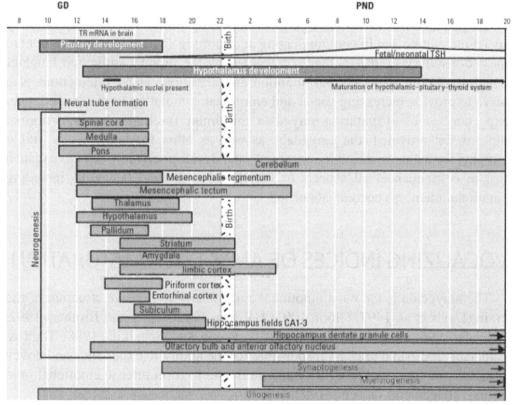

Therefore, activation of these tissues can also trigger smiling and social behavior. However, as these neurons are "experience-expectant" and require social-emotional stimulation in order to develop, establish neural pathways, and thrive, if this form of input is insufficient or abnormal, these neurons are likely to die (Joseph 2016). Hence, as the infant matures and its ability to attend to and perceive specific social emotional stimuli becomes more pronounced, so too does its ability to produce a "social" smile (Joseph, 2016b)--a capacity that first appears around 3-months of age (Snow & McGaha 2002; Sroufe, 1996; Tronic 2007) and which is likely produced by amygdaloid influences on the striatum and brainstem. Over the next three months these smiles become increasing social as they are produced most frequently during greeting and when making face-to-face and eye-to-eye contact, especially with their mothers (Ainsworth, 1973); perceptions and behaviors which activate the amygdala. Moreover, these smiles may be accompanied by genuine laughter--vocal expressions associated with the amygdala (as well as the hypothalamus).

By 4-months, laughter similar to adult laughter can be reliably evoked (Sroufe, 1996), and from 4- to 6- months of age, it takes progressively less vigorous stimulation to produce laughter which in turn is evoked by a broader range of auditory and visual stimuli (Sroufe, 1996; Tronic 2007). Therefore by 3-4 months the infant appears fully capable of experiencing as well as expressing pleasure as demonstrated through smiling and laughing--that is, so long as it is provided sufficient social-emotional stimulation.

Laughter, and the social smile plays an exceedingly important role in promoting social interaction and in communicating and forming an emotional attachment to the mother. That is, the mother is rewarded by the infant's smile and laughter which thus promotes maternal attention and affection. These interactions also serve to provide increasing social and emotional stimulation to the "experience-expectant" and still maturing amygdala and limbic forebrain. Again, if normal input is not provided, the amygdala, as well as other forebrain nuclei, might atrophy, form abnormal interconnections, and develop seizure-like activity, such that in consequence, all aspects of social and emotional behavior (including emotional memory) become abnormal.

VOCALIZING INDICES OF AMYGDALA MATURATION

The amygdala is the most emotional and socially responsive structure of the brain (Davis et al. 1997; Gloor, 1997; Halgren, 1992; Kling and Brothers 1992; LeDoux 1996; Pessoa & Adolphs 2010; Rosen and Schulkin, 1998; Todd & Anderson 2009) and appears responsible for the ability to experience and covey complex emotions including love and guilt, and to form intense emotional (and sexual) attachments (Joseph, 1992a, 2016b).

Nevertheless, at birth and over the course of the ensuing several weeks, the amygdala is so immature that its contributions appear to be rather negligible, which is which is why, for example, infants remain fearless until after 6 months of age. Fear is a primary emotion associated with the amygdala (Chapman, 1960; Davis et al. 1997; Gloor, 1997; Halgren, 1992; Pape & Pare 2010; Poulos et al., 2009; Rosen and Schulkin, 1998; Ursin and Kaada, 1960).

As discussed, neurons within the immature amygdala (and overlying temporal lobe), are responsive to faces and eyes (Blackford et al., 2009; Hasselmo et al. 1989; Kawashima et al., 2016; Morris et al., 1996; N'Diaye et al., 2009; Rolls, 1984; Rule,et al., 2010). Moreover, these facial-detecting-neurons are richly interconnected with amygdala-temporal lobe neurons concerned with social emotional functioning, including those which trigger smiling, laughter, and even a crying, sobbing, and a fear response (e.g., Chen and Forster, 1973; Offen et al., 1976; Sethi and Rao, 1976). Therefore, activation of these tissues can also trigger eye-to-eye facial contact, smiling, social behavior, as well as a variety of social-emotional vocalizations including feelings of fear or happiness.

The localization of these functions to the amygdala is exceedingly adaptive, as the face as well as the voice serve as major sources of information. When simultaneously employed these dual input/output channels promote social communication and thus language, and provide amygdala neurons and neural pathways with growth promoting stimulation (Joseph, 2016b). Face-to-face interaction provokes and reinforces the tendency to vocalize, and provides added meaning to what is heard and said, and also contributes to the formation of emotional attachments and the seeking of social contact and stimulation.

Therefore, as the amygdala increasingly attends to the human face, emotional vocalizations become more complex, and, around 3-4 months of age (in conjunction with increased forebrain control), smiling and crying become less reflexive, cooing increases in frequency, and the ability to produce a "social" smile becomes more pronounced (e.g. Hershkowitz et al. 1997). The infant becomes increasingly social, and coos and smiles during greeting, and when making face-to-face and eye-to-eye contact, especially with their mothers (Ainsworth, 1973; D'Odorico, 1984; Sroufe, 1996; Wolff, 1969).

Likewise, between the ages of 3 weeks to 4 months infants become increasingly capable of appropriately discerning, discriminating and responding to social-emotional vocalizations conveying approval, disproval, happiness, and anger (Fernald, 1993; Haviland and Lelwica, 1987; Snow & McGaha 2002; Tronic 2007). Infants are able to make these discriminations based merely on the perception of emotional prosody, in the absence of words and vocabulary, and in response to non-sense English, as well as to German and Italian vocalizations (Fernald, 1993).

WARINESS, STRANGER FEAR, AND THE AMYGDALA

For the first several weeks infants express distress in reaction to internal noxious stimulation, such as hunger and thirst, but remain largely unresponsive to noxious external stimuli (Wolff, 1969). Although the hypothalamus triggers distress in response to hunger and thirst, these initial, emotionally limited reactions are indications of forebrain-telencephalic immaturity. Indeed, the baseline EEG of a 3-month and even 6-month old infant consists of random, poorly organized low voltage slow waves, and it is not until 6-8 months that a transient regularity in EEG activity becomes apparent (Dekaban, 1970; Emde et al., 1976; Kellaway, 1979; Ohtahara, 1981). This diffuse and random slow wave neocortical activity appears to be a direct reflection of random and immature neural activity, and thus the diffusely overabundant, random, largely unmyelinated synaptic organization of the telencephalon and neocortex (Rakic, Bourgeois, Echenhoff, Zaecevic, & Goldman-Rakic, 1986) --much of which continues to mature well beyond the first decade (Blinkov & Glezer, 1968; Conel, 1937-2007; Flechsig, 1901; Holland et al., 1986; Huttenlocher, 1990; Yakovlev & Lecours, 2007).

Likewise, due to forebrain-amygdala immaturity, for the first several postnatal months the infant does not display any signs of wariness or fear. Wariness and fear, however, are associated with the functional integrity of the amygdala which does not reach adult levels of myelination until the end of the first year/ The medial and lateral amygdala mature at different rates and are concerned with somewhat different and more primitive vs more advanced emotional functions. Likewise, emotional reactions, such as pleasure, wariness and fear appear at different ages; which is exceedingly adaptive. As fear reinforces selective- as well as inhibits indiscriminate-social contact seeking, feelings of fear emerge much later in development; otherwise fear might interfere with the experience-expectant emotional needs of the developing brain by preventing or interfering with the reception of social stimulation. Thus initially the infant is fearless, and later, around 4 months they demonstrate wariness, which is followed, around 8-9 months of age, by true fear (Emde et al., 1976; Sroufe et al. 1974; Tronic 2007).

At this later age, infants may orient toward a novel, strange, or threatening stimulus, and then immediately express considerable fear and negativity coupled with heart rate deceleration (Emde et al., 1976; Sroufe et al., 1974). By contrast, at 4-months of age it takes up to 30 seconds before a wariness and a distress reaction can be triggered (Bronson, 1972).

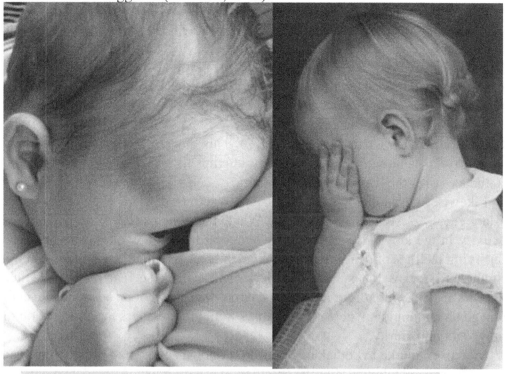

Hence the wariness versus the later appearing fear response can be taken as indications of increasing amygdala maturity, and both reactions can be evoked following depth electrode activation of the amygdala. Indeed, fear is the most common emotional reaction elicited from direct amygdala stimulation (Chapman, 1960; Davis et al., 1997; Gloor, 1992; Halgren, 1992; Rosen & Schulkin, 1998; Ursin & Kaada, 1960). The EEG becomes desynchronized, heart rate decellerates, respiration patterns change, the galvanic skin response significantly alters, the pupils dilate, the face contorts and will display extreme fear, and the subject will cringe, withdraw, and cower (Bagshaw & Benzies, 1968; Davis et al., 1997; Kapp et al., 2014; Ursin & Kaada, 1960). This cowering reaction in turn may give way to panic and the subject may attempt to take flight via amygdaloid influences over the brainstem and striatum.

Likewise, the human amygdala becomes activated when experiencing fear (Halgren, 1992; Rauch et al. 1996; Whalen & Phelps 2009) and abnormal activity in the amygdala or overlying temporal lobe can evoke overwhelming, terrifying feelings of death-like "nightmarish" fear (Herman & Chambria, 1980; Strauss, Risser, & Jones, 1982; Weil, 1956). Hence, the fear response which appears around 8 months of age, is an obvious indication of an advanced level of amygdala maturation, whereas the infant's initial fearlessness is an indication of amygdala immaturity.

Moreover, unlike hypothalamic on/off emotions, amygdala-fear reactions can last up to several minutes after the stimulation is withdrawn. Amygdala pathways may also remain potentiated for minutes, hours, and even days following fear induced stimulation (Clugnet & LeDoux, 1990; Rosen & Schulkin, 1998) such that it appears to contine to process--in the abstract--information that is no longer observable (O'Keefe & Bouma, 1969). Hence, the child or the adult may remain fearful long after the threat has been removed. Unfortunately, if the child or adult is repeatedly frightened, this will accentuate and promote the development of those neural pathways which mediate the fear response--a function of fear induced synaptic plasticity (e.g. Clugnet & LeDoux, 1990; LeDoux, 1996). In consequence, the child/adult who is repeatedly traumatized, later becomes easily startled, frightened and fearful and thus displays many of the classic signs of PTSD.

However, if both the right and left amygdala are completely destroyed, this results in a loss of fear, reduced aggressiveness, and docility even among purportedly ferocious creatures such as the agoutie and lynxe (Schreiner, & Kling, 1956; Weiskrantz, 1956; Vochteloo & Koolhaas, 1987). Likewise, adult humans who have undergone bilateral amygdala destruction become emotionally unresponsive and lose the ability to demonstrate or recognize vocally or facially conveyed fear or other emotions (LeDoux, 1996; Lilly et al., 2003; Marlowe et al., 2015; Ramamurthi, 1988; Scott et al., 1997; Terzian & Ore, 1955 Young et al., 1995). On the other hand, if sufficiently aroused or irritated, even the most placid of amygdalectomized animals can be induced to flee or fiercely fight (Fuller, Rosvold, & Pribram, 1957). However, these flight and aggressive responses are very short-lived and appear to be reflexively mediated by the hypothalamus (Joseph, 1992a; Wasman & Flynn, 1962).

DEVELOPMENT OF SOCIAL BEHAVIOR AND STRANGER-FEAR

Prior to developing fear, infants become increasingly socially oriented--an amygdala (and cingulate) mediated activity. Until 6-7 months of age the infant will smile at the approach of anyone, even complete strangers. The infant will also vigorously protest any form of separation from strangers (e.g. if they leave the room). It is the intense need for social and emotional stimulation which in part explains the infants indiscriminate tendency to welcome contact even from strangers--activities which maximizes opportunities for physical-social interaction and which provides the experience-expectant stimulation that the limbic system requires in order to develop and function in a normal manner. In fact, so intense is the need for physical and social contact that young animals raised in social isolation will form attachments to bare wire frames, to television sets, to dogs that might maul them, to creatures that might eat them, and among humans and non-human primates, to mothers that might abuse and even kill them (Cairn, 1966; Harlow & Harlow 1965a,b; Joseph, 1992a, 2016b).

It is not until about 7-months of age that infants become more discriminant in their interactions and it is during this time period that a very real and specific attachment is formed; for example, to one's mother --an attachment which normally becomes progressively more intense and stable (Snow & McGaha 2002; Sroufe, 1996; Tronic 2007). After these specific attachments have been formed, children increasingly display wariness, and then fear and even flight reactions at the approach of a stranger (Spitz & Wolff, 1946; Tronic 2007). By 9-months, 70% of children respond aversively to strangers, whereas by 10-months they might cry out if a stranger were to approach (Schaffer, 1966; Waters et al. 2015). By one year 90% of children respond aversively to strangers (Schaffer, 1966; ; Tronic 2007). The fear reaction, of course, is also exceedingly adaptive as strange people, animals, or objects, represent potential danger. Moreover, amygdala generated feelings of stranger-fear reinforce and promote the establishment of a safe and secure emotional attachment with the primary caretaker; e.g. the mother.

Indiscriminate contact seeking, followed by the establishment of specific attachments, and then the fear response are not only linearly linked but are manifestations of maturational and developmental changes occurring in the amygdala, followed by the septal nuclei and cingulate (Joseph, 1992a, 2016b), and (around the first year of life) the frontal lobes (e.g., Schore, 2014; Steklis & Kling, 2005).

AMYGDALA, FEAR, AND ATTACHMENT

As noted, medial forebrain structures begin to mature before lateral nuclei. Thus the medial hypothalamus begins to mature before the lateral nuclei, and the medial amygdala before the lateral amygdala. Thus, whereas the medial amygdala becomes increasingly well myelinated around 3-4 months (Yakovlev and Lecours, 2007), the functional maturation of the lateral amygdala is much more prolonged. It is the lateral amygdala which mediates the fear response (Chapman, 1960; Davis et al. 1997; Gloor, 1997; Halgren, 1992; Rosen and Schulkin, 1998; Ursin and Kaada, 1960); an emotion which, in conjunction with the development of "working memory" (Hershkowitz et al., 1997) and the maturation of the hippocampus, septal nuclei and cingulate, exerts significant influences on the development of attachment and fear of strangers (Joseph, 1992).

As the amygdala does not approach advanced levels of myelination until around 8-12 months of age, the infant remains basically fearless for the first 8 months of postnatal development. This is exceedingly adaptive. If fear were to emerge at an earlier age, the infant might withdraw from those who normally provide it with loving social-emotional stimulation. It is only as the medial and lateral amygdala reach an advanced stage of myelination and development that the fear response and related vocalizations emerge (Joseph, 1992a), that is, around the 8-12 months (Emde et al. 1976; Sroufe and Waters, 1976; Snow & McGaha 2002; Tronic 2007). Infants, therefore, become increasingly wary and fearful of strangers--emotions evoked by the amygdala. Therefore, if strangers approach, the child may look away or Cover their eyes. Or the child will try to get away.

Fear is the most common emotional reaction elicited from amygdala stimulation in human and non-humans (Chapman, 1960; Davis et al. 1997;

Gloor, 1992, 1997; Halgren, 1992; Rosen and Schulkin, 1998; Ursin and Kaada, 1960). Likewise, the human amygdala becomes activated when experiencing fear (Halgren, 1992; Rauch et al., 1996). Abnormal activity in the amygdala or the overlying temporal lobe can in fact evoke overwhelming, terrifying feelings of death-like "nightmarish" fear (Herman and Chambria, 1980; Strauss, Risser, and Jones, 1982). Hence, the fear response and the expression of fearful vocalizations, which appears around 8-12 months of age, are obvious indications of, and are correlated with, the later stages of amygdala maturation, a structure which also significantly contributes to the formation of specific social-emotional attachments (Joseph, 1992a, 2016b). Indeed, because the infant experiences fear, the fear response directly contributes to the formation of specific attachments and the avoidance of those who are unfamiliar.

Although the amygdala is associated with the fear response, this structure also promotes social contact seeking. Therefore, as noted, destruction of the amygdala abolishes social behavior, and animals and humans will actively avoid social contact. In the infant, however, social contact seeking is basically indiscriminate due to the immaturity of this structure and the paucity of counterbalancing influences normally exerted by the septal nucleus and cingulate gyrus on the amygdala and these tendendencies (Joseph, 1992a, 2016b). Thus, as the amygdala matures (and since the septal nuclei and cingulate do not begin to mature until later in development), until the infant is 6-7 months of age it will smile at the approach of anyone, even complete strangers. The child will also vigorously protest any form of separation from strangers (e.g. if they leave the room). This stage corresponds to the amygdaloid maturational period where septal and cingulate influences are still less well developed.

In fact, so intense is the need for physical and social contact that young animals raised in social isolation will form attachments to bare wire frames (Harlow, 1962), to television sets, to dogs that might maul them, to creatures that might kill them (Cairn, 1966) and among humans, to mothers that might abuse them.

In fact, among humans, so pervasive is this need for physical interaction and social stimulation that when grossly reduced or denied, the result is often death. For example, in several well known studies of children raised in foundling homes during the early 1900's when the need for contact was not well recongized, morbidity rates for children less than 1 year of age was over 70%. Of 10,272 children admitted to the Dublin Foundling home during a single 25 year period, only 45 survived (Langmeier and Matejcek, 2015).

However, as the septal nuclei and anterior cingulate begin to mature the infant becomes more discriminant in their interactions and around seven months of age a very real and specific attachment if formed; for example, to one's mother --an attachment which becomes progressively more intense and stable. This period represents septal and cingulate developmental influences such that global contact seeking becomes increasingly narrowed and restricted; attachment and avoidance

behaviors which are reinforced by the generation of the fear response. Therefore, by 9 months, 70% of children respond aversively, whereas by 12 months 90% respond aversively and will cry out and vocalize and display anxiety, fear and even flight reactions if the stranger were to approach (Schaffer, 1966; Spitz and Wolf, 1946; Tronic 2007; Waters et al. 2015).

SEPTAL SOCIAL BEHAVIOR

The septal nuclei does not begin to differentiate or mature until receiving axonal projections from the amygdala and extended amygdala (Brown, 2003; Humphrey, 2007), and does not begin to reach advanced stages of development until around after 3 years of age (Yakovlev and Lecours, 2007).

Phylogenetically the septal nuclei appears to be a derivative of the hypothalamus and hippocampus, and contributed to the evolution of the medial portions of the hemispheres (Sanides 1964) including portions of the cingulate gyrus. It also increases in relative size and complexity as we ascend the ancestral tree, attaining its greatest degree of development in humans.

Specifically, the septal nuclei lies in the medial portions of the hemispheres, just anterior to the 3rd ventricle near the hypothalamus and is comprised of the nucleus of the diagonal band of Broca and the nucleus of the medial septum. The septum projects heavily throughout the hypothalamus and maintains rich interconnections with all regions of the hippocampus (Mesulam et al. 2003; Siegel and Edinger, 1976) as well as the substantia innominata of the limbic striatum, the amygdala, the hippocampus and reticular formation (Amaral and Kurtz 2005; Nauta, 1956; Panula et al. 1984; Swanson and Cowan, 1979).

The septal nuclei is implicated in memory functioning (Bearer et al., 2007) and arousal, and in this regard contributes to the formation of specific attachments through memory functioning and the modulation of emotional arousal. Moreover, like the amygdala and cingulate, the septal nuclei also produces emotional vocalizations (MacLean 1990; Robinson 2007, 1972), and will become activated when mother's are exposed to a baby's cry (Numan & Sheehan 1997).

The septal nuclei is able to exert facilitatory or inhibitory influences on medial vs lateral hypothalamic arousal (Mogenson, 1976) and maintains a counterbalancing relationship with the amygdala particularly in regard to influences exerted on the hypothalamus (Joseph, 1992a). In addition, the amygdala acts to either facilitate or inhibit septal functioning whereas septal influences on the amygdala are largely inhibitory.

For example, whereas the lateral amygdala may activate the lateral hypothalamus, the septal nuclei may activated the medial hypothalamus (Kolb and Whishaw, 1977; Mogenson, 1976; Petsche et al. 1962, 1965) and can counter lateral hypothalamic self-stimulatory activity (Mogenson, 1976). As noted, the medial hypothalamus (and the septal nuclei) are associated with unpleasant mood states. In fact, electrophysiological alterations in septal activity which correspond to subjective feelings of aversion have been reported in humans (Heath, 1976).

Electrical stimulation of the septal nuclei counters and inhibits aggressive behavior (Rubenstein and Delgado, 1963) and suppresses the expression of rage reactions following hypothalamic stimulation (Siegel and Edinger, 1976). If the septal nucleus is destroyed, these counterbalancing influences are removed such that initially there results dramatic increases in aggressive behavior, including rage (Ahmad and Harvey, 1968; Blanchard and Blanchard, 1968; Brady and Nauta, 1953; King, 1958). Bilateral lesions in fact give rise to explosive emotional reactivity to tactile, visual, or auditory stimulation which can take the form of attack or flight. However, if the amygdala is subsequently lesioned, the septal rage and emotional reactivity are completely attenuated (King and Meyer, 1958). Hence, septal lesions appear to result in a loss of modulatory and inhibitory restraint which are normally exerted, in part, on the amgydala as well as the hypothalamus (McClary, 1961, 1966; Poplawsky, 1987).

Because of the loss of this inhibitory restraint, the amygdala begins to promote indiscriminant socializing and, as is the case with a five month old infant, will display an extreme need for social and physical contact (Joseph, 1992a). That is, in contrast to amygdaloid lesions which produce a severe social-emotional agnosia and social avoidance and withdrawal, septal lesions produce a dramatic and persistent increase in social cohesiveness and contact seeking (Jonason and Enloe, 1971; Jonason et al., 1973; McClary, 1961, 1966; Meyer et al. 2014).

With complete bilateral destruction of the septal nuclei in animals, the drive for social contact appears to be irresistable such that persistent attempts to make physical contact occurs--due in part, presumably, to the disinhibitory release of the amygdala. Septally lesioned animals will in fact seek contact with other species, including animals that might kill and eat them. If a group of septally lesioned animals are placed together, extreme huddling results. So intense is this need for contact comfort following septal lesions, that if other animals are not available they will seek out blocks of wood, old rags, bare wire frames or walls and then attempt to cuddle. Similar behaviors are demonstrated by human and non-human infant primates who are denied sufficient emotional and maternal stimulation (Joseph, 2016b,c).

Among human infant, and most mammals, the desire for maternal and physical-emotional contact is a normal aspect of development.

Humans with right sided or bilateral disturbances in septal functioning (such as due to seizure acitivity being generated in this region that may well involve the anterior cingulate), a behavior referred to as "stickiness" is sometimes observed. These individuals may seek to make repeated, prolonged, and often inappropriate contact with anyone who is available or who happens to be near by so as to tell them stories, jokes or merely pass the time. They don't readily take a "hint" and are difficult to "get rid of". In hospital situations they can be found intruding on other patients and their families, hanging out by the nurses station, or incessantly visiting other rooms to chat.

However, in some cases, similar behaviors can be triggered by amygdala as well as anterior cingulate hyperactivation It is probably the abnormal interactions of these nuclei that account for stalking behaviors and the formation of delusional attachments to actresses, sports stars, coworkers, and so on.

SEPTAL NUCLEI, AMYGDALA, SOCIAL-EMOTIONAL DEVELOPMENT & ATTACHMENT

That the amygdala promotes social emotional behavior and attachment is evident from the consequences of amygdala destruction. Social interest is abolished, animals that were formerly dominate become subordinate or social outcasts, and humans no longer react in an emotionally and socially appropriate manner and lose interest or no longer seem to recognize friends, relatives, and loved ones including their own offspring and parents (Dicks et al., 1969; Jonason & Enloe, 1971; Kling, 1972; Kling & Brothers 1992; Lilly et al., 2003; Marlowe et al., 2015; Terzian & Ore, 1955). Although they may behave in a sexually inappropriate fashion and masturbate and expose themselves to others, they also become socially unresponsive, and ignore, avoid, fail to recognize, or respond cruelly to others, and prefer to sit in isolation.

These disturbances, particularly those secondary to abuse or insufficient or abnormal early stimulation, is also related to environmental lesions which affect other limbic structures, including the septal nuclei and the anterior cingulate (Joseph, 1992a, 2016b). The amygdala maintains a mutually influential and counterbalancing relationship with the septal nuclei as both are richly interconnected via the stria terminalis. In general, these structures exert mutually inhibitory and excitatory influences on each other, with septal influences tending toward the inhibitory and emotionally dampening. For example, when the septal nucleus is electrically stimulated for brief periods, animals generally reduce their activity, and may lay down as if resting, and may even become unresponsive or oblivious to threat or other disturbances in the environment (MacLean, 1990). If the amygdala is destroyed, the septal nucleus becomes disinhibited, which in turn results in increased septal inhibitory and modulating influences on emotion and behavior.

However, if septal stimulation is prolonged and at high voltages, such that seizure-like spiking develops in the EEG, animals or humans may respond with pleasure (Heath, 1976; Olds & Forbes, 1981), and display increased sexual feelings coupled with erection or clitoral engorgement and genital manipulation, or conversely with rage, anger, and oppositional feelings of negativity (MacLean, 1990). Presumably, these latter behaviors are due to disruption in septal inhibitory functions, and are thus secondary to activation of the amygdala and hypothalamus. However, as noted, if the amygdala is destroyed, the septal nucleus may also become disinhibited and over active, which may result in severe disturbances in social as well as sexual behavior. This may explain why with amygdala lesions, although the desire for social contact is abolished, animals and humans may continue to engage in sexual behavior and may even attempt to have sex with members of their own sex or animals of other species (Kluver & Bucy, 1937).

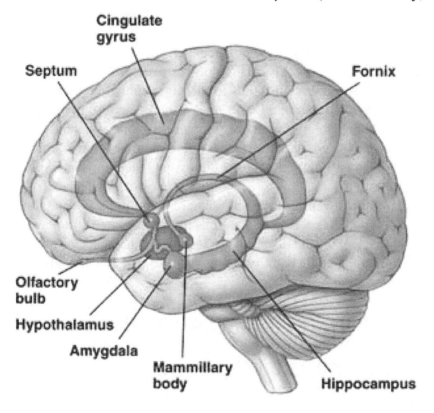

For much of the first year, septal influences are minimal as this nucleus functionally matures at a much later age than the amygdala (Brown, 2003; Joseph, 1992a, 2016b; Yakovlev & Lecours, 2007). In fact, the maturation of this structure appears to be rather prolonged as septal volume continues to increase well into late childhood and early adulthood (Jernigan et al., 1990), which may reflect the effects of pubertal hormones. Hence, infants behave in a socially indiscriminate manner as the developing amygdala is not subjected to septal inhibitory influences until later in development. As the septal nucleus matures, these indiscriminate socializing tendencies are restricted, which assists in the strengthening of specific attachments, such as to one's mother and family. This also insures that the infant or "toddler" does not wonder off with strangers. Thus, the latter maturation of the septal nuclei is exceedingly adaptive.

In fact, the initial development of the septal nuclei is influenced if not triggered by the extended amygdala, the tuberculum olfactorium (Humphrey, 2007), and later, it is only upon the receipt of amygdala afferent fibers that the septal nuclei begins to differentiate (Brown, 2003). Hence, in part, the maturation of the amygdala influences and promotes the later maturation of the septal nucleus which begin to myelinate until around the 4th fetal month; a process which is "extraordinarily protracted" and which can take well over 3 years to reach advanced stages of development (Yakovlev & Lecours, 2007), with the septal nuclei, including the hypothalamus and pituitary increasing in volume until well into puberty (Jernigan, et al., 1990).

As the septal nuclei is also implicated in sexual, aggressive as well as oppositional behavior the later maturation of this structure (including the frontal lobes, Schore, 2014) likely contributes to the oppositional and defiant childish attitude that emerges around age two: the so called "terrible twos," as well as the tendency of some youngsters to begin exploring their genitals at this age. Moreover, in response to the increased secretion of gonadal hormones, this structure likely plays a significant role in the sexual behavior of adolescents and adults.

In this regard, the development of the septal nuclei, in part is coordinated by the maturing amygdala, and as the infant develops, these two structures interact so as to promote selective and discriminate social, and then later, sexual behavior and the formation of specific emotional, and later, sexual attachments.

LIMBIC LOVE, HATE AND RELATIONSHIPS

The limbic system makes it possible to experience and communicate social-emotional nuances via multiple modalities, such as is reflected in the evolution and development of emotional speech, including the ability to laugh, cry, and to express sympathy and compassion, or the desire to form or maintain an emotional attachment. It is the evolution and development of these limbic nuclei (i.e. the amygdala, septal nuclei, cingulate gyrus) and their differential rates of maturation, which in fact enable humans and other higher mammals to form long lasting emotional and loving attachments, including the need and desire for contact comfort during infancy and early childhood.

Moreover, it is probably via the interactions mediated by these structures that emotions such as jealousy, rage or fear of abandonment are also generated, as well as feelings of possessiveness for a mate. Indeed, that some individuals respond with considerable grief, depression, anger and even uncontrollable rage when a "loved one" has ended their relationship, probably can also be explained from a limbic (infantile hypothalamic/amygdala) perspective.

Unfortunately, when the limbic system has been activated in this manner, feelings of rage may soon be manifested as acts of murder. For example, the frontal lobes and the rest of the brain may be overwhelmed by these limbic upheavals and the person may act on his or her limbic attachment needs, either in an extremely dependent and despairing fashion ("Don't leave me or I'll kill myself") or violent and enraged manner ("Don't leave or I'll kill you"). Loss of love, such as occurs when a relationship ends, seconded only by jealousy and money are prime elicitors of such murderous feelings and are due to the high involvement of the limbic system in all affairs of the heart.

Thus, if a person who has met another individuals primary needs for love, affection and physical intimacy were to leave, or want to end the affair, the limbic system of the male or female, being "abandoned," may respond in an infantile fashion; i.e. with desperation, frustration, anger, rage or depression and dispair -similar to the emotional stages demonstrated by children who are progressively deprived of mothering.

For example, children who are temporarily separated from their mothers and placed in a hospital, children's home, or what not, will pass through three stages of emotional turmoil, the first of which is characterized by a protest period where they frequently cry and scream for their mommy, and display signs of rage. This is followed by a stage of despair in which the child ceases to cry, loses interest in his environment and withdraws, and this too can persist for months. In the final stage he ceases to show interest in others, loses his appetite, and fails to respond to the affection offered by others and becomes quite passive and unresponsive. He may sit or lay for long periods with a frozen expression on his face, staring for hours at nothing. If the separation continues he deteriorates further and becomes physically ill and may die (Spitz 1945). In general, males are more severely affected than females (Bowlby, 1960; Spitz 1945).

Those who were only temporarily removed, once they were returned home would desperately cling to their mother, follow them everywhere, and became extremely fearful when left alone even for short time periods. Those who were deprived of maternal contact for 6 months or more instead behaved in a withdrawn, depressed manner and showed no interest in and were unable to reestablish their normal attachment to their mother. According to J. Bowlby (1940, 1960), children who suffer long term or repeated separations during the first three to five years of life are usually permanently affected.

However, when this same boy (or girl) grows to be an adult, instead of scrying, screaming, and raging helplessly when abandoned or neglected, he may plead as well as threaten, stalk, beat or even kill his former spouse or girlfriend and perhaps even his own children. Or, if its his job he's lost, he may threaten, attack, or kill his boss and coworkers.

Fortunately, it is a small percentage of the population who act on these limbic impulses. Nevertheless, even among those humans who maintain high levels of frontal inhibitory control in regard to all matters of the heart, the amygdala, cingulate, septal nuclei, hypothalamus, inferior temporal lobe, make possible not only intense feelings of emotion for a mate or lover, but correspondingly (at least in some people), an occasional "irrational" urge to throw them in front of a train (metaphorically speaking of course).

Indeed, because it provides the neurological foundation for emotion, attachment, jealously and desire, the limbic system enables human beings not only to coo words of love and sorrow but to experience all the joys, lusts, warmth, thrills, romance, passions, sexual excitement, and "craziness" of "true love."

Summary

In summary, during the amygdaloid maturational phase of early infant development, there is indiscriminate approach and contact seeking, which, if thwarted, may lead to emotional contact-seeking behaviors directed at inanimate objects. During the septal-cingulate stage (see below), indiscriminate social contact seeking is inhibited whereas specific attachments are narrowed, strengthened, reinforced and maintained due to the influences of these structures and the generation of fear response. However, if sufficient maternal emotional stimulation is not provided or is denied for long time periods, the infant will become enraged and then increasingly depressed.

The differential rates of amygdala and septal-cingulate development are crucial in promoting survival and social interaction with significant others. If these structures matured at an earlier age and if the infant experienced fear or wariness, social contact seeking might be prevented or avoided, and the result, might be severe social emotional and limbic system abnormalities (Joseph, 2016b,c) and even death.

CINGULATE GYRUS

The five layered cingulate gyrus sits atop the corpus callosum and can be broadly divided into two segments: the anterior cingulate (areas 24, 25, and 33) which is concerned with vocalizing and emotional and motoric functioning involving the hands, and regulating autonomic and endocrine activities; and the posterior (area 23) cingulate which is involved in visual-spatial and tactile analysis as well as motor output and memory.

POSTERIOR CINGULATE

The posterior cingulate gyrus is richly interconnected with the superior parietal lobe (area 7) the parahippocampal (inferior) temporal and superior temporal lobe (area 22), frontal lobe, caudate, putamen, substantia nigra, pulvinar of the thalamus, and dorsal hypothalamus (Beleydier and Mauguiere 1980; recently reviewed in Devinksy et al. 1995). In addition, the posterior cingulate projects to the red nucleus in the midbrain (which also receives frontal motor fibers) and to the spinal cord. Presumably the posterior cingulate acts to integrate visual input with motoric output and is not concerned with emotional stimuli per se, with the possible exception of nocioceptive functions (Devinksy et al. 1995).

However, the posterior cingulate may also be involved in visual-spatial and memory-cognitive activities, particularly as relates to the body and movement -hence the interconnections with the superior parietal lobe and the parahippocampal gyrus. The posterior cingulate may have, at least in part, evolved from the dorsal hippocampus (e.g. Sanides, 1964).

ANTERIOR CINGULATE GYRUS

The anterior cingulate (areas 24, 25, 33) is associated with processing and modulating the expression of emotional nuances, emotional learning and vocalization, the formation of long-term attachments and maternal behavior, including the initiation of motivationally significant goal directed behavior, as well as influencing and in part regulating endocrine and autonomic activities (Devinsky et al., 1995; MacLean 1990; Newman 2007, 2010; Shin et al., 2009; Vogt 2009).

The anterior cingulate maintains rich interconnections with the septal nuclei, amygdala, hypothalamus, mammilary bodies, hippocampus, dorsal medial nucleus of the thalamus and the periqueductal gray (Beleydier and Mauguiere 1980; Powell, 2014; Powell et al. 1974; Muller-Preuss and Jurgens 1976), as well as with the limbic striatum, caudate and putamen and the frontal motor areas (Vogt 2009).

The anterior cingulate thus appears to be a supra-modal area that is involved in the integration of motor, tactile, autonomic, and emotional stimuli, as well as with the production of emotional sounds (see below) and the capacity to experience psychological "pain and misery." In fact, the cingulate has long been associated with the experience of psychic and even physical pain (e.g. identifying the affective attributes of noxious and psychic stimuli).

Hence, during the 1930's and 1940's, bilateral cingulotomies were frequently performed to eliminate severe depressive and psychotic states as well as obsessive compulsive tendencies involving the hands (Le Beau, 1954; Whitty and Lewin 1957). However, following surgery, patients tended to become apathetic, emotionally blunted and/or socially and emotionally inappropriate or unresponsive.

Nevertheless, more recently it has been reported that 25% to 30% of patients with obsessive-compulsive disorder who were unresponsive to medication and behavioral treatment, significantly improve following cingulotomy (Baer et al. 1995), though these authors stress surgery is "a last resort treatment."

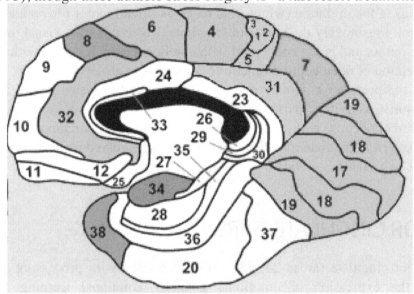

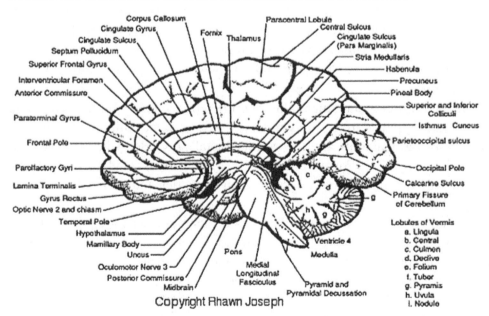

Copyright Rhawn Joseph

ANTERIOR CINGULATE GYRUS

As the forebrain matures in a caudal to rostral, paramedial to medial/lateral arc, paramedian structures such as the amygdala begin to mature in advance of the medially located septal nuclei and the medially situated anterior cingulate; developmental patterns which are reflected behaviorally and emotionally. Like the amygdala, the anterior cingulate is exceedingly important in affective-motor activities, including those involving the hands (e.g. grooming, cuddling), and the oral-laryngeal musculature; i.e. vocalization (Joseph, 1993, 2016b). The anterior cingulate is also associated with emotional learning, attention and concentration, the development of play, fantasy, and affectionate behavior, and the formation of long-term attachments and infant-maternal interactional behavior including separation anxiety (Devinsky, Morrell, & Vogt, 1995; Joseph, 2016b; MacLean, 1990; Slotnick, 2007; Smith, 1945, Stamm, 1955; Ward, 1948). In fact, electrical stimulation of the anterior cingulate can produce a separation cry identical to that of a frightened infant (MacLean 1990; Robinson, 2007).

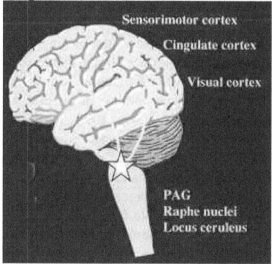

In this regard, capacities associated with the anterior cingulate (e.g. play, separation anxiety) also emerge later in development and thus parallel the functional maturation of this structure. Specifically, although the posterior cingulate begins to myelinate around the second to third postnatal month, the anterior cingulate begins to myelinate and mature around the fourth postnatal month and then reaches an advanced stage of myelination around the end of the first year (Benes, 2014; Brody et al., 1987; Yakovlev & Lecours, 2007)-- the age at which attachment behaviors, and separation anxiety and stranger fear become most pronounced (Schaffer, 1966). However, like other limbic structures, myelination of the cingulate continues for several years (Brody et al., 1987; Yakovlev & Lecours, 2007).

Thus the maturation and myelination of the anterior cingulate parallels and appears to contribute to the development of those social-emotions which emerge during the latter half of the first year; i.e. separation anxiety, stranger fear, the development of playfulness and affectionate behavior, and the formation of long term emotional attachment. Moreover, the maturation of the anterior cingulate also parallels and promotes the development of complex social emotional vocalizations, including "late" and canonical babbling, including the emerging ability to engage in sound play and to produce sounds which do not correspond to the infant's (or adult's) true mood state.

Indeed, the cingulate is capable of producing exceedingly complex social emotional vocalizations which sometimes have no bearing on the organism's mood or true emotional state (Jurgens, 1990; Jurgens & Muller-Preuss, 1977; Meyer et al., 1973), and completely different emotional calls can be elicited from electrodes which are immediately adjacent (Jurgens, 1990). Thus the cingulate is capable of considerable vocal flexibility and enables an individual to modulate, disguise or emphasize the emotional, prosodic, melodic components of speech so that one's true feelings can be disguised or emphasized in order to produce sounds suggestive of, for example, incredulity, hilarity, empathy, maternal concern, or separation anxiety.

As detailed below, it has been demonstrated that the anterior cingulate can generate a separation cry which is identical to that produced by a frightened infant (MacLean 1990; Robinson, 2007), including those vocalizations which infants produce in accompaniment to those produced by their mothers (Bayart et al. 1990; Jurgens, 1990; Wiener et al. 1990). As argued by MacLean (1990), the cingulate produces these infantile/maternal vocalizations and associated emotions so as to maintain maternal-offspring contact and maternal care. When mothers and infants mutually vocalize, these interactions reinforce and promote attachment behaviors, and contribute to the development of language. Again, however, just as the cingulate of the infant appears to be responsible for producing infantile sounds and behaviors, including the separation cry, these maternal vocalizations also appear to be produced by the anterior cingulate (and right frontal lobe), as it is this structure which enables a speaker, including a mother to vary and emphasize prosodic vocalizations--a characteristic of mothers when interacting with their infants (Fernald, 2005, 1991, 1992). In this regard it appears that the cingulate and limbic system of the mother is essentially communicating with the cingulate and limbic system of the infant, thereby promoting maternal-infant attachment as well as the development of human speech.

The importance of the cingulate in emotional vocalization and affectionate, playful behavior becomes most evident following injury to this region of the brain. For example, adult, non-human primates who have suffered cingulate destruction cease to display acts of affection, cease to vocalize, engage in abnormal maternal behavior, and will even walk and step on their offspring "as though they were inanimate objects" (Ward, 1948). Likewise, human adults who have experienced cingulate destruction become mute, inattentive, and socially and emotionally unresponsive and will ignore loved one's including their children (Barris & Schuman, 1953; Devinksy et al., 1995; Laplane, Degos, Baulac, & Gray, 1981; Tow & Whitty, 1953). Similarly, infants with anterior cingulate destruction cease to engage in affectionate behavior, no longer play with siblings or conspecies, and lose all interest in establishing or maintaining affiliative behavior, and generally become mute and no longer vocalize (MacLean, 1990; Newman 2009).

Thus, the maturation of the anterior cingulate promotes the formation and strengthening of emotional attachments, including various aspects of speech, as well as those infantile behaviors which stimulate maternal behavior which in turn are also, in part, mediated by the cingulate. Hence, this structures in parts serves as a mother-infant interface, and in fact, it appears that the evolution of this structure, some 200 million years ago, coincided with and ushered in the development of long term maternal behavior and the establishment of the first families with infants remaining attached until reaching the juvenile period.

Of course, the anterior cingulate has also continued to evolve, culminating in complexity with the emergence of primates and modern humans. Moreover, as it evolved, it appears to have contributed to the evolution of the medial frontal neocortex (which is also involved in vocalization), as well as the lateral frontal neocortex including Broca's area and the emotional-melodic speech area in the right frontal lobe with which it maintains extensive interconnections. In fact, it is via these extensive neocortical-anterior cingulate (as well as amygdala) interconnections that enables a child or adult to hierarchically subserve and express, as well as punctuate limbic vocalizations so as to produce word-rich grammatically complex human language.

THE CINGULATE GYRUS AND EMOTIONAL SPEECH

Electrical stimulation of the anterior cingulate can induce feelings of anxiety, pleasure and fear (Meyer et al. 1973) as well as changes in heart and respiratory rate and blood pressure accompanied by pupil dilation, gonadal and adrenal cortical hormone secretion, penile erection, and aggression (Buchanan and Powell 1982; Devinsky et al. 1995; MacLean 1990). The cingulate also plays a role in maternal behavior (Bartels & Zeki 2004; Leibenluft et al., 2004; Lorberbaum et al., 2016, 2002; Renote et al. 2004; Salmaso et al., 2011; Sander et al. 2007; Seifritz et al., 2003). Stimulation also induces a wide range of divergent vocalizations including growling, crying, high pitched cackling, and sounds similar to an infant's separation cry (MacLean 1990; Newman 2007, 2010; Robinson, 2007).

The cingulate interacts with the amygdala. The amygdala is able to produce complex social-emotional vocalizations via the stria terminals and amygdalafugal pathways to the hypothalamus and periaqueductal gray which acts on the oral-laryngeal musculature. The amygdala also increasingly interacts with the rapidly maturing cingulate gyrus which is one of the most vocal structures of the brain (Hage 2010; Jurgens, 1990, 1992, 2009; MacLean, 1990; Newman 2007, 2010; Ploog, 1992; Robinson, 2007, 1972) and which becomes activated in response to and when producing human speech (Passingham, 1997; Paulesu et al., 1997; Peterson et al., 1988). For example, the anterior cingulate (as well as the left frontal lobe) become highly active when generating as many words as possible for a given category, e.g. words beginning with "F" (Frith and Dolan, 1997). Conversely, if the anterior cingulate is severaly damaged, the ability to initiate speech may be abolished (Chang et al., 2007).

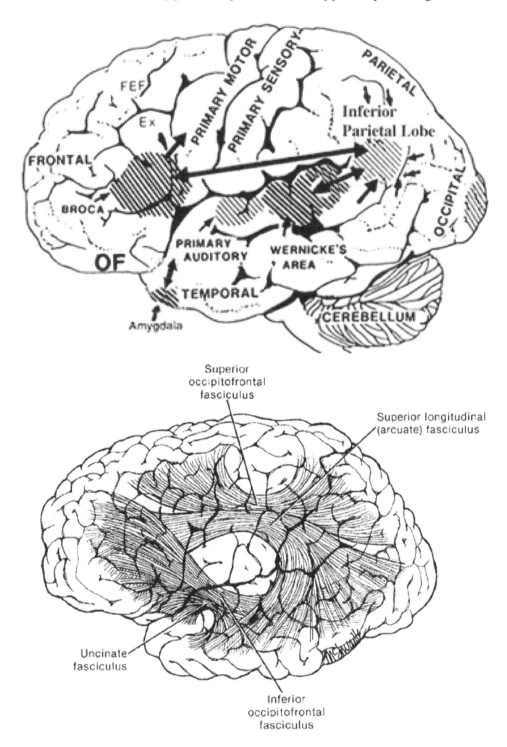

The anterior cingulate gyrus is also directly linked to the neocortical expressive speech areas located in the left and right frontal lobe, as well as with the hypothalamus and periaqueductal gray (Powell, 2014; Powell, Akagi, and Hatton, 1974; Jurgens, 1990, 2014)--which explains why the anterior cingulate and left frontal lobe become active simultaneously during language tasks (Frith and Dolan, 1997; Peterson et al., 1988). Indeed, Broca's expressive motor-speech (and oral-facial/hand) area in the left frontal lobe, and the emotional-melodic speech (and oral-facial/hand) area in the right lateral frontal lobe, appear to have evolved from the anterior cingulate gyrus/medial frontal lobe (Joseph, 2016e). Therefore, the right and left frontal lobes responds to cingulate (and posterior neocortical) impulses by vocalizing. If the anterior cingulate/medial frontal lobe were destroyed, the patient would become mute (Barris and Schuman, 1953; Devinksy et al. 1995; Joseph, 2016a; Laplane et al., 1981; Tow and Whitty, 1953)

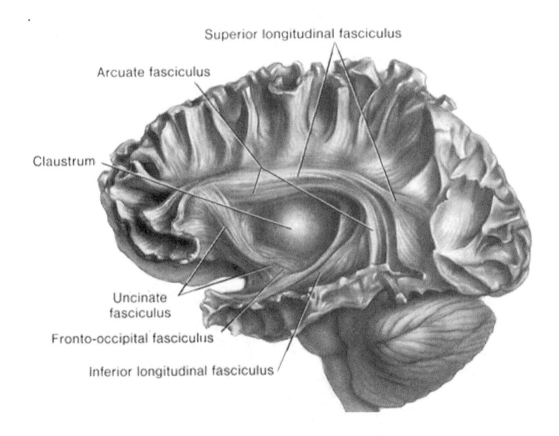

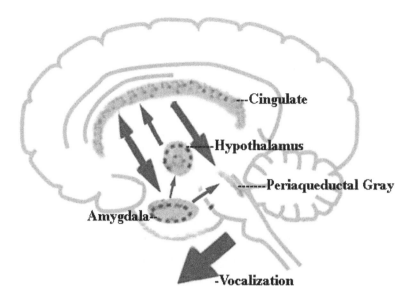

Among its many functions, the anterior cingulate (Brodmann's areas 24, 25, 33) is associated with processing and modulating the vocal expression of emotional, melodic, and prosodic nuances, emotional learning, identifying the affective attributes of noxious psychic stimuli, maternal behavior, separation anxiety, and the formation of long-term attachments (Shin et al., 2009; Devinsky, Morrell, and Vogt, 1995; Joseph, 2016b; MacLean 1990; Powell, 2014; Salmaso et al. 2011). As based on functional imaging, the anterior cingulate also becomes activated by hot, painful, and noxious stimuli (Casey et al., 2014), and has been considered by some to be the seat of pain and misery (Vogt 2009).

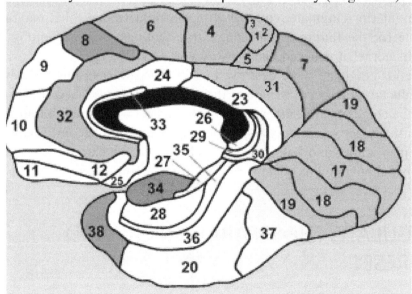

Depth electrode stimulation of the anterior cingulate can induce feelings of anxiety, pleasure and fear as well as a wide range of divergent vocalizations including growling, crying, high pitched cackling, laughing, and sounds similar to an infant's separation cry (Devinsky et al. 1995; Jurgens, 1990; MacLean 1990; Meyer et al. 1973; Robinson, 2007). The anterior cingulate also assists in setting thresholds for vocalization (Jurgens and Muller-Preuss, 1977; Robinson, 2007), including modulating some of the prosodic and melodic features which characterize different speech patterns, e.g. happiness vs sadness, and thus laughing vs crying. The vocalizing capabilities of the cingulate are made possible via subcortical connections with the periaqueductal gray (Jurgens 1990, 2014; Newman 2007, 2010; Siegel et al., 2010), and its axonal projections to the right and left frontal speech areas.

Whereas vocalizations triggered by excitation of the amygdala, hypothalamus, or septal nuclei are usually accompanied by mood-congruent behaviors (Gloor, 1960; Jurgens, 1990; Robinson, 2007; Ursin and Kaada, 1960) the cingulate is capable of producing exceedingly complex social emotional vocalizations which sometimes have no bearing on the organism's mood or true emotional state (Jurgens, 1990; Jurgens and Muller-Preuss, 1977; Meyer et al. 1973; Newman 2007, 2010). In addition, completely different emotional calls can be elicited from electrodes which are immediately adjacent (Jurgens, 1990, 2009).

Thus the cingulate is capable of considerable vocal flexibility and apparently enables an individual to modulate the emotional-prosodic-melodic components of speech so that one's true feelings can be disguised or emphasized in order to produce sounds suggestive of, for example, sarcasm, incredulity, or hilarity. The anterior cingulate may well contribute to the "deceptive" vocalizations and behaviors demonstrated by innumerable mammalian and avian species, such as when attempting to lure a predator away from one's helpless infants. Conversely, however, the anterior cingulate, coupled with the right frontal lobe, may also be responsible for the failure to hide one's true feelings, thus generating the complaint: "Its not what you said, but the way you said it!"

If the anterior cingulate were destroyed, of if the pathways linking it with the periaqueductal gray were severed, the individual would become mute. However, if the cingulate and surrounding medial tissue were mildly injured, or became abnormally active, emotional-prosodic speech would become abnormal and patients may stutter and repeat words such that, in the extreme, they may uncontrollably babble (Devinksy et al. 1995; Dimmer and Luders, 1995).

THE CINGULATE, THE SEPARATION CRY AND "MOTHERESE"

The medially located cingulate gyrus begins to myelinate around the second postnatal month and achieves an advanced stage of myelination by the end of the first year (Debakan, 1970; Gibson, 1991; Yakovlev and Lecours, 2007); around the same time the amygdala increasingly vocalizes feelings of fear. However, in addition to fear, the anterior cingulate contributes to the experience of unpleasant and negative emotions (Cao et al., 2009; Casey et al., 2014; Coghill et al., 2014; Eto et al. 2011; Nitschke et al., 2009; Shin et al. 2009) including separation anxiety and vocalizes a separation cry which is similar if not identical to that produced by a frightened infant (MacLean 1990; Newman 2007, 2010; Robinson, 2007). In fact, abnormal activity in the anterior cingulate has in some cases induced not just anxious vocalizations, but infantile behavior, such as assuming the fetal position (Devinksy et al. 1995). By contrast, lesions of the anterior cingulate significantly reduce crying upon separation in primates (MacLean and Newman 1988).

Likewise, infant vocalizations including crying significantly alters the activity of the cingulate in human mothers and female listerners (Lorberbaum et al., 2016, 2002; Sander et al. 2007; Seifritz et al., 2003). Cingulate activity also changes when mothers view pictures of their infants (Bartels & Zeki 2004; Leibenluft et al., 2004; Renote et al. 2004). Maternal behavior, including pregnancy, are also associated with neuroplasticity and alterations in metabolism in the cingulate (Salmaso et al., 2011). By contrast, anterior and posterior cingulated lesions impair maternal behaviour in non-human mammals (MacLean 1990).

The anterior cingulate is thus responsible for producing and responding to complex emotional-prosodic vocalizations, including, perhaps, the prosodic variations which mothers employ when speaking to their babies and vice versa; i.e. "motherese." As is well known, considerable vocalizing typically occurs between mothers and their infants; and the infants of many species will often sing along or produce sounds in accompaniment to those produced by their mothers. These interactions appear to be limbically mediated and reinforce and promote mutual vocalization, attachment behaviors, and may contribute to the development of language. Among animal and human mothers, much of this initial mutual sound production consists of exaggerated emotional prosody (Cooper and Aslin, 1990; Fernald, 1991, 1992; Fernald et al., 1989; Jurgens, 2009; Newman 2007); i.e. "limbic language."

The cingulate is also sexually differentiated (MacLusky et al. 1987, 2014; Salmaso et al., 2011). Thus there is a "male" vs a "female" cingulate which in turn likely contributes to sex differences in melodic speech patterns as well as in "maternal" vs "paternal" behaviors. For example, regardless of culture, mothers not only produce emotional-prosodic-melodic vocalizations but emphasize and even exaggerate social-emotional, and melodic-prosodic vocal features when interacting with their infants (Fernald, 1992; Nakazima, 2015). Presumably, it is these limbic foundations which explain why the acoustics of these nuances are basically identical regardless of culture (Nakazima, 2015), and why even mothers or infants who are born deaf produce these same prosodic vocalizations when speaking to their deaf babies (Oller et al., 2005; Woll & Kyle, 1989).

These emotional-melodic vocalization greatly influence infant-emotional behavior and attention as infants not only produce but prefer and are more responsive to these exaggerated prosodic vocalizations (Cooper and Aslin, 1990; Fernald, 1991). In fact, by 5 months of age infants become quite adept at perceiving and distinguishing between different emotional vocalizations so as to determine the mood state and intentions of the speaker (Fernald, 1993; Haviland and Lelwica, 1987). Likewise, mothers are generally able to determine the mood and desires of her 5-month old offspring when it produces similar emotional vocalizations (D'Odorico, 1984; Wolff, 1969).

In many respects these mutual mother-infant social-emotional interactions appear to be a reflection of the limbic system of the mother communicating with the limbic system of her infant. The infant-neocortex is much too immature to comprehend non-emotional words and sentences.

The female limbic system (and the right frontal-temporal speech areas) are in fact adapted and organized so as to promote social-emotional communication with her young, and with each other. That is, the cingulate gyrus, amygdala and hypothalamus are sexually differentiated such that there is a "male" and a "female" limbic system. Being in possession of a "female" limbic system presumably confers a superior ability to perceive and express social-emotional nuances and vocalizations (Joseph, 2000a); capacities at which females excell (Brody, 2005; Buck, 1977, 1984; Buck, Miller, and Caul, 1974; Fuchs and Thelan, 1988; Heller and Levy, 1992; Proverbio et al., 2007, 2008; Soloman and Ali, 1972; Strayer, 1980). Indeed, in contrast to males, females are not only more emotionally perceptive and expressive, but tend to employ 5-6 different prosodic variations and utilize the higher and fluctuating registers when conversing (Joseph, 1993, 2016e), especially with their infants (Fernald, 1992; Fernald, et al. 1989). Human (as well as non-human) infants are not only more responsive to the emotional-prosody conveyed by a female voice, but are most responsive to the higher as well as fluctuating registers (Fernald, 2005; Hauser, 1997).

However, in contrast to the infant, adult females (and males) also rely on the neocortices of the right frontal-temporal lobe to produce and comprehend emotional-melodic-prosodic vocalization. As noted, over the course of evolution the anterior cingulate appears to have contributed to the evolution of the frontal motor-speech areas, whereas the auditory areas in the superior temporal lobe appear to be evolutionary derivatives of as well as richly interconnected with the amygdala (Joseph, 2016e). The frontal and temporal auditory areas, however, do not begin to significantly mature until around the first year after birth; a process which can take 7 to over 20 years to complete (Blinkov and Glezer, 1968; Brody, et al. 1987; Conel, 1939, 1941; Huttenlocher, 1990; Yakovlev and Lecours, 2007).

MATERNAL BEHAVIOR & THE EVOLUTION OF INFANT SEPARATION CRIES

Sharks, teleosts, amphibians, and reptiles possess a limbic system, consisting of an amygdala, hippocampus, hypothalamus, and septal nuclei. It is these limbic nuclei which enable a group of fish to congregate and "school", and which makes it possible for reptiles to form territories which include an alpha female, several sub-females, and a few juveniles. These nuclei promote social attachment and interaction.

However, sharks, fish, and the first amphibians and reptiles, like their modern counterparts lacked the four to five layered cingulate gyrus. Moreover, these creatures do not possess an inner ear or true middle ear, though amphibians and reptiles are attuned to hear low level vibrations and sounds, such as croaking, tails thumped on the ground, and a few distress calls and those of contentedness. Limbic language capabilities are not well developed in these creatures. As they also lack a cingulate gyrus, amphibians and most but not all reptiles show little or no maternal care, and rarely vocalize. They will also greedily cannibalize their infants who in turn must hide from their parents to avoid being eaten

When reptiles began to differentiate and evolve into the repto-mammals some

181

250 million years ago, and then, twenty-five million years later, when the first tiny dinosaurs (who diverged from a different line of reptiles, the theocondants) began to roam the Earth, major biological alterations occurred involving cranial and post-cranial skeletal structure, mammillary development, thermo-regulation, sexual reproduction, and limbic system function and structure (Bakker, 1971; Crompton & Jenkins, 1973; Duvall, 1986; Paul, 1988; Quiroga, 1980; Romer, 1966) --all of which coincided with tremendous advances in the ability to engage in audio-vocal communication and the capacity to nurse the young.

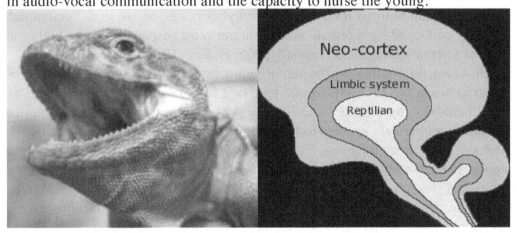

It was not until the appearance of the the therapsids, around 200 to 150 million years ago, that mammilary glands, and thus the capacity to nurse, came into being (Duvall, 1986). It was at this time that the middle ear began to undergo tremendous modification and the first rudiments of an inner ear developed (Broom, 1932; Brink, 1956; Crompton & Jenkins, 1973; Romer, 1966). Although the hypothalamus, septal nuclei, and amygdala continued to evolve, it was also around this time that the cingulate gyrus began to appear and increasingly enshroud the dorsal surface of the limbic forebrain -an event which corresponded with the appearance of nursing nipples (Duvall 1986) and the inner ear. When this began to occur, sounds came to serve as a means of purposeful and complex communication, not only between potential mates or predator and prey, but between a mother and her infant (Joseph, 1993, 2014; Maclean, 1990). This ability in turn was probably made possible by the amygdala and in particular, the evolution of the four to five-layered transitional neocortex, the cingulate gyrus.

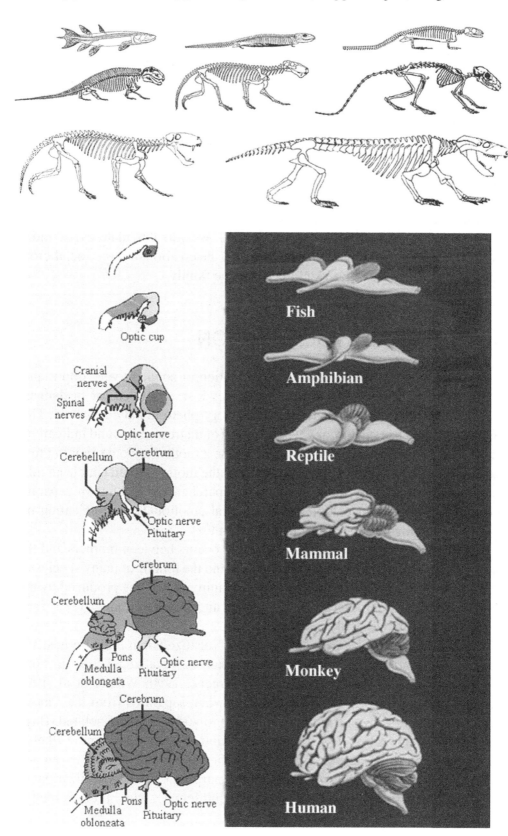

As noted, it is the limbic system and the interactions of limbic nuclei such as the amygdala and the cingulate gyrus which not only stimulates the desire to communicate, but to form attachments, social groups, and eventually, the formation of the family. In fact, many of the late repto-mammals, as well as some dinosaurs and the later appearing therapsids, lived in packs or social groups, and presumably cared and guarded their young for extended time periods lasting until the juvenile stage (Bakker, 1971; Brink, 1956; Crompton & Jenkins, 1973; Duvall, 1986; Paul, 1988; Romer, 1966). Presumably long term attachments were made possible via the evolution of the anterior cingulate.

As also noted, the first appearance of rudimentary nipples coincided with therapsid development. Hence, one of the hallmarks of this evolutionary transitional stage, some 200 million years ago, was the cingulate gyrus and the first evidence of nursing, maternal feeling, and the creation of large social groups and hunting packs, and what would become the family.

MOTHER INFANT VOCALIZATION

Among mammals and primates the production of sound is very important in regard to infant care, for if an infant becomes lost, separated, or in danger, a mother could not quickly detect this by olfactory-pheromonal cues alone. These conditions would have to be conveyed via a cry of distress or a sound indicative of separation fear and anxiety; which would cause a mother to come running to the rescue. Conversely, vocalizations produced by the mother would enable an infant to continually orient and find its way back if perchance it got lost or separated. Hence, the first forms of complex limbic social-emotional communication may well have been first produced in a maternal context.

As noted, considerable vocalizing typically occurs between mothers and their infants (be they human, primate, or mammal); and the infants of many species will often sing along or produce sounds in accompaniment to those produced by their mothers. These mutual interactions reinforce and promote mutual vocalization which is often initiated by the mother.

In fact, primate females are more likely to vocalize when they are near their infants versus non-kin, and infants are more likely to vocalize when their mother is in view or nearby (Bayart et al. 1990; Jurgens, 1990; Wiener et al. 1990). Similarly, infant primates will loudly protest when separated from their mother so long as she is in view and will quickly cease to vocalize when isolated (Bayart et al. 1990; Wiener, et al. 1990). However, adult males are also more likely to call or cry when in the presence of their mother or an adult female vs an adult male (Jurgens, 1990). It thus appears that the purpose of these vocalizations are to elicit a vocal response from mother, or an adult female, who in turn is likely to respond with soothing limbic language.

Hence, ontogentically and phylogenetically, the initial production of emotional sounds is limbically based, and increasingly, over the course of evolution, and as evident during early development, the production of these sounds is associated with maternal-infant care, and/or interactions with an adult female. As noted, the cingulate is sexually differentiated (MacLusky et al., 1987, 2014), and regardless of culture, human mothers tend to emphasize and even exaggerate social-emotional, and melodic-prosodic vocal features when interacting with their infants (Fernald, 1992; Fernald et al., 1989), which in turn appears to greatly influence infant emotional behavior and attention (Fernald, 1991). Similarly, human infants prefer listening to and are more responsive to these exaggerated limbic vocalizations, as compared to "normal" adult speech patterns (Cooper and Aslin, 1990) particularly when produced by a female; i.e. by a female cingulate gyrus.

FEMALE SUPERIORITIES IN LIMBIC LANGUAGE

In addition to the cingulate, the amygdala and hypothalamus are also sexually differentiated (Allen and Gorski, 1992; Allen et al., 1989; Blier et al., 1982; Gorski et al. 2014; Goy and McEwin, 1980; Raisman and Field, 1971; Swabb and Fliers, 2005; Swabb and Hoffman, 1988). In addition, the rope of nerve fibers which interconnect the right and left amygdala and inferior temporal lobes (the anterior commissure) is 18% larger in females than males (Allen and Gorski, 1992), which in turn likely contributes to sex differences in language, emotion, and maternal vs paternal behavior. Thus, females tend to produce a greater range of limbic (social-emotional) vocalizations than males (Glass 1992; Joseph, 1993, 2000a, 2011a,b; Tannen 1991) and they tend to employ 5-6 different prosodic variations and to utilize the higher registers when conversing. They are also more likely to employ glissando or sliding effects between stressed syllables (Brend, 2015; Coleman, 1971; Edelsky, 1979).

Men tend to be more monotone, employing 2-3 variations on average, most of which hovers around the lower registers (Brend, 2015; Coleman, 1971; Edelsky, 1979). Even when trying to emphasize a point males are less likely to employ melodic extremes but instead tend to speak louder. Perhaps this is why men are perceived as more likely to bellow, roar, or growl, whereas females are perceived as more likely to shriek, squeal, coo, and purr. Nevertheless, although influenced by sex differences in the oral-laryngeal structures, these differential capacities are also reflected in the greater capacity of the female brain to express and perceive these nuances (chapter 7), which also appears to be the case in female primates. Thus female monkeys and apes are more vocal and engage in more social vocalizations, and in fact vocalize more often that males who in turn are more likely to vocalize when threatening or engaged in dominance displays

(Cross and Harlow, 1965; Erwin, 1980; Fedigan, 1992; Goodall, 1986, 1990; Mori, 2015; Mitchell, 1979).

It has been repeatedly demonstrated that human females are also more emotionally expressive, and are more perceptive in regard to comprehending emotional verbal nuances (Burton and Levy, 1989; Hall, 2014; Soloman and Ali, 1972). This superior sensitivity includes the ability to feel and express empathy (Burton and Levy, 1989; Safer, 1981). From childhood to adulthood women appear to be much more emotionally expressive than males in general (Brody, 2005; Burton and Levy, 1989; Gilbert, 1969); abilities which confer upon her a greater emotional sensitivity to the needs and feelings of others, especially her babies. These superiorities assist her in being a good mother.

MATERNAL BEHAVIOR, ATTACHMENT, AND THE FEMALE LIMBIC SYSTEM

It has been proposed that these limbic system sex differences are responsible for and are an evolutionary consequence of woman's role in bearing and rearing children and the female desire to form long term attachments, and engage in maternal care and verbal communication (Joseph, 1993). Female humans, primates and mammals apparently find these activities rewarding in-themselves, due to these same limbic system sex differences.

That is, given that the sexually differentiated anterior cingulate, at least in part, evolved in a maternal context and promoted the development of maternal feelings and long term mother-infant attachment, whereas the amygdala and hypothalamus are also sexually differentiated, it appears that these structures may account for why human and non-human female primates differentially respond and desire to nurture, hold, cuddle, and stare at infants. Indeed, female humans, chimps, baboons and rhesus macaques cuddle more and more closely, and are cuddled more by their sisters, mothers and other females (Jensen et al., 1968a, Hansen, 1966; Mitchell, 1968; Goodall 1971, 1990), whereas males are much more resistant to being held, and will kick and fuss, and actively attempt to escape their mothers much more so than females (Elia, 1988; Fedigan, 1992; Freedman, 1974, 1980; Mitchell, 1968, 1979; Goodall 1971, 1990; Kummer, 1971). In part this sex differences also reflects a struggle against potential physical domination which most males find aversive (Joseph, 1993). Hence, be it a male dog, chimpanzee, baboon, or child, they are far more likely than females to struggle, squirm, or resist attempts to hold or pick them up, and may even respond as if they find it aversive.

Mothers are therefore more willing to hold female babies and for longer time periods as they are also easier to calm and are more fun to hold as they seem to enjoy it more than males. Since females demonstrate greater social responsiveness and are more likely to employ facial, vocal and social signals, mothers are more likely to physically, socially and vocally interact with their infant daughters and vice versa (Moss, 1974).

Being similarly socially inclined, mothers find it more socially rewarding and enjoyable to interact with their daughters who are also in possession of a "maternal" (albeit immature) limbic system and cingulate gyrus.

Be it a female chimpanzee, baboon, rhesus macaque, or human, females also begin to demonstrate an extraordinary interest in babies and in play-mothering during even the earliest phases of their own childhood (Devore, 1964; Elia, 1988; Fedigan 1992; Goodall 1971, 1990; Jolly 1972; Kummer, 1971, Mitchell, 1979; Strum, 1987; Suomi, 1972). When girls play together, much of their fantasy and conversation concerns fashion and making out and revolves around adult relationships, including the raising of a family and the behavior and misbehavior of children (their dolls). Babies are of enormous interest to females, be they human, ape or monkey, and social primates and female humans who have babies usually become tremendously popular and the center of attention (Fedigan 1992; Jolly 1972, Mitchell 1979, Strum ,1987). Even among women enslaved in a harem, once she becomes pregnant and has a child, her status is quickly and permanently elevated.

Mothers, grandmothers, young and adolescent females, and even women who describe themselves as "feminists" show much more interest in babies than do men, even when the baby is not their own (Azhn-Waxler et al., 2003; Berman, 1990; Berman and Goodman, 1984; Blakemore, 1981, 2005, 1990; Frodi & Lamb, 2014; Melson and Fogel, 1982; Nash and Fledman, 1981). Adolescent girls spend significantly more time talking about new baby's than boys (Berman, 1990), and mothers spend more time talking about the baby with their daughters than their sons (Berman, 1990).

Girls not only talk more but play and care for their infant sisters and brothers significantly more and show consider amounts of nurturant interest in the babies well being (Blakemore, 1990) even when there has been no request or pressure to do so. Indeed, girls often demonstrate an intrusive interest in babies (Berman, 2003), and will give infants much more care than they require (Ainsworth & Wittig, 1969), as if often the case with mothers (Stewart, 1990). These behaviors also appear to be limbically mediated, as they are demonstrated by females of other species.

Non-human female primates, be it gorilla, chimpanzee, baboon, rhesus macaques, lemur, and so on, will eagerly seek to groom, cuddle, and carry not only their own infants but those of other females (Jolly, 2005; Devore, 1964; Kummer 1971, Strum 1987; Suomi, 1972; Mitchell, 1979; Goodall, 1971). These primates may also spend all day passing them back and forth. Like human females, some will even steal these infants. Those female primates who show the greatest interest, however, are young females who had not yet had babies.

Moreover, among almost all social primates, the birth of a new baby has an extremely excitatory effect on all the other females of the troop who will gather around and touch, stare, hold, and cuddle it. This female interest, of course, is certainly quite adaptive, at least for those living in the dangerous condition of the wild for it insures that if a mother dies another will adopt her baby.

Such behavior is obviously not the result of sexist training for it is typical of almost all social female primates, whereas males, including young males show relatively little interest in babies. For example, boy chimpanzees show little interest in their younger infant siblings, whereas girl chimps become increasingly fascinated and will hold and cuddle them and will attempt to model their mother's interactions with the infant (Goodall, 1971). If a new mother dies but her baby has older male siblings, less than 25% will adopt the little orphan whereas females siblings are quite anxious and happy to take this role.

THE MALE LIMBIC SYSTEM AND INFANT CARE

With the exception of the baboon (Rowell et al., 1968; Kummer, 1968, 1971; Mitchell, 1968, 1979, Fedigan, 1992), lack of interest in infants is characteristic of most social male primates and almost all male mammals, reptiles, amphibians and fish, as well as human fathers and men and boys in general who generally have little or no interest in babies and generally provide little or nurturant care for their own or the children of others (Rossi, 2005; Gordon and Draper, 1982).

In fact, be it male chimps attacking another troop, or male humans attacking other humans, infants are often the victim of male aggression. Males will kill other humans including the babies of those who have done them no harm.

Of course, there are always exceptions; particularly among males who may possess a "female" limbic system. Rather, like other social primates, boys seek boys for playmates and engage in considerable amounts of rough housing, wrestling, and hitting; behavior that is completely inappropriate in regard to infant interactions. When boys or male primates begin to separate from their mothers, they show no interest in younger siblings but seek out adolescent and adult males to play with. Although they may on occasion seek nurturance they seldom provide it in return.

Human males and fathers rarely behave in any manner that approximates normal female maternal behavior (Belsky et al., 1984; Clarke-Stewart, 2014; Frodi et al., 1982) as this is simply not an activity they find interesting, pleasurable or rewarding. This is why, for example, child care professions and those jobs involving high levels of child interactions, such as elementary school teacher, are overwhelmingly made up of women (Gordon and Draper, 1982); a function not of pay but lack of heterosexual-male interest (Blakemore et al., 1988). Rather, fathers and adult heterosexual males tend to express interest in younger males (and females) only when they reach adolescence, and this is also true of most male primates.

Given that these sex differences are obviously innate, it could therefore be argued that in contrast to male humans, primates, and mammals who have little or no interest in child care, that the female limbic system is designed to promote these interests. Just as the male limbic system rewards males for engaging in competitive and aggressive actions, the female limbic system probably generates rewarding feelings, coupled with appropriate emotional vocalizations, when females look at, hold, care for, and form attachments to their babies, infants, young children. Although this has yet to be determined, the female limbic system probably contains nuclei, neural networks, and individual neurons which respond selectively to infant visual and auditory related stimuli; e.g. baby faces, infant cries.

Again, consider that the anterior cingulate, in part, evolved in a "maternal" context and acts to promote the development of maternal behavior and mother-infant communication. Indeed, sex specific structural differences in the limbic system probably account in large part for most all sex differences in emotionality and related behavior, including childcare, the desire to have and nurture babies, and the greater female propensity for developing affective and mood disorders.

However, these sex differences also make her a more communicative mother.

CINGULATE MATERNAL INFANT COMMUNICATION

The anterior cingulate gyrus, in conjunction with the amygdala and right frontal lobe, appears to provide the foundation for mother-infant communication, the generation of separation anxiety, as well as the desire to provide as well as receive prolonged maternal care (Davidson and Fox, 1989; Joseph, 1993, MacLean, 1990). Long-term mother-infant communication and prolonged maternal care is unique to human and non-human primates, as well as some mammals (e.g. Hauser, 1997), and appears to be directly associated with the rather recent evolution of the five-layered neo-limbic mammalian cingulate gyrus (Joseph, 1993, MacLean, 1990). Again, animals lacking the more recently evolved cingulate gyrus, but who possess a hypothalamus, amygdala, and brainstem (e.g. such as reptiles, amphibians, teleosts, and sharks) fail to provide even short-term maternal care and sometimes cannibalize their young.

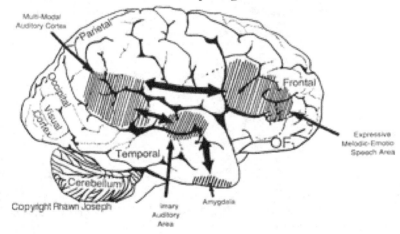

As noted, with the evolution of the cingulate and mammal-like therapsids, it appears that vocalization came to serve as a means of complex communication, not only between potential mates or predator and prey, but between mother and infant (for related discussion see MacLean, 1990; Ploog, 1992). Hence, in humans, whereas the anterior cingulate is one of the most vocal structures of the brain and becomes highly active when speaking (Frith and Dolan, 1997; Passingham, 1997; Paulesu et al., 1997; Peterson et al., 1988), destruction of the anterior cingulate abolishes emotional speech production, and results in severe abnormalities in social and emotional behavior and a loss of maternal responsiveness (Barris and Schuman, 1953; Laplane et al. 1981; Maclean, 1990; Tow and Whitty, 1953). Behavior, in fact, becomes reptilian, and human and non-human primates become mute, cease to groom or show acts of affection, and treat their infants as if they were inanimate objects that might be walked on and discarded. In non-human primates, the majority of infants whose mothers have suffered anterior cingulate destruction, die from lack of care (MacLean, 1990).

BABBLING, LIMBIC LANGUAGE, AND NEUROANATOMICAL MATURATION

The capacity to vocalize is initially the province of the brainstem and midbrain periaqueductal gray which responds reflexively to the immature hypothalamus. Thus, for the first 30-days following birth, infants tend to cry, cough, belch, grunt, and express displeasure and distress. These initial sounds are likely produced reflexively by the periaqueductal gray, perhaps in reaction to the hypothalamus which may trigger crying when experiencing hunger or thirst. However, as the brainstem, hypothalamus, and then the amygdala and cingulate continue to mature the infant begins to babble and increasingly expresses feelings of pleasure and other social-emotional nuances.

For the first six months of life, with the exception of the somatomotor areas, much of the neocortex is so immature that its influences are negligible. However, the somatomotor areas begin to mature quite early; reflected in dendritic and pyramidal neocortical development (Flechsig, 1901; Joseph, 1982; Gibson, 1991; Gilles et al. 2003; Scheibel, 1991) and the growth and myelination of the corticospinal tracts which invades the brainstem several months before birth (Kertesz and Geschwind, 1971; Yakovlev and Rakic, 1966). However, the corticospinal tracts (which project from the motor areas to the brainstem and spinal cord), take well over a year to reach advanced levels of myelination (Yakovlev and Lecours, 2007).

The myelination of the corticospinal tract coincides with the descent of the larynx, the myelinization and development of the amygdala and the amygdalafugal brainstem pathway, and later, the maturation of the cingulate gyrus and its pyramidal brainstem pathways (Debakan, 1970; Langworthy, 1937; Yakovlev and Lecours, 2007; Yakovlev, and Rakic, 1966). These overlapping maturational and physical events also coincide with vocal development and the onset of early and late babbling followed by canonical and jargon babbling.

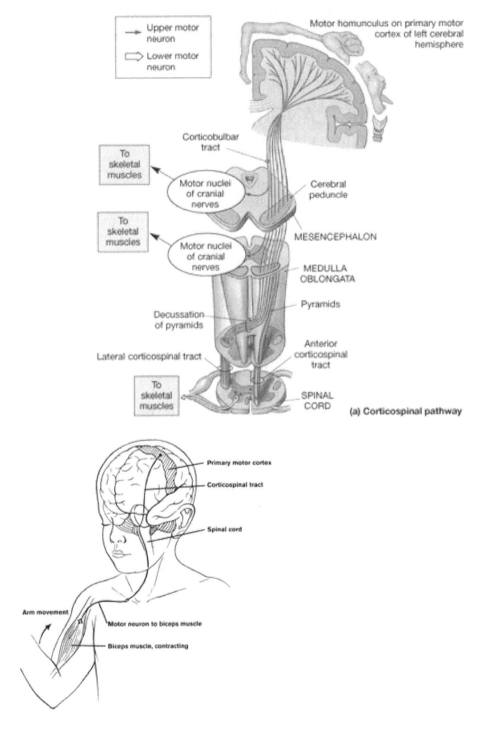

(a) Corticospinal pathway

EARLY BABBLING, PROBABLE MEANINGS, AND PROSODY

By 2-3 months of age amygdala-brainstem pyramidal fibers as well as corticospinal axons have already begun to myelinate. These maturational events coincide with an initial shift in the emotional utterances of the infant which become progressively complex and prosodic and increasingly subject to sequencing and segmentation. The infant begins to "coo," "goo," and babble.

Specifically, as the amygdala (followed by the anterior cingulate) matures and begins establishing hierarchical control over the hypothalamus, midbrain periaqueductal gray, and the brainstem masticatory centers with which it maintains a massive fiber pathway (Takeuchi et al., 1988) the infant will laugh, becomes increasingly oral, displays genuine pleasure, stares and smiles at the human face, and while so doing, will phonate and babble.

This early babbling stage generally involves the repetition of pleasant friction and voicing sounds which tend to be produced while making face-to-face and eye-to-eye contact and while engaged in social interaction (Kent and Miolo, 1995; Hoff & Shatz, 2009; Owens, 2011; Tronic 2007). Moreover, whereas the expression of pleasant sounds are in the ascendant, crying tends to become less frequent but more variable in tone, and can be differentiated into requests, calls, and sounds of discomfort (D'Odorico, 1984; Wolff, 1969).

As the amygdala, corticospinal tracts, and cingulate continue to mature, and the larynx continues to assume an adult pattern of orientation, the infant not only babbles but vocalizes a variety of sounds which increasingly convey probable meanings which may signify to the listener a variety of diffuse feelings and needs (D'Odorico, 1984; Wolff, 1969). Infants produce different noncry vocalizations depending on context and in reaction to people vs objects. The 3-4 month old infant can in fact produce at least four different pitch contours differering in fundamental frequency, each of which conveys probable meanings regarding affective state (Fernald, 1992; Hauser, 1997).

For example, if the 4 month old infant coos and babbles "mama," to the primary caretake (and depending on context, facial expression, and prosody/fundamental frequency) this may be interpreted to mean: "mama come here," "mama I hurt," "mama I thirst," etc. (e.g., D'Odorico, 1984; Fernald, 1992; Joseph 1982, Piaget, 1952; Vygotsky, 1962; Wolff, 1969). Hence, although the infant's utterances are not referential and may at times represent little more than the random universal babbling produced by all infants, they can also convey meaning and serve as a means of communicating with the primary caretaker (Fernald, 1992; Hauser, 1997; Hoff & Shatz, 2009; Owens, 2011; Tronic 2007).

MATURATION OF THE AMYGDALA, CINGULATE, AND EARLY AND LATE BABBLING

As detailed above, the increased complexity of the infant's utterances likely reflect the maturational influences of the amygdala, and later, the cingulate, coupled with physiological/anatomical changes in the position and orientation of the larynx. These same maturational events are also correlated with different babbling stages.

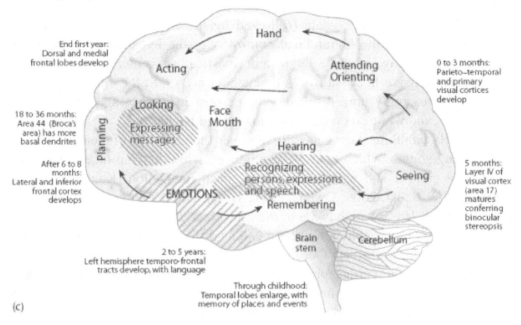

(c)

Activation of the amygdala can trigger lip smacking, rhythmic jaw movement, babbling, and manidibular-teeth "chattering" (Gloor, 1997), which, when coupled with sound production may induce babbling. Infant's display similar behaviors, which is presumably a direct consequence of the immaturity of the amygdala and its projections to the masticatory centers in the brainstem. Indeed, early babbling appears to be a direct function of reflexive and spontaneous jaw movement (e.g, MacNeilage and Davis, 1990; Moore and Ruark, 1996; Weiss, 1951) and lip smacking. Hence, early babbling may reflect immature amygdala (as well as amygdala-striatal and motor neocortical) influences on the brainstem masticatory centers and the periaqueductal gray which reflexively triggers the oral musculature thereby inducing rhythmic movement of the jaw.

"Early" babbling is soon replaced by "late" babbling which has its onset around 4 months of age (de Boysson-Bardies et al.,1981; Hoff & Shatz, 2009; Oller, 1980; Oller and Lunch, 1992; Owens, 2011). Late babbling is sometimes described as "repetitive babbling" (Mitchell and Kent, 1990), and at later stages of development may include the repetitive production of CV syllables in which the same consonant is repeated, such as "dadada" (Hoff & Shatz, 2009; Owens, 2011). As noted, electrical stimulation in the cingulate and surrounding medial frontal tissues can trigger the repetitive babbling of certain words and sounds, such as "dadadada" (Dimmer and Luders, 1995; Penfield and Welch, 1951).

The development of late babbling also occurs in conjunction with the infant's increased ability to produce sophisticated social-emotional nuances, and appears to be associated with increasing cingulate (as well as amygdala) influences. For example, around 4-months, the infant's intonational-melodic vocal repertoire becomes more elaborate and tied to a variety of specific feeling states (Piaget, 1952; Tronic 2007); which may reflect increasing amygdala maturational dominance.

Human Brain Development
Neural Connections for Different Functions Develop Sequentially

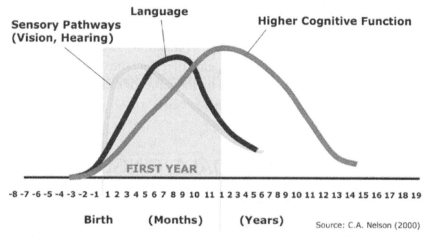

Source: C.A. Nelson (2000)

However, over the ensuing months vocalizations also begin to assume an imitative quality (Hoff & Shatz, 2009; Nakazima, 1980; Owens, 2011; Tronic 2007) which are often context specific but which do not necessarily reflect the infant's internal state--a characteristic also of cingulate vocalizations. Some infant vocalizations are produced in mimicry and in play (Piaget, 1952), and the cingulate is also associated with mimicry and play behavior (MacLean, 1990). The late babbling stage has also been repeatedly described as a form of "sound play;" an activity which increasingly contributes to phonetic development (de Boysson-Bardies et al. 1981; Ferguson and Macken, 2003). As the cingulate is associated with mimicry and the onset of play behavior and since the production of these sounds do not necessarily reflect the infant's true emotional state, the cingulate, therefore, is implicated in all aspects of the late babbling stage.

As noted, late, repetitive babbling consists of sequences of CV syllables in which the same consonant is repeated, e.g. dadadada. However, infants will also produce what has been referred to as non-duplicated, variegated, and concatenated babbling (Hoff & Shatz, 2009; Oller, 1980; Owens, 2011; Mitchell and Kent, 1990). That is, they will increasingly vocalize phonetically-varied-multisyllables which are periodically inserted into what is otherwise a repetitive sequences of CV syllables. These latter tendencies in fact, appear to be present even at the onset of the late babbling stage (Mitchell and Kent, 1990).

Repetitive, late babbling increases in frequency until around the seventh to tenth month of postnatal development (de Boysson-Bardies et al. 1981; Ferguson and Macken, 2003; Nakazima, 1980; Oller, 1980; Oller and Lunch, 1992), at which point the tendency to produce phonetically varied multisyllables becomes dominant. Thus the late babbling stage comes to be largely replaced by what has been termed "variagated" or "canonical" babbling (Oller, 1980; Oller and Lunch, 1992) which in turn is followed by "jargon" babbling (around 12 months).

Likewise, during these latter babbling periods the infant is also able to express fear, separation anxiety, and a variety of subtle social-emotional nuances. Although it appears that there is considerable overlap between these so called stages (e.g. Mitchell and Kent, 1990), the onset and increased frequency of late babbling followed by the increased production of variagated/canonical and then jargon babbling (Hoff & Shatz, 2009; Nakazima, 1980; Oller, 1980; Oller and Lunch, 1992), coincides with and appears to reflect the (overlapping) maturational influences of the amygdala followed by the anterior cingulate and then the frontal motor neocortex (which produce true speech).

BABBLING AND AMYGDALA, CINGULATE, NEOCORTICAL MATURATION

The maturation of the amygdala is associated with the onset of early babbling, whereas the anterior cingulate likely contributes to the development of late (repetitive) babbling, and the increased production of canonical/variagated babbling. These latter maturational events, however, also correspond to those taking place in the motor areas of the neocortex and may represent increasing pyramidal influences on the brainstem and oral-laryngeal musculature. In fact, jargon babbling appears to be a function of the immature neocortical somatomotor areas slowly gaining control over the limbic system, midbrain inferior-colliculus, and periaqueductal gray (Herschkowitz et al. 1997).

For example, pyramidal fibers from the somatomotor neocortex to the brainstem become increasingly well myelinated from 4 to 12 months of age (Debakan, 1970; Yakovlev and Lecours, 2007). Likewise, the somatomotor areas of the neocortex begin to rapidly mature around the first postnatal year (Brody et al. 1987; Chi et al. 1977; Gilles et al. 2003; Scheibel, 1991, 1993). Hence, the neocortex likely increasingly contributes to the development of jargon babbling, especially around one year of age.

Moreover, just as the pyramidal/corticospinal tracts as well as the somatomotor areas continue to mature and myelinate over the first and second years (Conel, 1937, 1941; Debakan, 1970; Yakovlev and Lecours, 2007) and beyond (Paus et al., 2016), babbling continues throughout the first and second years. It is during these same time periods in which the child gradually acquires and develops the phonetic structure which underlies speech production (de Boysson-Bardies et al.

1981; Hoff & Shatz, 2009; Oller, 1980; Oller and Lunch, 1992; Owens, 2011). This implies considerable forebrain as well as right and left neocortical influences over vocal behavior (see below). Once the neocortical speech area establish hierarchical control, and begin to program the oral-laryngeal motor areas, a new form of (neural-muscular) vocalization emerges which appears somewhat distinct from its precursors. The infant begins to speak their first words.

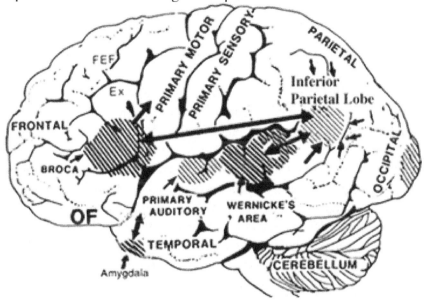

IMMATURITY OF THE NEOCORTICAL SPEECH AREAS AND JARGON BABBLING

The overlapping transition from the initial amygdala-brainstem-babbling stage to late babbling, around 4 months of age, may represent the onset of an amygdala to cingulate transition in vocalization control. Around 7-10 months, and as the cingulate become ascendant, the late babbling stage is transformed into the overlapping (cingulate-) canonical babbling stage. Canonical babbling, such as "dadada," involves the rhythmic and repetitive production of identical consonant vowel (CV) syllables (da, ba). Temporal sequencing motor capabilities are the province of the left hemisphere as well as the anterior cingulate gyrus. As the neocortex becomes ascendant and increasingly exercises (albeit immature) motor control, (cingulate-) canonical babblings is followed by (neocortical-) jargon babbling around one year of age (Hoff & Shatz, 2009).

The somewhat latter to appear "jargon" (or "conversational") babble resembles actual speech. At a distance it sounds as if the infant were talking, although the infant is in fact spouting prosodically sophisticated nonsense. Jargon babbling appears to reflect the increasing influences of the still exceedingly immature right and left frontal-temporal neocortex.

Jargon babbling is generally produced in a social context and while making eye contact and in many respects is similar if not identical to Wernicke's ("jargon") aphasia. Jargon aphasia is associated with severe injuries to Wernicke's area and the temporal-parietal junction which transmits abnormal streams of neologistic jargon to Broca's area (via the arcuate fasciculus) which then spouts nonsense words; a condition also referred to as "fluent aphasia." However, rather than a function of brain damage, jargon babbling is probably an indication of the extreme immaturity of the superior temporal lobe and Wernicke's area (as well as the left frontal lobe).

In general, "jargon" babbling (like jargon aphasia) consists of normal stress and intonational patterns that have been abnormally sequenced and chunked together. Hence, the infant expresses normal emotional-melodic prosody (probably via the limbic systm and right frontal lobe) coupled with nonsense words (via Broca's area), which makes it sound as if the child is truly attempting to communicate. Indeed, while jargon babbling the infant may appear to be engaging in a two-way discussion, or they may seem to be making requests for help or a desire to direct the other's attention to some object or activity (Kent and Miolo, 1995). Patient's with Wernicke's aphasia behave in an identical fashion. As with Wernicke's aphasics, children who jargon babble are attempting to communicate yet appear oblivious (or agnosic) to the fact they what they are spouting is emotionally meaningful verbal nonsense.

As jargon babbling coincides with the emergence of the infant's first words, this babbling stage heralds a hierarchical shift from the limbic system to the neocortex which increasingly acts to perceive and express social-emotional nuances and to punctuate and impose temporal sequences on what had been purely emotional speech. That is, beginning around 12 months and over the following years, the neocortex of the right hemisphere increasingly subserves the perception and expression of emotional-melodic-prosodic speech--as it does in adulthood (Gorelick and Ross, 1987; Heilman et al. 2015; Lalande et al. 1992; Ross, 1993; Shapiro and Danly, 2005; Tucker et al. 1977). By contrast, the left hemisphere motor areas increasingly act to punctuate, segment, and impose temporal sequences on sound production and perception (Joseph, 1982, 1988a, 2016e). Thus, as the neocortex of the left hemisphere gains motor control over the brainstem and oral musculature, what had been purely limbic language becomes grammatical, vocabulary-rich human speech.

RIGHT AND LEFT HEMISPHERE LANGUAGE ACQUISITION

During the last phase of fetal development the corticospinal tract of the left hemisphere descends and establishes brainstem and spinal synaptic contact in advance of the right (Kertesz and Geschwind, 1971; Yakovlev, and Rakic, 1966). These include pyramidal axons from the left amygdala (and amygdala-striatum), which is more concerned with motor control than the right amygdala, as reflected in its heavier concentrations of dopamine (Bradbury, Costall, Domeney, and Naylor, 2005; Stevens, 1992). Moreover, the left frontal primary motor areas representing the oral-facial and laryngeal muscles and cranial nerves, matures more rapidly than the right frontal primary motor areas (Joseph, 1982; Schiebel, 1991, 1993). In consequence, the left hemisphere is provided with a competitive expressive-motor advantage over the right, which is demonstrated not only in control over the oral-laryngeal musculature, but handedness.

By contrast, right frontal non-motor and secondary-motor gyral development, and right frontal dendritic growth within the emotional, melodic, prosodic speech area, initially develops faster than Broca's area (Chi et al. 1977; Gilles et al. 2003; Scheibel, 1991, 1993). Although the right hemisphere remains functionally dominant in the non-motor, non-linguistic, sensory-affective modalities (Chiron et al., 1997; Joseph, 1982), neuronatomically, Broca's area overtakes its right-sided counterpart around one year of age (Scheibel, 1991, 1993) and the infant increasingly produces jargon babbling, and then later, its first words.

Specifically, due to the earlier development of the right cerebral sensory receptive and non-motor areas, which in turn correspond to the development of the limbic system, sensory-limbic-receptive and expressive emotional functions come to be hierarchically represented in the right half of the brain (Joseph, 1982, 1988a). By contrast, the motoric and associated temporal-sequential aspects of expressive functioning, including right hand dominance, becomes the province of the left hemisphere whose motor areas and corticospinal tract develop more rapidly, which enable it to overtake, and thus gain a competitive advantage over the right.

As the left hemisphere matures and establishes dominance over motor control and expressive speech, temporal sequences and syllabication are imposed on emotional, intonational, and melodic vocalizations which come to be puctuated, segmented, reorganized, classified, and shaped so that vowel, consonantal elements, and words are produced.

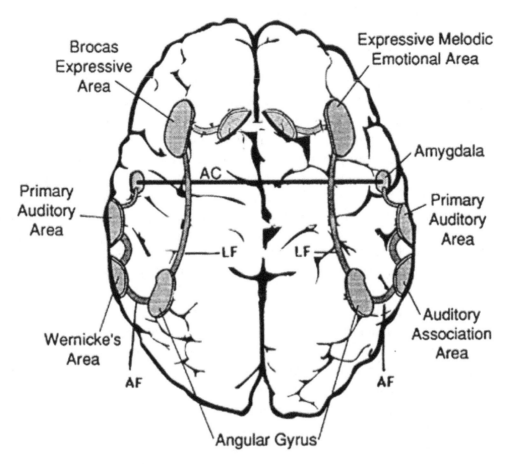

Specifically, Broca's expressive speech area, upon receiving linguistic input from the inferior parietal lobule and Wernicke's area and emotional-prosodic input via the cingulate/medial frontal lobe (Joseph, 1993, 2016e), acts on the adjacent primary and secondary frontal motor areas which subserve the oral-laryngeal musculature (Foerster, 1936; Fox, 1995; LeBlanc, 1992; Petersen et al. 1989). In this manner, speech units are motorically organized and vocalized. Thus, left hemisphere speech comes to be superimposed over limbic (and right hemisphere) speech and by one year of age a second form of language emerges, initially one word at a time.

However, as the left and right frontal and temporal areas interact interhemispherically via the corpus callosum, and intra-hemispherically through the arcuate fasciculus, and as these neocortices are linked with the amygdala and cingulate gyrus, language remains emotional and melodic even as it becomes increasingly grammatical and descriptive. Thus even among adults, language remains emotional, melodic, and prosodic, as these nuances continue to be produced not only by the limbic system, but by the right frontal lobe.

CONCLUSIONS

Based on an extensive review of animal and human studies, the preponderance of evidence indicates that the roots of language and social emotional and maternal behavior, originate within the limbic system. Laughter, fear, cries, warning calls, and a variety of emotional vocalizations have been produced via electrode stimulation of wide areas of the limbic system including the hypothalamus, amygdala, cingulate gyrus, and septal nucleus; and these same areas often become activated in response to certain emotional sounds. The limbic system is more vocal than any other part of the brain.

Nevertheless, the type of vocalizations elicited, in general, depends upon which limbic nuclei has been activated. This is because different limbic nuclei, and in fact, different divisions within these nuclei, subserve unique functions and maintain different anatomical interconnections with various regions of the brain. In addition, some areas are more evolutionarily advanced such as the five-layered cingulate gyrus, and/or have expanded and added additional nuclei, such as the lateral amygdala. The vocalizations and emotional behaviors mediated by these recent evolutionary acquisitions are also more complex than those produced by more ancient nuclei such as the medial hypothalamus and brainstem periaqueductal gray.

In some instances ontogeny replicates phylogeny and over the course of early development the medial hypothalamus (and periaqueductal gray) becomes functionally active and produces primitive vocalizations indicating distress, and later, pleasure. The later to develop medial and lateral amygdala experiences, perceives, and vocalizes joy, wariness, anger, and fear, whereas the neo-limbic cingulate gyrus is capable of producing a wide range of complex social emotional vocalizations such as separation anxiety and those which disguise the individual's true feelings.

As these nuclei and structure interact and mature at different and overlapping rates, over the course of early development the infant's emotional and babbling repertoire expands as does its ability to perceive, vocalize and express social-emotional nuances. The acquisition of infant speech, and the progressive expansion and increased complexity of limbic speech and social emotional behaviors parallels the maturation of these limbic structures.

Likewise, since all humans are in possession of a limbic system which is organized and which develops in a similar manner, the emotional and babbling precursors to language also appear to develop and are expressed in a similar manner regardless of culture. Thus early babbling is associated with the amygdala, late and canonical babbling with the cingulate, and jargon babbling with increasing, albeit immature neocortical influences.

As the neocortex matures and the amygdala and cingulate gyrus establish interconnections with the superior temporal and frontal lobe, emotional speech and limbic language is slowly transformed into segmented units of prosodic speech and grammatical utterances. That is, the maturing right frontal lobe, via the emotional-melodic speech area, hierarchically comes to express emotional-melodic and prosodic nuances.

By contrast, the left frontal motor and Broca's expressive speech areas and the left cerebral inferior parietal lobule increasingly punctuate, fractionate, and impose temporal sequences onto the stress, pitch, and melodic intonational contours of the infant's speech output. Hence, vowel, consonantal elements, and then words are produced. Left and right hemisphere speech comes to be superimposed over limbic speech and by one year of age a second form of language emerges, initially one word at a time.

Although language is commonly associated with the left hemisphere and is discussed in terms of grammar and vocabulary, the underlying foundations are and remain emotional and have their source in the limbic system. It is limbic (and right hemisphere) emotional mediation which explains why patients suffering from severe left hemisphere injury and profound receptive or expressive aphasia retain the capacity to express and comprehend these nuances and the meanings they imply (Boller et al., 1979; Boller and Green, 1982; Joseph, 1982, 1988a; Smith, 1966; Smith and Burklund, 1966).

It is due to these same limbic linguistic nuances which enable speakers to convey, and listeners to comprehend, the connotative and contextual implications of what is being said, even when words have been filtered or eliminated (Blumstein and Cooper, 1974; DeUrso, Denes, Testa, and Semenza, 1986; Dwyer and Rinn, 1981; Kramer, 1964), or when interacting with those from other cultures and who speak foreign dialects (Beier and Zautra, 1972; Fernald, 1992; Joseph, 1988a, 1993; Kramer, 1964). Again, consider the famous aside: "I don't know what they're saying, but I sure don't like the sound of it."

Language is both emotional and grammatically descriptive, limbic and neocortical. It is precisely because all humans possess a limbic system which is organized, and which develops in an identical fashion, that a listener is able to comprehend not only the content and grammar of what is said, but the emotion and melody of how it is said --what a speaker feels, even when that speaker is a cooing, gooing, babbling infant.

Part III
The Hippocampus, Amygdala, Memory, Amnesia, Neural Networks & Long Term Synaptic
Potentiation
Cognitive & Emotional Memories, Frontal Lobes, and Dorsal Medial Thalamic Nucleus

What is Memory?

What is memory? Is memory an accurate representation of what has taken place in the past, or is it an interpretation or a reconstruction based on emotion, guilt, hope, wishes, personality, or fragments of perceive reality?

You are driving to work and see a young woman in red riding a bicycle and immediately recall a dream from the night before--a dream which might have been recalled and forgotten forever if not for that chance event. The fragrance of flowers and freshly baked bread while listening to a song on the radio triggers the recall of a childhood experience at grandma's house which had long been forgotten. Where were these forgotten memories stored?

Your lover reminds you of a conversation you shared just days before--a conversation you cannot remember, but which she can't forget. Two soldiers witnesses a blast which kills and maims their comrades; days later one can remember nothing of the battle whereas the other cannot forget the scenes replaying themselves over and over, even in his dreams. Why do we remember? Why do we forget?

Some memories decay. Others fail to be stored. Yet others are stored, and although the memory is retained, their location cannot be found and they come to be misplaced. Yet others are replaced by similar memories which may be laid one atop the other, until they merge or become displaced. Yet others are actively blocked their recall actively prevented by the frontal lobes; or they come to be isolated as the neurons or networks which maintained them decay from lack of use, or reform to maintain newer memories.

Then there are emotional factors, stress, context, and personal biases, all of which effect memory. Further, different regions of the brain play differential and often overlapping roles in memory, the amygdala, for example, processing emotional and personal memories, the hippocampus visual-spatial and verbal memories, and the frontal lobes directing attention and acting to block or retrieve memories.

Then there is the problem of short-term vs long-term memory. The nervous system is bombarded by impressions, most of which are filtered out and never committed to memory. Yet other impressions, conversations, sights, thoughts, ideas, are considered briefly and then forgotten, whereas others are transferred from short to long term memory and are stored within the brain.

Neural Networks

Over a century ago it was proposed that learning and memory were paralleled by physical changes in neuronal structure and function, as well as the establishment of new neuronal connections where before there had been none (Cajal, 1911; Tanzi, 1893, cited by Cajal 1954) such that the brain continually rewires itself by forming new synapses and interconnections between neurons. Cajal (1911) proposed that long term memories were stored via the establishment of these new synaptic links; that the new synapses formed networks which maintained the memory.

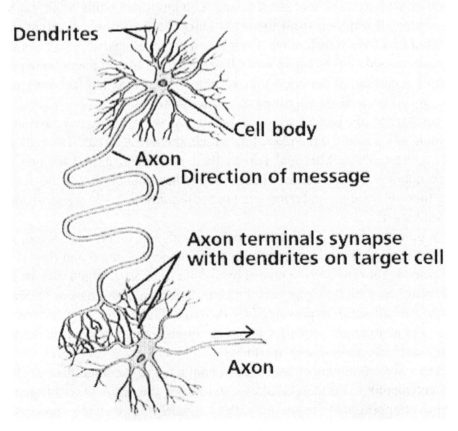

Subsequently, it was discovered that primate nerve cells can regenerate, establish new connections, acquire new functions (Joseph & Casagrande 2014, 1980; Casagrande & Joseph 2014, 1980), and that neurons continue to be born in the hippocampal region of the mammalian brain (Joseph 1998) such that the brain continually rewires itself.

Hilgard and Marquis (1940) and Hebb (1949), basing their hypothesis in part on the neuroanatomical work of Lorente de No (1938) and Cajal (1911), proposed that perceptual activity continues in neurons even after the cessation of stimulus input, thereby inducing structural alterations, which in turn makes learning and memory possible. Hebb (1949) also proposed that different neurons are linked together via this activity so as to form reverberating neural circuits that can fire with minimal stimulation. According to Hebb (1949, p. 62), "when an axon of cell A is near enough to excite cell B or repeatedly or persistently takes part in firing it, some growth process or metabolic change takes place in one or both cells." Hebb (1940) also presumed that memories are represented via a specific pattern of activity across a network of neurons; a consequence of permanent reverberating structural changes. Behaviorally the establishment of these plastic, reverberating neural networks is represented by increases in learning efficiency, enlargement of the memory store, and the formation of long term memories.

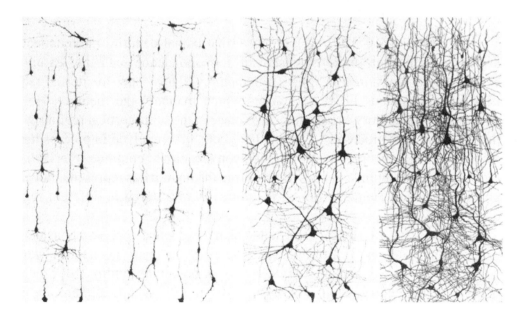

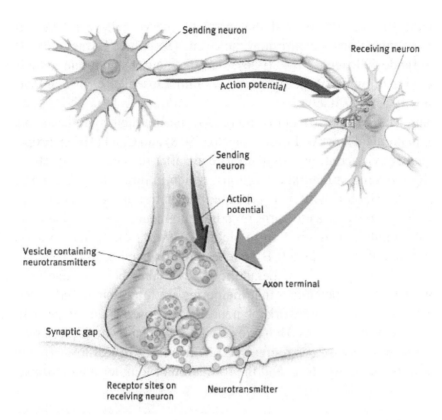

Hebb (1949), like Cajal (1911), proposed that axonal-dendritic interconnections are likely to become more extensive in correspondence with the learning of events which are stored in long term memory. Thus, new memories require new interconnections between neurons which maintain the memory. He also postulated that memory storage may take place in the same cortical regions where the information is processed. That is, those cells first involved in processing this information (e.g. people, places, events, conversations) continue to reverberate creating these structural changes, thus storing the memory as represented by these physical changes. Hence, different memories can be stored in different regions of the brain.

The theorizing of Hebb, Cajal, and others has since received considerable experimental support. In fact, because there are so many available synapses, cognitive complexity and memory capacity is potentially unlimited. Since the neocortex alone contains anywhere from 10^{14} to 10^{17} synapses, there are more than enough for all possible information storage requirements. Synapses make very low energy demands, so the system is energy efficient and requires little to maintain the memory stores. However, not just neurons, but synapses show neuroplasticity, such that dendrites can grow additional spines--the small protuberants that are the sites of excitatory input-- a growing process which also facilitates or is associated with new learning and memory (Lang et al., 2004; Less et al., 2009; Restivo et al., 2009) and the storage of long term memories in various regions of the cerebrum. In fact, synaptic plasticity occurs throughout the brain, including in excitatory and inhibitory neurons (Kullmann and Lamsa 2007). Moreover, dendritic spines can grow 4-fold within 2 min of forming a new memory (Lang et al., 2004) which in turn would effect neural transmission and increase the number of interconnections between neurons. Likewise, new neurons are constantly being generated, and these new neurons are also believed to play a major role in the formation of long term memory (Bruel-Jungerman et al. 2005) and forgetting (Willshaw and Buckingham, 1990).

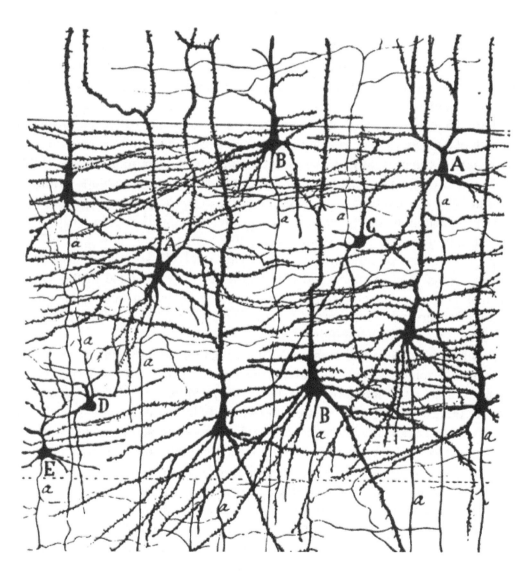

As a growing number of neurons come to be linked via perceptual and cognitive activity, complexity in mental functioning also increases and is maintained via a vast system of interconnected memories and semi-independent neural networks which allow for the addition of new, albeit associated memories (Buchel et al.,

2016; Joseph 1982; Miltner et al., 2016; Quartz & Sejnowski, 1997).

These physical changes include alterations in gene expression (Alberini et al., 2008; Romcy-Pereira et al., 2009) and protein synthesis (Alberini et al., 2008; Bekinschtein et al., 2007), which are associated with fluctuations in neural activity which are linked to learning and memory (Pang et al., 2004; Pastalkova 2006; Vertes 2005). These activation phenomenon include long term synaptic potentiation (LTP) and which is believed to underlie the consolidation and transformation of short-term memories into long term memories (Morris 2003; Enoki et al., 2009; Less et al, 2009; Okada et al., 2009; Whitlock et al., 2006). LTP is associated with the growth of dendritic spines, but also occurs presynaptically (Zakharenko and others, 2001; Bayazitov et al. 2007) as well as postsynaptically. LTP could be likened to a form of reverberatory activity, such that the synapse carrying the information which is to be preserved in memory, remains active for varying lengths of time.

Through correlated activity both pre and post synaptically, and with the growth of dendritic spines, a new memory can be added to a neural network and/ or the circuit can be modified so as to accommodate new learning (Joseph 1982). Moreover, a new set of activated neurons can be added to the network so long as their activity and interconnections become linked to the previously established pattern of excitation associated with a specific neural network (Buchel et al., 2016; Enbert & Bonhoeffer, 2016; Miltner et al., 2016; Quartz & Sejnowski, 1997; Xu et al., 1998). That is, certain forms of activity involving specific neurons, may represent a specific memory, and new memories may be added to this circuit when other neurons develop similar patterns of activity which then bind them in a circuit of experience. Behaviorally this may be expressed as associative learning and even classical conditioning.

Presumably, due to the creation of these neural circuits which are linked together via spines, synapses, and various forms of activity, widespread and complex associated memories can be formed. Moreover, this reverberatory activity increases the synaptic strength (which links these synapses), such that specific synapses are already highly active. Thus complex actions can be initiated in an effortless and routine fashion due to the strength of the connections which maintain the pattern (Hebb, 1949; Joseph 1982). Hence, these neural circuits can be associative, such that a variety of memories are linked as a whole, and in parallel, and they may also be temporal-sequential, such that one neuron or synapse can predict or trigger the next step in the behavioral sequence by activating the next neuron and so on thereby giving a memory a beginning, middle and end but which can be replayed or modified. Based on Hebb's theory it could be predicted that memories can be activated by a variety of simple and even fragmentary cues, each of which can trigger activation of a portion or the entire circuit which is already potentiated.

NEURAL CIRCUITS & LONG TERM POTENTIATION

Long term synaptic potentiation, first discovered by Lomo (1966) in the dentate gyrus and which lasted for several days, is a form of "reverberating" neural activity that has been noted to occur in both pre but predominantly in postsynaptic neurons, and has since been directly associated with new learning. Long term potentiation (LTP) is thus associated with what Hebb (1949) described as reverberation. LTP is associated with the creation of long lasting memories as represented by neuronal circuits that are highly active.

Synaptic changes have been found to occur in conjunction with the development of long-term synaptic potentiation in dendrites and axons, especially in the hippocampus (Enbert & Bonhoeffer, 2016; Enoki et al., 2009; Gustafsson & Wigstrom, 1988; Hardt et al, 2010; Lang et al., 2004; Less et al., 2009; Lynch et al. 1990; Romcy-Pereira et al., 2009; Whitlock et al., 2006). Long-term synaptic potentiation has been correlated with learning and increased environmental input and is associated with an increase in synaptic contacts and changes in the morphology and number of dendritic spines (Enbert & Bonhoeffer, 2016; Lang et al., 2004; Less et al., 2009; Lynch et al. 1990; Restivo et al., 2009). This long lasting synaptic activity in turn appears to bind the pre and post-synaptic surfaces so that future neuronal activity is correlated as well. The proliferation of dendritic spines and associated synapses would allow for the creation of wide spread neuronal networks.

LTP is best described as a long lasting post synaptic depolarization which is induced through the repetitive stimulation and summation of excitatory post-synaptic potentials (EPSP). Presumably the prolonged and repetitive nature of these EPSPs counter inhibitory influences of GABA (Davies et al., 1991). In addition to countering GABA, or activating MNDA receptors (Collingridge

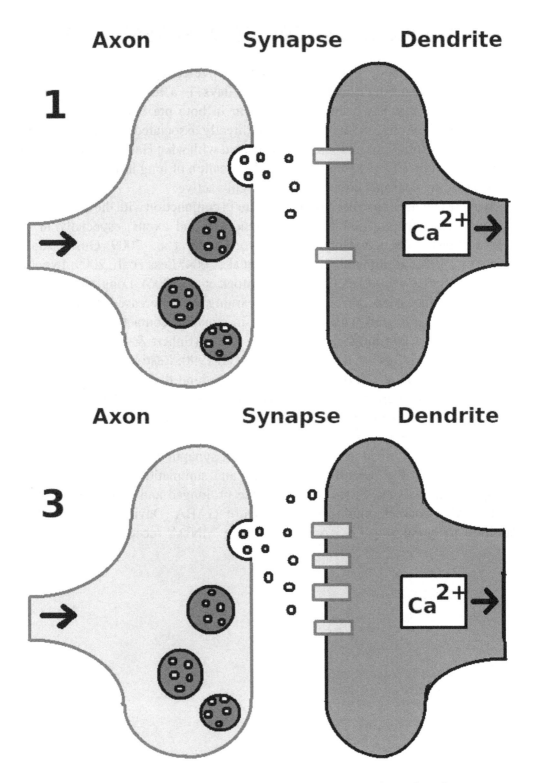

2003; Zakharenko et al,m 2001), LTP is most often attributed to increases or alterations in glutamate (Enocki et al., 2009). Specifically, it has been shown that the induction of LTP is directly associated with increases in glutamate secretion with each subsequent stimulation (Bliss & Collingridge, 1993). As glutamate is excitatory, this would account for increased excitation in the post synaptic dendrite.

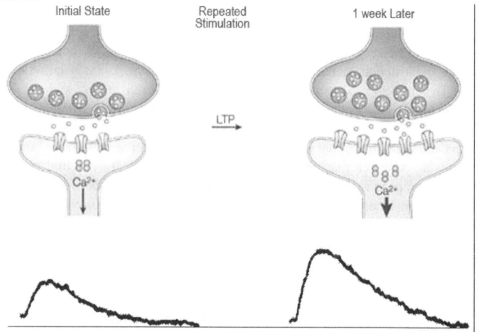

LTP can also be triggered by very brief periods of repetitive excitation, and may persist from hours to days to weeks to months (Barnes, 1979; Bayazitov et al., 2007; Bliss & Lomo, 1973; Davies et al., 1991; Enoki et al., 2009; Kitamura, et al. 2009; Lomo, 1966; Pastalkova et al. 2006; Villarreal et al., 2002). There are in fact different types of LTP depending on their length. The short version of LTP is referred to as short-term potentiation (STP) and may last from a few minutes to up to 30 minutes, whereas the longer version of LTP is divided into LTP1, LTP2, LTP3, depending on how long it lasts.

LTP is both a pre and post synaptic phenomenon (e.g. Bashir et al., 1991; Bayazitov et al. 2007; Gloor, 1997; (Zakharenko and others, 2001) and appears to interlock the pre and post synaptic junction (Davies, et al. 2007; Kauer, et al. 1988) of the various interacting neurons such as through synaptic growth and the addition of dendritic spines (Enbert & Bonhoeffer, 2016). It also appears that postsynaptic LTP develops and declines quickly, and presynaptic LTP develops slowly and is sustained for a long period.

NEURAL NETWORKS

LTP is believed to be a major factor in the establishment of wide spread neural networks as LTP has been observed in the hippocampus, amygdala, entorhinal cortex, frontal lobes, parietal lobes, temporal lobes, visual cortex, and the motor areas of the frontal lobes (Artola & Singer, 1990; Chapman et al., 1990; Kitamura et al, 2009; Sigurdsson et al., 2007; Sutor & Hablitz, 2007). Possibly, the development of LTP in different cortical areas may represent the binding together of these areas when engage in certain types of learning.

Temporal and spatial contiguity in axonal-dendritic synaptic activity has been postulated to be very important in establishing neural networks including those specific to particular memories (Gustafsson & Wigstrom, 1988; Kitamura et al, 2009; Lynch, 1986; Singer, 1990). Presumably different axons and dendrites must be highly active whereas yet others must be silenced and at the same time for these exclusionary networks to form (Xu et al., 1998), thus creating networks for specific memories. That is, since a dendrite may receive input from hundreds of axons all of which may fire at different times, in order for a neural circuit to be formed so as to maintain a particular memory, the activity between a number of specific presynaptic and post synaptic surfaces must be correlated and thus linked together, whereas others must remain at a low level of excitation so that they do not become linked with the emerging network. A large number of specific axons and dendrites must be activated simultaneously which in turn allows these pathways to consolidate (Singer, 1990) whereas yet others are silenced (Xu et al., 1998).

For example, Lynch and colleagues (1990), sequentially stimulated three different afferents which terminated at the same dendrite, such that each burst of activity overlapped somewhat with the next. They found that the degree of LTP induced was greatest at the synapse which was first stimulated, intermediate for the second, and least of all for the third. Hence, LTP appears to bind together those neurons which initially share parallel activity--a process that must occur in numerous synapses which are activated simultaneously to process the same event (or different aspects of the same event).

As described by Singer (1990, p. 225), "the integration interval during which presynaptic and postsynaptic activation must coincide in order to lead to stabilization of a pathway...(and)...excitatory and inhibitory inputs to the same dendrite must be activated and silenced respectively. The efficiency of stimuli to induce modifications of cortical circuitry will increase to the extent that the stimuli not only match the response properties, but also conform with the resonance properties of more distributed neuronal assemblies."

However, it may be necessary for yet other neural networks to become silenced so that specific circuits can be formed. For example, if two neurons form synapses with the same dendrite but with different dendritic spines, the more active of the two may inhibit the activity of the other (Artola & Singer, 1993). Even synaptic links that have developed LTP may be inhibited and develop long-term depression (Artola & Singer, 1993) --which may be associated with forgetting. As summed up by Xu et al. (2008, p. 891), "extensive long-lasting decreases in synaptic efficacy may act in tandem with enhancements at selected synapses to allow the detection and storage of new information by the hippocampus."

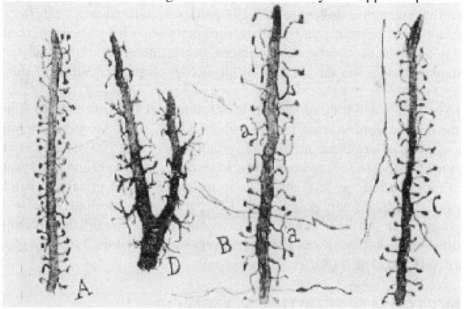

Hence, it appears that various neocortical and limbic regions may come to be linked via spatially and temporally correlated synaptic activity coupled with decreases in the activity of yet other circuits so that specific stimuli can be attended to, learned, and stored in memory (Kitamura et al, 2009). Similarly, structural alterations and synaptic links may be induced by processing similar or associated perceptual experiences.

SYNAPTIC GROWTH AND DENDRITIC SPINE PROLIFERATION

LTP is also associated with synaptic growth and an increase in dendritic spines; all of which would obviously improve the quality and amount of information being received and processed, thus enhancing memory. LTP is commonly associated with excitatory glutamate activity (Enocki et al., 2009) protein synthesis (Alberini et al., 2008; Bekinschtein et al., 2007) and activation of an assemble of neural-genes (Alberini et al., 2008; Romcy-Pereira et al., 2009), including c-fos, jun-B, and zif/268 (Katche et al., 2010; Richardson, et al., 1992) which are associated with neural growth and differentiation including the proliferation of dendritic spines.

The proliferation and growth of dendritic spines during LTP consists of a very rapid transient phase in which the spine may grow 4-fold in 2 min and then slowly decline over a period of 30 minutes several hours (Lang et al 2004; Tanaka et al 2008). The expansion and growth of spines naturally effects the morphology and physiology of the synapse including concentrations of glutamate and other extracellular factor that influence LTP. LTP and spin proliferation would effect the presynaptic and postsynaptic terminals, forming a bond between them, thereby creating an interlinked network of neurons which interact both pre-and post to maintain memories via the creation of physiological and activational feedback loops.

The growth of dendritic spines during or following LTP leads to the likelihood that the post-synaptic surface may be inducing LTP in the presynaptic terminal via some type of retrograde messenger system (Lynch et al 2003); like a key that grows to fit inside the lock. This would also account for both pre and post synaptic LTP. Further, a retrograde feedback loop mediated by the growth of dendrite spines might explain why postsynaptic LTP develops and declines quickly, and presynaptic LTP develops slowly and is sustained for a long period. As noted, the growth of dendritic spines also occurs very rapidly, within 2 minutes of LTP induction (Lang et al 2004).

LONG TERM POTENTIAL & MEMORY

According to Stevens (2007, p. 461), "the glutamate that is released from the axon terminal... acts on the postsynaptic membrane to change the postsynaptic voltage and --under the right circumstances-- permits an influx of calcium ions" which allows for the develop of postsynaptic LTP.

In this regard, LTP appears to be, at least in part, a function of increased transmitter levels (due to the release of more vesicles) as well as the changes in the post synaptic receptors which appear to increase in size which allows them to absorb more of the excess transmitter. In this manner the post synaptic membrane becomes increasingly sensitive which reduces the threshold for activation thus allowing LTP to develop (Davies, et al. 2007).

Hence, corresponding with the development of LTP it is presumed that a neuron can fire more easily, particularly in response to input from the same exact source. In addition, axons and dendritic spines become linked due to LTP and associated neuroplasticity. Hence, LTP is strongly related to the coupling of different neurons which repeatedly interact, thus forming a neural network that can be easily activated and which represents the totality of an experience. By contrast, neuronal sources that provide a different or later form of stimulation, come to be excluded from this particular circuit and may be stored in a different neural network representing separate and distinct memories and thus different experiences.

The short durations of LTP are referred to as STP. Longer versions of LTP have been classified as LTP1, 2, 3, and so on depending on their length. LTP1 lasts for about 6 hours and appears to be maintained not only by countering the influences of GABA but through the buildup of protein kinases (in the post synaptic dendrite). The increase in kinases appears essential for transforming STP to LTP1 and thus prolonging this activity (Bliss & Collingridge, 1993). LTP2 lasts for about 10 hours and is associated with a buildup in dopamine and activation of (excitatory) glutamate receptors. LTP3 lasts for weeks and is associated with dendritic growth, and thus reflects genetic activity and protein synthesis (Bliss & Collingridge, 1993).

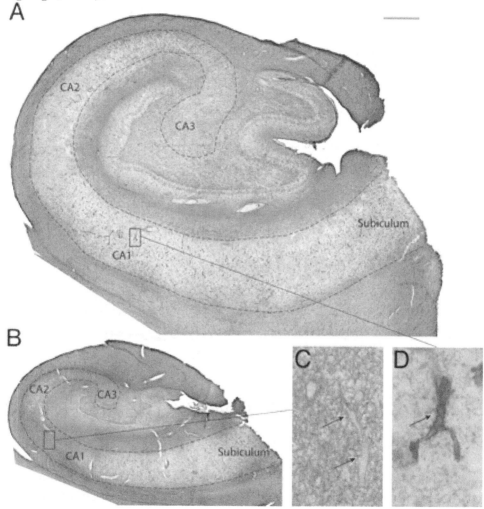

The differing lengths of LTP and the rapid growth of dendritic spines during the course of or following learning appears to corresponds to the development of short-term and then long-term memory (Enoki et al., 2009; Less et al, 2009; Okada et al., 2009; Morris 2003; Pang et al., 2004; Pastalkova 2006; Vertes 2005; Whitlock et al., 2006). Thus, short-term memories might be attributed to the shortest periods of LTP and a paucity of dendritic spine proliferation, whereas long-term memories are created through the establishment of numerous new synaptic connections formed through LTP-induced synaptic growth and the longest periods of LTP.

As is well established, the hippocampus plays a primary role in the storage and consolidation of long term memories. Thus, we see that LTP is a primary feature of hippocampal neuronal activity and the hippocampus is largely responsible for the conversion of short-term memories into long term memories with different regions of the hippocampus playing different roles (Chadwick et al. 2010; Gartner & Frantz 2010) . For example, it is believed that the anterior hippocampus may prepare short-term memories for consolidation by the posterior hippocampus. Thus, we see that within the hippocampus, LTP occurs at multiple locations and uses different mechanisms to effect excitatory synapses between CA3 and CA1 pyramidal neurons (Bayazitov et al. 2007; Remondes & Schuman 2004; Zakharenko et al 2001).

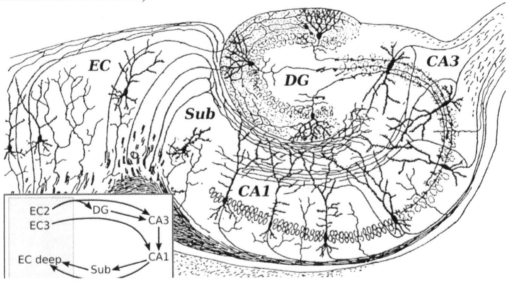

SHORT & LONG TERM MEMORY: THE ANTERIOR & POSTERIOR HIPPOCAMPUS

In humans, the hippocampus, the anterior and ventral hippocampus in particular, is usually associated with learning and memory of cognitively relevant information e.g. the long term storage and retrieval of newly learned information ((Chadwick et al. 2010; Fedio & Van Buren, 1974; Milner, 1966; 1970; Penfield & Milner, 1958; Gartner & Frantz, 2010; Gloor, 1997; Kim et al., 2011; Nahum et al, 2011; Rawlins, 2005; Scoville & Milner, 1957; Squire, 1992).

During learning activities LTP has been repeatedly found to occur within the hippocampus (Barnes & McNaughton, 2005; Enbert & Bonhoeffer, 2016; Gartner & Frantz, 2010; Lynch, 1986; Xu et al., 1998). Dendritic proliferation and the creation of specific neural circuits, as well as LTP, also occurs in the hippocampus during learning (Barnes, 1979; Enbert & Bonhoeffer, 2016; Less et al., 2009;

Lynch, 1986; Restivo et al., 2009; Tanaka et al., 2008; Whitlock et al. 2006). It has also been demonstrated that hippocampal pyramidal cells undergo synaptic modification when flexible stimulus response associations are being formed (Enbert & Bonhoeffer, 2016; Rolls, 1987, 1988). Similar correlations between hippocampal LTP and learning have been found on tasks involving memory for visual-spatial relations (Barnes, 1979; Bird & Burgress 2008; Pastalkova et al., 2006; Remondes & Schuman 2004) and object locations (Piekema et al., 2006). Moreover, during acquisition, not only does LTP increase but so to does EEG evoked responses within the hippocampus (Barnes & McNaughton, 2005) including the generation of theta (Vertes 2005).

Many of these synaptic and activational changes, in turn, are most apparent within the anterior regions of the hippocampus (Gartner & Frantz, 2010; Lynch, 1986) --which maintains rich interconnections with the amygdala (Amaral et al. 1992; Whalen & Phelps 2009). Moreover, this same region of the hippocampus will become electrophysiologically potentiated during learning tasks. As noted, long term potentiation lasting up to several days have been observed in the hippocampus following successful learning trials, which in turn may reflect the transition of information from short-term, to long term memory, at which point LTP ceases to be a factor in further memory maintenance. These findings are consistent with the notion that the longer the potentiation, the stronger might be the memory, and the more likely it will persist over time. These findings also support the likelihood that the hippocampus is primary concerned with converting short-term memories into long term memories, and is thus largely responsible for long term memory consolidation. Data from neuropsychological studies (Eichenbaum et al. 2014; Gloor, 1997; MacKinnon & Squire, 2007; Nunn, et al., 2016; Squire, 1992; Victor & Agamanolis, 1990), also indicate that the hippocampus plays a major role in the storage of long term memories, but a less significant role in the maintenance of short term memories.

Squire argues (1992, p. 222) that "the hippocampal formation is essential for memory storage for only a limited period of time. A temporary memory is established in the hippocampal formation at the time of learning in the form of a simple memory, a conjunction, or an index. The role of the hippocampus then gradually diminishes, and a more permanent memory is established elsewhere that is independent of the hippocampus...and... the neocortex alone gradually becomes capable of supporting usable, permanent memory. This reorganization could depend on the development of cortico-cortical connections between separate sites in neocortex, which together constitute the whole memory."

It thus appears that the formation of long term memories (LTM) is dependent on the hippocampus, the growth of dendritic spines, and the binding action of LTP which creates links between different synapses thus allowing for the transition from short to long term memory. However, because it acts as an interface between long term and short term memories (STM), not surprisingly damage to the hippocampus not only profoundly effects LTM but interferes with short term memory (Nee & Jonides 2011). For example, patients with hippocampal damage and amnesia show significant problems remembering the locations of novel objects within seconds (Jonides et al., 2008). Jonides et al., (2008) "hypothesize that the associative properties of the hippocampus serve to inter-relate information actively maintained in ST) which not only promotes strong STM, but also lays the foundations for subsequent LTM.

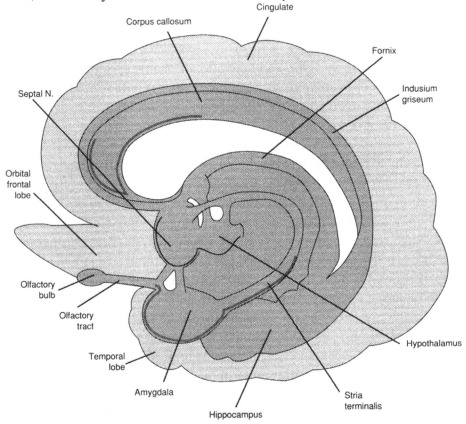

Data from neuropsychological studies indicate that the anterior hippocampus is important in establishing or preparing memories for long-term storage, and that the memory must migrate from the anterior to the posterior hippocampus to be placed in long term storage (Penfield and Mathieson 1974). For example, if the anterior hippocampus is injured or functionally suppressed, very little new cognitive learning occurs and potentiation does not appear. However, once these memories have been established in long term memory, the role of the anterior regions of the human hippocampus appears to diminish. This would explain why long term memory for long ago events is spared with hippocampal destruction. On the other hand, there is some human evidence which indicates that the more posterior human hippocampus may be responsible for long term memory access which is why retrograde amnesia has been reported with damage to or electrical stimulation of this area (Fedio & Van Buren, 1974; Penfield & Mathieson,

1974). Indeed, Penfield and Mathieson (1974) suggested that memories might actually migrate over time along the length of the hippocampus in a posterior direction, and that the ability to retrieve these memories follows this posterior movement. However, this does not mean that long-term memories are stored in the hippocampus. Rather, these memories may be stored in the neocortex. Once these memories are placed in long-term storage, the role of the hippocampus significantly diminishes.

As noted, LTP also decays over time within the hippocampus (Villarreal et al., 2002). However, LTP also develops in the neocortex. Thus, there appears to be an interaction and exchange between the hippocampus and the neocortex where information is consolidated and the stored, by the hippocampus, within the neocortex. Therefore, the processing of acquired memories appears to be initially dependent on the hippocampus but this dependency lessens over time as these memories come to be stored in the neocortex (Dudai, 2004; Frankland and Bontempi, 2005; Marshal & Born 2007; Remondes & Schuman 2004; Squire and Bayley, 2007; Warburton & Brown 2009; Wiltgen et al., 2004) .

SHORT VS LONG TERM VERBAL & VISUAL MEMORY LOSS, RETRIEVAL & HIPPOCAMPAL DAMAGE

When the hippocampus has been damaged the ability to convert short term memories into long term memories (i.e. anterograde amnesia), is significantly impaired in humans (Eichenbaum et al. 2014; Gloor, 1997; MacKinnon & Squire, 2007; Nunn, et al., 2016; Squire, 1992; Victor & Agamanolis, 1990) and primates (Zola-Morgan & Squire, 1984, 2005a, 1986). Lesions of the hippocampus can also disrupt time sense and temporal sequencing such as involving timing tasks (Meck et al. 1984). And, memory for words, passages, conversations, and written material is also significantly impacted, particularly with left hippocampal destruction (Frisk & Milner, 1990; Joseph 1996; Squire, 1992).

Visual spatial memory is dependent on the hippocampus (Barnes, 1979; Bird & Burgess 2008; Pastalkova et al., 2006; Remondes & Schuman 2004); whereas spatial memory is significantly impaired among a variety of species with hippocampal lesions (Mishkin, et al. 1984; Nunn et al., 2016; Weiskrantz, 1987). In fact, the capacity to cognitively map, or visualize one's position and the position of other objects and individuals in visual-space is dependent on the hippocampus (Nadel, 1991; O'Keefe, 1976; Piekema et al., 2006; Wilson and McNaughton, 1993). The hippocampus contains "place" neurons which are able to encode one's position and movements in space. Specifically, O'Keefe, Nadel, and colleagues, found that hippocampal pyramidal cells became sensitive to particular spatial coordinates and the location of objects in visual space, but that these spatial maps were also very plastic. These authors also found that as the subject moves about in that environment, entire populations of cells would fire but only when in a particular spot, whereas other cells would fire when in a different location. Moreover, some cells respond not just when moving about, but in reaction to the speed of movement, or when turning in different directions. Moreover, some cells are responsive to the movements of other people in that environment and will fire as that person is observed to move around. (Nadel, 1991; O'Keefe, 1976; Wilson and McNaughton, 1993).

The hippocampus, therefore, can create a cognitive map of an individuals environment and their movements within it. Presumably it is via the hippocampus that an individual can visualize themselves as if looking at their body from afar, and can remember and thus see themselves engaged in certain actions, as if one were an outside witness (Joseph, 1998b, 2016d). Therefore, patients with hippocampal destruction may demonstrate severe visual-spatial memory disturbances and may easily lose their way, forget where they place items, or where things are located (Nunn et al., 2016; Squire, 1992); particularly with right hippocampal injury (Joseph 1988a, 1996). However, abnormal activation of the hippocampus may also induce sensations of dissociation, such that the person feels they are floating above their body watching their movements as if from afar (Joseph 1996; 2016; 2000).

There is considerable evidence that the left hippocampus is crucial for the long term storage of verbal memories (Frisk & Milner, 1990; Joseph 1982, 1996; Squire, 1992; Zimmerman et al., 2008). Thus, whereas right temporal-hippocampal injuries effect visual-spatial memory, verbal memory is impaired following left sided damage.

BILATERAL HIPPOCAMPAL DESTRUCTION & AMNESIA

Although memories may be transferred to the neocortex with the aid of the hippocampus, the hippocampus (along with the frontal lobes) appears to help keep track of where those memories are stored, so they may be recalled at a later date. Hence, if the hippocampus is damaged, the ability to find certain memories is often compromised.

Bilateral destruction of the anterior hippocampus results in striking and profound disturbances involving almost all aspects of cognitive and recognition memory and new learning (i.e. anterograde amnesia); and is associated retrograde amnesia (RA) for events that may extend 2-3 years in time (Marslen-Wilson & Teuber, 2015; Milner, 1966; Murray, 1992; Penfield & Milner, 1957; Scoville & Milner, 1956, Squire, 1992), particularly if the posterior hippocampus has also been injured or removed (Fedio & Van Buren, 1974).

H.M, who underwent bilateral hippocampal removal lost the ability to recall almost anything experienced after surgery. If you introduced yourself to him, left the room, and then returned a few minutes later he would have no recall of having met or spoken to you. Dr. Brenda Milner has worked with H.M. for almost 20 years and yet she was an utter stranger to him.

H.M. was in fact so amnesic for everything that had occurred since his surgery (although memory for events prior to his surgery is comparatively exceedingly well preserved), that every time he rediscovered that his favorite uncle died (actually a few years before his surgery) he suffered the same grief as if he had just been informed for the first time.

H.M., although without memory for new (non-motor) information, had adequate intelligence, was painfully aware of his deficit and constantly apologized for his problem. "Right now, I'm wondering" he once said, "Have I done or said anything amiss?" You see, at this moment everything looks clear to me, but what happened just before? That's what worries me. It's like waking from a dream. I just don't remember...Every day is alone in itself, whatever enjoyment I've had, and whatever sorrow I've had...I just don't remember" (Blakemore, 1977, p.96).

H.M.,however, not only suffered profound anterograde amnesia, but a dense retrograde amnesia which extended over 11 years prior to his surgery (Corkin, 1984). However, as H.M. also had severe epilepsy, this extensive loss of pre-surgery memory may due to this preexisting lesion.

In yet another case, a 37-year old Lt. Colonel (LC) who had sustained bilateral posterior temporal lobe and hippocampal destruction secondary to prolonged anoxia in 1969, had no memory of his injury, and no memory of major events that had transpired two years prior to his injury. Although he could recall the death of President J.F. Kennedy, he could not recall the assassination of his brother, senator Robert Kennedy, though he could recall that Robert Kennedy had been attorney general and was running for president (Joseph 1996). As part of his "memory retraining" LC read and reread short newspaper style articles including those describing the death of Robert Kennedy, and was asked questions about the story. Each time LC read this latter article he had the same exact emotional and behavioral reaction, expressing surprise, shock, and sorrow. LC had absolutely no memory of having read the same exact article just 30 minutes earlier--though he had answered all questions correctly immediately following each reading. Thus, LC demonstrated profound RA, as well as profound anterograde amnesia, as he not only failed to recall these stories, but has no memory of the trainer who worked with him three times a week for a three month period of time.

In yet another case, an 18 year old man who sustained bilateral inferior-anterior-medial temporal lobe and hippocampal destruction (following a car accident immediately after high school graduation), demonstrated both retrograde and anterograde amnesia. For example, he believed he was sixteen years old and a "junior or a senior" in high school. His father described his son's memory as "like a sieve. You fill it up with information and 30 minutes later its all leaked away. If you leave him alone for half an hour he will completely forget where he is, how he got there, and so on. Then he begins to panic for he forgets he was in a car accident and has lost his memory." In fact, while this examiner "was examining this young man when he suddenly looked up at me in astonishment and had no idea who I was, where he was, why he was there, and so on." These episodes were repeated approximately every 30 minutes. Nevertheless, his anterograde memory loss was not global as he was capable of learning new motor routines and was able to get a job performing electronics assembly. He also learned to carry a note pad with "reminders" to tell him where he was, why he was there, etc (Joseph 1996).

LEARNING AND MEMORY IN THE ABSENCE OF THE HIPPOCAMPUS

As noted, the 18-year old mentioned above was capable of learning simple motor tasks. Similarly, monkeys with hippocampal destruction, including those with bilateral destruction, although demonstrating severe memory impairments are capable of learning motor skill tasks and acquiring habits (Squire, 1992; Zola-Morgan & Squire, 1984, 2005a).

It has been repeatedly demonstrated that various aspects of learning and memory are retained in the absence of the hippocampus (see Eichenbaum et al. 2014; Horel, 2014; Seldon et al., 1991; Squire, 1992; Zola-Morgan, et al. 1986). This includes the learning of skilled and coordinated motor programs -as these "memories" appear to be dependent on the basal ganglia (Heindel et al. 1988; Packard, et al. 2007; Wang et al. 1990), cerebellum (Schmahmann, 1997; Thompson, 1986), inferior parietal lobule, the supplementary motor areas, and the lateral frontal motor areas (Joseph 1996). The role of the hippocampus is minimal in these forms of learning (Squire, 1992).

Classical conditioning is also independent of the hippocampus which may be a function of the repeated nature of stimulus presentation -the hippocampus soon ceases to respond to repetitive experiences. In contrast, single learning associations are more dependent on the hippocampus (Squire, 1992).

The learning of emotional information also appears to occur largely independent of the hippocampus --being dependent on the amygdala (Gloor, 1997; LeDoux, 1996; Pape & Pare 2010; Pessoa & Adolphs 2010; Seldon et al., 1991; Whalen & Phelps 2009), and perhaps the interactions of the amygdala with the hippocampus (Joseph 2016; Lang et al. 2009). LTP has been induced in the amygdala and amygdala pathways (Chapman, et al. 1990; Clugnet & LeDoux, 1990), which is presumably a function of its involvement in most aspects of emotional memory formation (Gloor, 1997, Halgren, 1992; Kesner, 1992; LeDoux, 1996; Pape &

Pare 2010; Pessoa & Adolphs 2010; Poulos et al., 2009; Rolls, 1992; Roozendaal et al., 2009), and the creation of emotional memory neuronal networks.

In summary, it is clear the hippocampus plays a major role in the storage and consolidation of visual, spatial, and verbal information, and less so with motor, skilled, and emotional material. Further, the hippocampus appears to help maintain certain forms of information in short-term memory, in preparation for long-term storage. However, the hippocampus does not act alone, but in association with the neocortex, the frontal lobes, amygdala, and other structures including the immediately adjacent entorhinal cortex.

THE HIPPOCAMPUS AND ENTORHINAL CORTEX

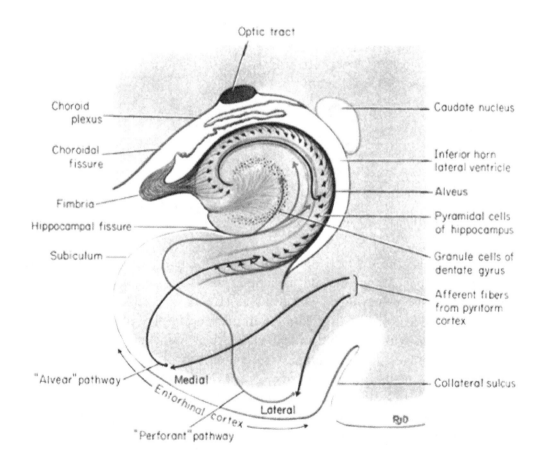

The hippocampus does not receive direct neocortical input. Moreover, the data it does receive, at least from the neocortex, originates in the neocortical association areas and is first transmitted to the entorhinal cortex or amygdala, and is then relayed to the hippocampus (Andersen et al., 2006; Brun et al., 2008; Horel et al. 1987; Issausti et al. 1987; Fyhn et al.,, 2007; Squire, 1992). This includes auditory input which is transferred directly from the primary auditory areas to the entorhinal cortex. It is also via the overlying entorhinal area that the hippocampus receives amygdaloid projections (Andersen et al., 2006; Carlsen et al., 1982; Gartner & Frantz, 2010; Gloor, 1955, 1997; Krettek & Price, 1976; Steward, 1977) and axonal projections from the orbital frontal and temporal lobes (Andersen et al., 2006; Van Hoesen, et al., 1972). Thus, the hippocampus only receives neocortical input indirectly, and for the most part this is relayed by the entorhinal cortex which is considered the "gateway to the hippocampus."

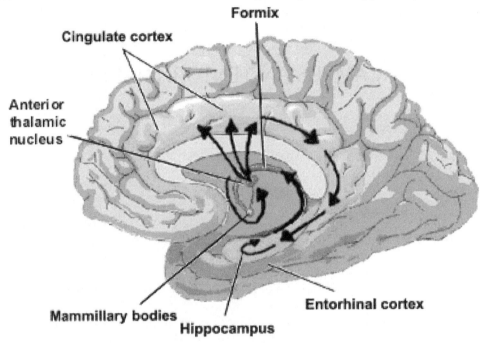

The entorhinal cortex is truly unique, not only because it serves as an interface between the hippocampus and the neocortex, but because this medial located structure consists of between 7 and 8 layers (Braak & Braak, 1992; Ramon y Cajal, 1902/1955; Rose, 1926). The entorhinal cortex also maintains massive interconnections with all multi-modal neocortical association areas (as well as with the amygdala, hippocampus, septal nuclei, olfactory bulb, etc.) but apparently none of the primary sensory areas (Leichnetz & Astruc, 1976; van Hoesen, et al., 2015). Hence, the entorhinal cortex must play a supramodal role that is exceedingly unique and profoundly important in memory and cognitive processing, and may play different roles, in for example, recognition vs recall vs short term and long-term memory.

For example, some believe that the neocortex of the temporal lobe is the repository of those long term memories initially processed by the entorhinal cortex and hippocampus and that these latter structures are more important in recognition memory and act to store this material in the neocortex. Consider, for example, patients who undergo "hippocampal removals" whereas the overlying neocortex was spared (Milner, 1990) and patients such as the famous H.M., who underwent bilateral mesial temporal removals: amygdala, hippocampus, entorhinal cortex (Milner, 1968). These patients (particularly those with right sided destruction) perform exceedingly poorly on visual recognition memory tests, including those involving recurring nonsense figures (Kimura, 1963) and human faces (Milner, 1990).

For example, it has been shown that hippocampal lesions produce mild deficits in recognition memory (Mishkin, 2014, 1990), though if the lesion includes the adjacent medial temporal cortex including the perirhinal cortex, recognition memory is severely impaired--which suggests that mesial structures play their own unique role in memory. It has also been reported that recognition memory is severely disrupted with damage to the entorhinal cortex but is spared when the hippocampus is intact (Murray, 1992; Squire, 1992). Thus recognition memory appears to be more dependent on the entorhinal cortex as well as the amygdala. Recognition memory has also been reported to be somewhat (but not always) spared when the medial thalamic nuclei and/or the frontal lobe destruction are the source of the amnesic disturbance (Graff-Radford, et al. 1990; Jetter et al. 1986); in which case retrieval may be severely disrupted. Therefore, retrieval may be more dependent on frontal-thalamic interactions (Aggleton & Mishkin, 2003; Graff-Radford et al. 1990; Squire, 1992; Victor et al. 2007) with the right frontal lobe becoming activated when searching for visual and episodic memories, and the left frontal when searching for verbal memories (Brewer et al., 1998, Wagner et al., 1998). The hippocampus appears to be more involved in the actual storage of non-emotional memories, including those which are visual, spatial, and involving language.

FRONTAL LOBES, HIPPOCAMPUS, & MEMORY

Reverberating LTP activity takes place in various regions of the neocortex, and this activity may be linked to the storage of long term memories, These different neocortical areas and neurons apparently come to be bound together via the simultaneous activity and steering influences involving the frontal lobes (Joseph, 1986a, 2016a), dorsal medial thalamus, and in particular the amygdala and hippocampus (Dudai, 2004; Frankland and Bontempi, 2005; Gloor, 1997; Graff-Radford, et al. 1990; Lynch, 1986; Marshal & Born 2007; Remondes & Schuman 2004; Rolls, 1992; Squire, 1992; Squire and Bayley, 2007; Warburton & Brown 2009; Wiltgen et al., 2004), thereby forming a circuit of experience which may maintain certain memories, thoughts, images, and so on. The frontal lobes, dorsal medial thalamus, and amygdala are all interlinked and highly involved in attention, arousal, and memory functioning, and probably act together so as to establish and maintain specific neural circuits and networks associated with specific memories (e.g., Brewer et al., 1998; Lang et al., 2009; Squire, et al,. 1992; Tulving et al., 2014; Wagner et al., 1998).

For example, these different networks and neurons may be linked via the steering influences exerted by the frontal lobes (Joseph 1988a,b; 1990, 1996, 2016), which can selectively activate or inhibit these memories and associated tissues in a coordinated fashion, and which can tie together certain perceptual experiences so as to form a complex multi-modal memories (e.g., Dolan et al., 1997; Joseph, 1982, 1986a, 1988a, 2016a; Kapur et al., 1995; Squire, et al,. 1992; Tulving et al., 2014; Dolan et al., 1997; Brewer et al., 1998; Wagner et al., 1998).

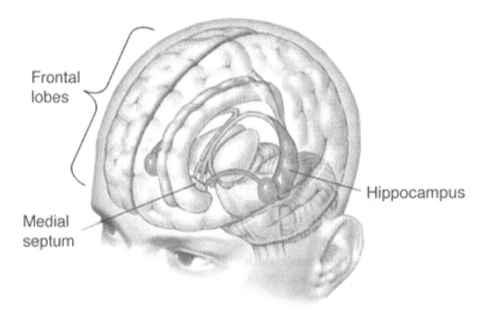

Frontal lobes

Medial septum

Hippocampus

Likewise, since the hippocampus is a prime location for the development of LTP and is significantly involved in many aspects of memory functioning, it is also presumably able to exert steering influences on different neocortical sites with which it is also richly, albeit indirectly interconnected via the entorhinal cortex. Via LTP (and the entorhinal cortex and dorsal medial nucleus) the hippocampus presumably acts to bind these divergent neocortical sites together so as to form a circuit of experience, which takes the form of memory.

Thus, both the frontal lobes and the hippocampus appear to be involved in the storage of information within specific locations within the neocortex. However, in contrast to the hippocampus, the frontal-thalamic system is more involved in retrieval and so called "working memory," as well as keeping something in mind and the focus of attention so that it can be remembered and performed later (Brewer et al., 1998; Cabeza et al. 2002, Cabeza & Nyberg 2000; Joseph 1986, 1990, 1996, 2016; Prabhakaran et al. 2000; Squire, et al,. 1992; Tulving et al., 2014; Wagner et al., 1998; Wager & Smith 2003; Zhang et al. 2004).

AMYGDALA, HIPPOCAMPUS & MEMORY

LTP is not an exclusive property of the hippocampus but also appears in entorhinal cortex, the frontal lobes, visual cortex, the motor areas of the frontal lobes (Artola & Singer, 1990; Chapman et al., 1990; Sutor & Hablitz, 2007) and the adjacent amygdaloid nucleus (Chapman et al., 1990; Sigurdsson et al., 2007; Whalen & Phelps 2009) with which the anterior hippocampus is richly interconnected. Mishkin (2014) showed that lesions of the hippocampus and amygdala results in severe recognition memory deficits, whereas damage restricted to the hippocampus does not. Mishkin also proposed that the hippocampus and amygdala form two parallel memory systems, which together form the main memory system (Mishkin, 1990).

Amygdaloid neurons show plasticity in response to learning (Lynch, 1986; Whalen & Phelps 2009), and LTP has been induced in amygdala neurons (Chapman, et al. 1990; Sigurdsson et al., 2007; Whalen & Phelps 2009). Moreover, fear induced neural plasticity in the form of LTP has been repeatedly observed in the amygdala (Clugnet & LeDoux, 1990; Sigurdsson et al., 2007; Whalen & Phelps 2009). This is presumably a consequence of the amygdala's involvement in most aspects of emotional experience, including the formation of cross-modal emotional associations and memories (Gloor, 1992, 1997; Halgren, 1992; Lang et al., 2009; Kesner, 1992; Kensinger et al., 2011; LeDoux, 1992, 1996; Poulos et al., 2009; Rolls, 1992; Roozendaal et al 2009; Sigurdsson et al., 2007).

The amygdala is also intimately interlinked with the anterior hippocampus and appears to exert reinforcing and modulating influences on this nuclei (Gloor, 1997; Halgren, 1992; Lang et al., 2009). That is, the amygdala may signal the hippocampus as to the motivational or emotional importance of various experience such that both structures interact to create linked memories, the hippocampus providing the visual, spatial, contextual or verbal attributes, and the amygdala the personal and emotional attributes. Moreover, both project to adjacent thalamic relay neurons which raises the possibility they act conjointly to form separate but closely aligned neural networks concerned with different aspects of memory.

ANTEROGRADE & RETROGRADE AMNESIA

There are all types of memories; i.e. verbal, visual, short-term, long-term, episodic, explicit, implicit, tacit, procedural, etc., and so on--and some investigators use different labels to describe the same type of memory; e.g., conscious/declarative/explicit vs unconscious/nondeclarative/implicit. Hence, some memories are easily consciously accessible and are therefore easy to declare because they are explicit, whereas there are other memories which are unconscious such that the individual may have no idea as to how they acquired these memories. For example, amnesics may display implicit knowledge and memory, though they may have no idea as to how they obtained that information (Penfield & Milner, 1958; Scoville & Milner, 1957; Squire, 1992, 2006).

Amnesic conditions are most frequently encountered by physicians and therapists following an injury to the brain, such as due to head trauma, stroke, neoplasm, or encephalitic condition (Hodges & Warlow, 1990; Lynch & Yarnell, 1973; Miller, 1993; Russell, 1971; Yarnell & Lynch, 1970, 1973). Following a significant head injury or stroke there may be a period of amnesia for events which occurred just before and just after the time of injury (Hodges & Warlow, 1990; Russell, 1971; Squire 2006), even if consciousness is not lost (Yarnell & Lynch, 1970, 1973).

In more severe cases, such as those involving a brief or prolonged loss of consciousness, the brain may remain dysfunctional for some time even after the trauma and the return of consciousness, and memory functioning and new learning may remain deficient for long time periods (Miller, 1993; Russell, 1971). Indeed, following the recovery of consciousness patients may be unable to recall little or anything that occurred for days, weeks, or even months after their injury. This condition has been referred to as post-traumatic, anterograde amnesia.

Anterograde amnesia is a consequence of continued abnormal brain functioning. Because the brain is functioning abnormally, information is not processed or stored appropriately and cannot be accessed .

POST-TRAUMATIC/ANTEROGRADE AMNESIA

Individuals who suffer extended periods of emotional stress, and particularly those who suffer unconsciousness and coma such as following a head injury, may experience protracted periods of disorientation and confusion (Levin et al., 1982; Joseph 1990, 1996; Nemiah, 1979; Russell, 1971). Attention, new learning, and memory is necessarily compromised.

Frequently, with moderate or severe brain injuries there is a period of complete amnesia for continuously occurring events for some time after the return of consciousness (Russell, 1971). Amnesia may also occur following horrific emotional traumas (Donaldson & Gardner, 2005; Grinker & Spiegel, 1945; Joseph, 1998b, 2016d, 2003; Parson, 1988). That is, although consciousness has returned, and the patient can talk, respond to questions, and even perform simple arithmetical operations, because the brain is impaired or since the effects of the emotional shock have not completely waned (such as in conditions of post-traumatic stress disorder) information processing and thus memory remain faulty for a variable length of time. The time length, however, may depend on the severity of the trauma, or the location and extent of the injury. This has been referred to as post-traumatic amnesia (PTA).

Nevertheless, PTA is not due to an inability to register information, for immediate recall may be intact whereas short- and long term memory remain compromised (Squire, 1992; Yarnell & Lynch, 1970, 1973). Although patients are responsive and may interact somewhat appropriately with their environment, they may continue to have difficulty consolidating and transferring information from immediate to short to longer term memory. However, the PTA may not be global, and may be selective for verbal vs visual material, or inclusive of both whereas motor and emotional learning may remain intact.

It is also important to bear in mind that the first appearance of normal memory or personality or conscious functioning following an injury or an emotional trauma, does not indicate the end of the amnesic period. That is, although behavioral functioning seems ostensible normal, brain functioning may not be. Hence, the "normality" may be temporary and followed by another period of PTA such that the person may suffer repeated absences of memory (Hodges & Warlow, 1990; Myers, 1903). Memory functioning may remain abnormal even after 10-20 years have elapsed (Brooks, 1972; Schacter & Crovitz, 1977; Smith, 1974).

RETROGRADE AMNESIA

Frequently following a stroke or severe head injury, or in cases of extreme and prolonged emotional turmoil and trauma, the amnesia may include events which occurred well before the trauma or moment of impact. This retrograde amnesia (RA) may extend backwards for seconds, minutes, hours, days, months or even years depending on the severity of the injury, extent of degenerative damage (Blomert & Sisler, 1974; Fugjiwara et al., 2008; Hodges & Warlow, 1990) or degree of emotional trauma (Grinker & Spiegel, 1945; Janet, 1927; Myers, 1903; Nemiah, 1979; Prince, 1939; Strange et al., 2008).

Be it physically or emotionally induced, retrograde amnesia is often reflective of disturbances involving the posterior-ventral hippocampus, frontal or inferior temporal lobes, and/or the dorsal medial nucleus of the thalamus (see below) and possibly the amygdala. However, the RA may also be due to disconnection and dissociation, such that the Language Axis is no longer able to gain access to select neural networks and thus the missing information.

Retrograde amnesia is seldom inclusive for public facts or the entirety of an individuals life, for the remote past appears to be better preserved than the more recent past in these cases (Fugjiwara et al., 2008; Squire, 1992, 2006). Even when personal identity has been forgotten, facts, city names, the ability to read and write, and other forms of non-emotional memory may be retained. However, this also depends on the nature, location and laterality of the trauma. For example, with traumatic injuries to the left hemisphere, public facts, as well as reading, writing, math, and even the ability to speak may be severely compromised, whereas with right temporal lobe injuries, personal and emotional memories may be seemingly erased.

In general, the extent and severity of the RA is measured by determining the last series of consecutive events recalled prior to the trauma. That is, a patient aged 50 who has suffered a severe head injury may be able to remember events from late childhood, early adulthood, but have almost no memory for events which occurred between ages 30-40, and no memory for anything that occurred during the last 10 years. The more extensive the RA, the more severe the underlying brain damage.

Be it due to physical or emotional trauma, patients may show islands of memory, such that in actuality they may only be able to recall a few events for early adulthood, and only a few from middle age. If they are not carefully examined, one might erroneously conclude that memory and brain functioning is not severely impaired. Moreover, individuals with amnesia, when repeatedly questioned at different time periods can often recall information that previously was not available to the speaking half of the brain (Squire et al. 2007). In this regard, these amnesics are somewhat like young children who report different details at different times making them appear inconsistent. Unfortunately, this inconsistently may be viewed as malingering when this is not the case.

Rather, what this variability indicates is that amnesia is variable and that when alternate neural networks and pathways become accessible, information or memories can be accessed when formerly they seemed to have been forgotten. In other words, although an individual at one time may appear to have no memory for certain events and thus may be considered amnesic, at another time and under different circumstances, these memories may suddenly become available even in patients who are profoundly amnesic.

SHRINKING RETROGRADE AMNESIA

RA is not necessarily a permanent condition and memory for various events may return. However, with head injury or following a stroke, usually the older memories return before more recent experiences. This has been referred to as a shrinking retrograde amnesia (Sisler & Penner, 2015; Squire, et al. 2015; Squire 2006). The shrinkage is not complete as events occurring seconds or minutes before the trauma may be permanently forgotten (Sisler & Penner, 2015; Squire, et al. 2015; Squire 2006).

However, not all patients show a shrinking RA (Sisler & Penner, 2015), especially those with degenerative or functional disturbances. When secondary to degeneration, for example, the neurons making up various neural networks, and thus the networks themselves may be destroyed, in which case there can be no recovery of memory. Moreover, due to degeneration, the RA will expand.

Among those with emotionally induced amnesias, the forgotten material may be recovered in a haphazard, piece meal fashion over a series of minutes, hours, or days. Moreover, rather than a shrinking retrograde amnesia, in some cases (such as in fugue states) the forgotten memories (which may include almost all of the individuals prior life and childhood) may be quite suddenly recovered almost in total (Janet, 1927; Myers, 1903; Nemiah, 1979; Prince, 1939).

Thus it is important to emphasize that even in well documented cases of amnesia secondary to verifiable brain injuries or in those due to emotional trauma, that some memory recovery is not only possible, but likely. However, even in instances where memories appear to have been permanently lost or erased, or perhaps never even formed, the neural network which supports the memory may simply be disconnected, dissociated, and unavailable to the Language Axis and the language dependent regions of the conscious mind. With recovery and reconnection, or if presented with associated contextual cues, the amnesia may clear and what had been forgotten may be suddenly remembered; sometimes to the shock and dismay of all concerned.

CAUSES OF AMNESIA

Memory loss may be secondary or related to a number of factors, including aging, chronic emotional stress, degenerative disturbances and neurological disease or stroke, head injury, intense fear, physical traumas, rape, assault, and sexual molestation during childhood (Brier, 1992; Christianson & Nilsson, 2007; Donaldson & Gardner, 2005; Fisher, 1982; Frankel, 1976; Fredrikson, 1992; Fugjiwara et al., 2008; Grinker & Spiegel, 1945; Herman & Schatzow, 1987; Joseph, 1998b, 2016d, 2003; Kuehn, 1974; Miller et al. 1987; Parson, 1988; Schacter et al. 1982; Shrouping et al. 1980; Squire 2006; Williams, 1992). Even immersion in cold water and consensual sexual activity have been noted to give rise to transient amnesias (Miller et al. 1987; Shrouping et al. 1980); which is presumably a consequence of rapid depletion of serotonin and the release of opiates peptides which in turn negatively influence the hippocampus.

Severe stress, emotional shock, as well as a blow to the head or a stroke or tumor can induce sudden and drastic alterations in neurotransmitter and arousal levels as well as create structural alterations in the functional integrity of the brain -which is why memory may be effected. When the brain has been traumatized the ability to process information or retain, store and recall ongoing events may be seriously altered and disturbed thereby creating a functional amnesia (Donaldson & Gardner, 2005; Fisher, 1982; Grinker & Spiegel, 1945; Hodges & Warlow, 1990; Parson, 1988; Strange et al., 2008) --even when consciousness has not been lost (Clifford & Scott, 2014; Peters, 1991; Yarnell & Lynch, 1970).

However, depending on the nature of the trauma, the amnesia may be global and all encompassing, or include only those events which occurred at the moment of impact or emotional upheaval; and for a few seconds before or thereafter. That is, the patient may suffer from an extensive and prolonged or very brief period of amnesia which may include simple details which immediately preceded or followed the trauma.

In cases of very minor head injury or mild emotional shock, what is forgotten may be quite trivial. For example, Loftus and Burns (1982) reported that subjects who watched a 2.25 minute film of a violent (vs non-violent) bank robbery (which ended with a 15 second sequence where a boy is shot in the face), were unable to remember a number on the football jersey of a bystander. By contrast, those who had not seen the shooting could recall the number.

Clifford and Scott (2014) also found that the recall accuracy of witnesses viewing a video of an assault (vs a non-violent encounter), was significantly reduced, with women showing significantly poorer recall then men. Moreover, women rated the film as more violent than the men -a function of the differential structure and functioning of the female limbic system and a greater female sensitivity to emotional stimuli.

With mild head injury, such as often occurs among football players, the amnesia may include the previous or upcoming play (Lynch & Yarnell, 1973; Yarnell & Lynch, 1973) --even though consciousness was not lost. However, in these instances, it is not all unusual for the forgotten memories to be recovered; i.e. shrinking retrograde amnesia.

With more severe injuries, the memory loss may be much more enduring and extensive and even personal identity may be temporarily forgotten; for example, when subject to emotional and stressful extremes, and/or when the conditions are life threatening, such as in instances of repeated front line battle field exposure, or during a brutal rape (Christianson & Nilsson, 2007; Donaldson & Gardner, 2005; Grinker & Spiegel, 1945; Janet, 1927; Joseph, 1998b, 2016d; Myers, 1903; Nemiah, 1979; Parson, 1988; Prince, 1939). With severe and profound emotional stress, the individual may become so amnesic they cannot recall their name, occupation, and so on -which in turn may be due to injury to the hippocampus and amygdala, are or a temporary disconnection involving these nuclei. Even in less extreme instances involving non-life threatening emotional trauma and stress, the victim may have no memory for the trauma which preceded or accompanied the development of the amnesia, and they may suffer a retrograde memory loss for events which occurred weeks, months, or even years before hand (Janet, 1927; Myers, 1903; Nemiah, 1979; Prince, 1939). Amnesia victims such as these may also display a continuous anterograde amnesia such that they continue to forget events as they occur, including people whom they subsequently meet.

However, just as lost-memories may be recalled over time following a mild or severe head injury, those with emotionally induced traumatic amnesia may eventually recover much of this forgotten material, some of which may be retrieved while under hypnosis, via the assistance of a dream (Hilgard, 1986; Janet, 1927; Myers, 1903; Nemiah, 1979; Prince, 1939), or in response to a face that resembles a victim or perpetrator. Even those with head injury-induced amnesic states may experience memory recovery if exposed to related details or even through their dreams. Indeed, regardless of the etiology of the amnesia, although it is often presumed that the memory (such as memories at the moment of impact) was not formed, and that other memories were erased, this is not always the case. Sometimes the memory was merely stored abnormally and cannot be found.

Memory Gaps

Different memories are presumably represented by specific neuronal circuits, which when later activated, may recreate the original cognitive, emotional, and perceptual experience (Halgren, 1992; Gloor, 1997; Joseph 1982; Kitamura et al, 2009). Correspondingly, a complex memory may be triggered by a variety of stimuli as well as a single cue which initially activates only part of the neural network. When one region of the neural network is activated, associated neurons within the circuit are likely to become aroused in parallel or sequentially.

Not all neural networks, however, may be characterized by parallel processing. For example, neural networks may be sequentially linked, such that activation of one neuron within the network will result in a step-wise pattern of sequential activation of various parts of the circuit. This would allow for one neuron to predict or determine what stimulus pattern or sequence will come next (Gloor, 1997; Sejnowski & Tesauro, 1990). For instance, in getting dressed a whole sequence of associated actions take place which are so well learned that one need not even think about the different steps involved; e.g. putting on shirt, fastening clothes, etc. The entire circuit of experience is sequentially activated and occurs almost in reflex fashion. However, some neural circuits may be characterized by both parallel and sequential activation. Nevertheless, when a circuit of experience is activated, such that a routine behavior is performed, then the performance of that routine, that is, subsequent routines, may not be committed to memory; whatever happened during that routine and even doing the routine is forgotten.

It has been argued that temporary amnesic states may be common every day events that most people just do not remember (Reed, 1979; Hodges & Warlow, 1990); that is, they do not know they do not remember because they have completely forgotten these details. For example, it is not at all uncommon for individuals to drive across twisting mountain roads, or through busy city streets, only to arrive home and have absolutely no recall of having driven their car or any aspect of the journey. There are many such blank spots that fill the course of most every day. One need only attempt to account for what they did over the course of the previous week to realize there may be a number of gaps; what Reed (1979) refers to as "time-gap" experiences.

It has also been suggested, however, that these transient "time gap" amnesias may be the result of the verbal half of the cerebrum simply ceasing to attend to tasks which it normally does not perform (Joseph,1988a) and are a form of verbal amnesia. Consider the "driving" example mentioned above. It is the right half of the brain that is dominant for visual and depth perception and maneuvering through visual space (Joseph, 1988a). Therefore, the left hemisphere may not recall, for example, the driving experience as it was not engaged at the time and was possibly functioning at a lower level of arousal. It is the right half of the brain that would process, store, and be responsible for recalling this information. And, although this information may be stored by the right hippocampus, as there are no axonal connections between the right and left hippocampus, this data is not shared.

It is this same differential organization of the brain and the propensity for memories to be stored in one rather than in both hemispheres, which often gives rise to a verbal amnesia. This sometimes leads to the mistaken notion that an individual has either forgotten or failed to form certain memories, when in fact they are present but not available via verbal (or in some cases hippocampal) retrieval strategies.

ANESTHESIA & UNCONSCIOUS LEARNING

It has been repeatedly demonstrated that patients in a deep state of unconsciousness due to anesthesia, are capable of perceiving, storing in memory, and later recalling events which took place during surgery (Bennet, 1988; Furlong, 1990; Kihlstrom, et al. 1990; Millar, 1987; Polster, 1993). Patients may even recover sooner when provided therapeutic suggestions while unconscious (Evans & Richardson, 1988; Furlong, 1990). Moreover, they may later respond to suggestions made to them while unconscious.

For example, in one study anesthetized patients received suggestions that they should touch their ears when interviewed after the surgery. And this is exactly what they did, although they claimed to have no knowledge or memory of having heard this suggestion (Bennet, Davis & Giannini, 1981; cited by Schacter & Moscovitch, 1984).

Kihlstrom et al. (1990) reported that when word pairs were presented to unconscious patients during surgery that they were more likely to free associate these same words when presented with the other member of the pair. However, although learning and memory was demonstrated they claimed to have no memory of having heard this material. Control subjects did not show this effect

Other investigators, however, have failed to find evidence of memory storage even when recognition was employed (see Millar, 1987; Polster, 1993). In large part this may be a function of the type of anesthesia as well as the type of surgery, for these studies are clearly in the minority.

UNCONSCIOUS KNOWLEDGE: VERBAL & SOURCE AMNESIA

Amnesic disturbances due to anesthesia, drugs, or left frontal lobe or dorsal medial or left temporal lobe/hippocampal dysfunction (see below) typically and predominantly involve the verbal memory system. Moreover, the verbal memory system appears to be more vulnerable to disruption than the visual or emotional memories systems. The visual and non-verbal recognition memory is also much more robust than verbal recognition memory. For example, Adams (1973) found that subjects who inhaled nitrous oxide and who were then presented with words as well as non-verbal and melodic sounds, pictures and geometric shapes, were able to remember almost 100% of the visual and non-verbal acoustic stimuli but only about 50% of the words.

However, in some cases the verbal memory may be unconscious and cannot be accessed indirectly. There have also been numerous examples of individuals who although suffering from amnesia secondary to neurological dysfunction are nevertheless able to demonstrate the possession of knowledge and information which they in fact denied possessing or learning (e.g. Claparede, 1911; see also Schacter et al. 1984). This includes recalling details from a short story read to them previously as well as remembering names and addresses or little known facts provided to them during their amnesic period.

For example, when amnesics, when presented with words (which they quickly forgot), and were then later presented with incomplete words that they were to fill in, the previously viewed (albeit forgotten) information facilitated performance although subjects denied having seen this material before (Warrington & Weiskrantz, 1974; Tulving, et al. 1982). Similarly, Graf, Squire and Mandler (1984) found that when amnesics had been presented with a list of words and then later were presented with incomplete stems (e.g., "inc___ or mot___") that those who were told to form the first word that comes to mind, performed similar to normals. That is, they were able to recall the words they had been exposed to, although they denied having recently heard them.

In a similar study an amnesic patient was told some very unusual stories about various pictures. When he was later shown the same pictures, he claimed to have no recollection of having seen them or hearing the story. However, when asked to pick a title for each picture, he picked those which mirrored the theme that he had been told (Schacter & Moscovitch, 1984).

Some individuals with amnesia can also learn motor skills and related tasks and will, for example, perform a jigsaw puzzle faster on the second trial and improve as much as normals (Brooks & Baddeley, 1976). Amnesics have also been shown to be capable of learning musical stimuli (Starr & Phillips, 1970). Similarly some individuals suffering from profound amnesia are able to demonstrate recognition memory involving identification of visual objects and "picture puzzles," such that recognition time is reduced by over 100% on day 2 vs day one of training (Crobitz et al. 1981; Meudell & Mayes, 1981).

Many of the patients described above could therefore be considered to be suffering from "source amnesia" -an inability to recall how or in what context certain information was acquired. Hence, some amnesic syndromes are due to a source and contextual memory deficit (Stern, 1981; Winocur, 1982).

For example, when an amnesic patient was stuck by a pin when she tried to shake hands with a physician, she later refused to shake hands although she had no memory of ever having met the doctor before. When asked why she refused to shake, she answered that she didn't really know, but that sometimes people hid pins in their hands (Clarapede, 1911; see also Kebeck & Lohaus, 1986; Meudell & Mayes, 1981).

This patient thus demonstrated what has been referred to as a source amnesia. Moreover, the emotional link with the actual cognitive event associated with the original memory was ostensibly lost. That is, although she had an emotional memory of having been stuck with a pin when shaking hands, she could not recall when or where this occurred, or with whom. Hence, she experienced a hand shaking aversion but was amnesic as to why. Repression (which involves the frontal lobes and dorsal medial nuclei --see chapter 19) often gives rise to similar symptomology, as does hypnosis (Evans & Thorn, 1966; Hilgard, 1986; Myers, 1903).

Of course, in many instances, it is not the source but the information itself which amnesic individuals deny knowing or possessing. However, if also provided with forced choice testing situations, these same amnesiacs may be able to indicate they were in possession of that information all along.

Again, it is important to note that although patients may verbally claim to have no verbal memory, and although they are clearly amnesic, the amnesia is often due to verbal access failure and retrieval failure. This is why these same amnesic individuals may retain and even learn information which they verbally claim not to possess.

If a memory is stored, yet cannot be found, this may well implicated the frontal lobe and the frontal-thalamic system as the source of the amnesia. The frontal lobes are directly implicated in source amnesia, as it is these structures, the right frontal lobe in particular, which normally becomes quite active when retrieving this data. For example, in a test of unconscious memory, subjects were presented with word stems of complete words presented previously. When performing this task, there was increased blood flow in the right hippocampus and right frontal lobe (Squire, et al,. 1992). Right frontal activation was also seen in a recognition tasks involving sentences viewed the day before (Tulving et al., 2014). In fact, when engaged in episodic retrieval, there is a significant activation of the right frontal lobe, right thalamus, and right medial temporal lobe (Dolan et al., 1997); increases in activity being a function of retrieval effort.

FRONTAL LOBES & THE DORSAL MEDIAL & ANTERIOR THALAMUS

The dorsal medial nucleus of the thalamus, as well as the frontal lobes are exceedingly important in memory functioning and information retrieval (Aggleton & Mishkin, 2003; Barbey et al., 2011; Brewer et al., 1998; Dolan et al., 1997; Graff-Radford et al. 1990; Hales & Brewer, 2011; Hasegawa et al., 1998; Schott et al., 2011; Squire, 1992; Wagner et al., 1998; Victor et al. 2007), and both structures are intimately linked and interact with the temporal lobe and the amygdala and entorhinal cortex/hippocampus. For example, when engaged in episodic memory retrieval, there is increased activity in the frontal lobes (Hales et al., 2011; Schott et al., 2011) and thalamus (Dolan et al., 1997) as well as the temporal lobes (Brewer et al., 1998; Hales et al., 2011; Wagner et al., 1998). In fact, the ability to remember a visual or a verbal experience, is directly correlated with activation of the right or left frontal lobe and the temporal lobes during that experience (Brewer et al., 1998; Wagner et al., 1998).

According to Wagner et al., (1998, p. 1190), as per verbal memories, "what makes a verbal experience memorable partially depends on the extent to which left prefrontal and medial temporal regions are engaged during the experience." Moreover, according to Brewer et al., (1998, p. 1185) the degree of this activity can be used to predict which experiences will be "later remembered well, remembered less well, or forgotten." Hence, activity increases in the right frontal lobe as a function of retrieval effort (Kapur et al., 1995), or a function of effort exerted at preventing retrieval.

As first fully proposed and detailed elsewhere (Como, Joseph, Fiducia, et al., 1979; Joseph, 1986a; Joseph et al., 1981) the frontal lobes play a signficant role in human memory including memory retrieval failure (Joseph, 2016a), and the inability to remember traumatic events (The frontal lobes are also implicated in the failure to transfer these unpleasant memories from the right to left hemisphere (Joseph, 1992b; Hasegawa et al., 1998). That is, it has been proposed that although a memory may be recalled by the right hemisphere, through frontal lobe inhibitory action the memory may be suppressed or prevented from transferring to the left, such that the language regions of the brain remain amnesic. The individual thus knows, yet does not know, simultaneously, and may demonstrate the presence of unconscious memories.

Specifically, it appears that the frontal lobes, in conjunction with the hippocampus (Goldman-Rakic, 1990), reticular activating system, the amygdala and the dorsal medial thalamus (DMT), acts to gate and direct perceptual and cognitive activity occurring within the neocortex (Como et al., 1979; Joseph, 2016a; Joseph et al., 1981). That is, the frontal lobes, DMT, amygdala, and hippocampus interact when determining which neuronal circuits are created, linked together, inhibited or activated.

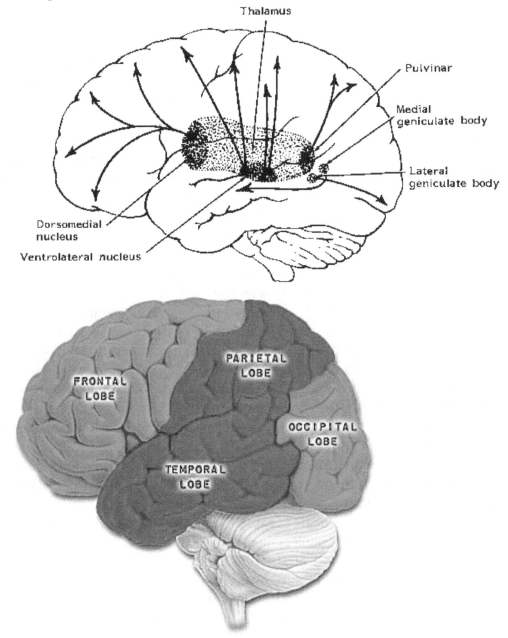

The frontal lobes, in fact, are highly concerned with arousal, attention, activation and neuronal inhibition (Como et al., 1979; Fuster, 2008; Joseph, 1986a, 2016a; Joseph et al., 1981; Stuss, 2011) as well as sustaining the creation of specific reverberating neural circuits. The frontal lobes are also particularly important in the capacity to retrieve previously stored information (Brewer et al., 1998; Fuster, 2008; Wagner et al., 1998), as well as prevent access to those memories and perceptions deemed irrelevant or undesirable. Presumably it can retrieve or inhibit particular memories by acting directly on the neurons and neural network where they are maintained or indirectly via the thalamus and reticular formation through which it can selectively effect arousal. In this manner, the frontal lobes can selectively sample, deactivate, or enhance neural activity depending on the information it is searching for.

Conversely damage to the frontal lobes can result in difficulty retrieving memories (Fuster 2008; Joseph, 1986a, 2016) but has little effect on recogniton memory (Jetter, et al. 1986) where search, activation, and retrieval are not as important. Recognition memory can be activated by direct stimulation of the neurons and the neural network which have stored similar information in the past.

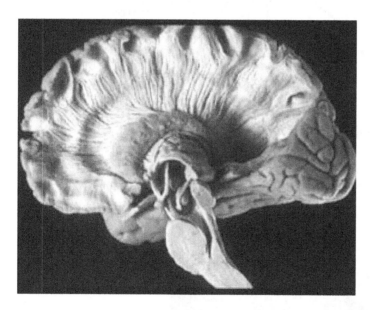

DORSAL MEDIAL THALAMUS

The frontal lobe, hippocampus, and the amygdala appear to share major roles in regard to neocortical activation and thus memory storage and retrieval, and all appear to partly rely on the dorsal medial thalamus (DMT) and anterior thalamus in this regard. The DMT (and the thalamus in general) are highly important in transferring information to the neocortex, and is involved in perceptual filtering, and exerting steering influences on the neocortex so as to direct attention. The

DMT plays a critical role in the storage of long term memories (Gaffan and Parker, 2000; Mitchell and Dalrymple-Alford, 2005; Mitchell et al., 2007) When damaged, there can result a dense verbal and visual anterograde amnesia (Graff-Radford, et al. 1990; von Cramon et al. 2005) as memories cannot be selectively stored or activated.

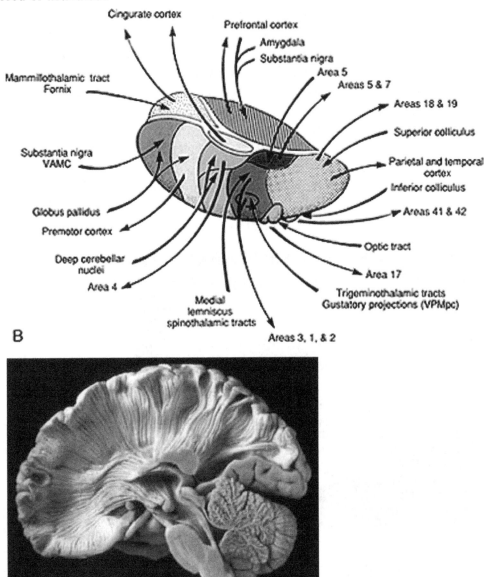

The DMT and anterior thalamus are able to perform these functions via inhibitory and excitatory influences (mediated by the frontal lobe and to a lesser extent, the hippocampus) on neurons located in the neocortex, limbic system, and reticular activating system. For example, the DMT and frontal lobes monitor and control, at the neocortical level, all stages of information analysis, and insure that relevant data and associations are shifted from primary to association to multi-modal associations areas so that further processing can occur. This is made possible since the frontal lobes are interlocked with the first, second, and third stage of neocortical information processing, and simultaneously projects to these neocortical regions and the DMT which enables it to exert inhibitory, facilitatory influences so as to selectively gating information reception and processing. Hence, the frontal-thalamic system can act to inhibit further processing and/or prevent this information from reaching the neocortex in the first place; i.e. at the thalamus prior to transfer to the neocortex, and at the level of the neocortex to prevent further processing. In this way, distractions and irrelevant stimuli may be filtered so that salient events may be attended to.

DMT, FRONTAL LOBES, KORSAKOFF'S SYNDROME, SEARCH & RETRIEVAL

Through the widespread interconnections maintained by the frontal lobes, hippocampus, and thalamus, specific neuronal networks and perceptual fields can be selectively inhibited or activated, so that information may be processed or ignored, and so that conjunctions between different neocortical areas can be formed. These nuclei therefore directly mediate information processing, memory storage, and the creation of or additions to specific neural networks via the control of neocortical activity.

The frontal lobe and anterior and dorsal medial thalamus are also involved in search and retrieval, for these aspects of memory are severely disrupted with damage to the frontal lobes and dorsal medial nuclei, whereas recognition memory may remain much more intact (Graff-Radord, et al. 1990; Squire, 1992). However, recognition memory may be impaired as well. For example, one such patient (who, however, also had atrophy involving the mammilary bodies) was not only unable to recall that he had been a patient at the hospital for over a month, but repeatedly claimed to be "working" as a "janitor," and that he would be "going home at quitting time." However, when he was shown his hospital room and clothes, although he recognized the items as his, he persisted in claiming he was at work and that was the reason his clothes were in the hospital room was so he could change before leaving to go home (Joseph 1986a). As per the mammilary bodies (a structure also associated with memory), the hippocampus also maintains interconnections with this tissue (Guillary, 1956; Nauta, 1958), and "diencephalic" amnesia is a not uncommon manifestations of mammillary injury (Victor & Adams, 1993; Victor et al., 1971).

Hence, when the frontal lobes and DMT and anterior thalamus are damaged, the ability to shift from one set of perceptions to another, or to selectively retrieve a specific memory, or to inhibit the activation of irrelevant ideas, associations, memories, and thoughts, is significantly impacted, and the patient may confabulate and produce "false memories" (Joseph, 1986a, 1988a, 2016a). The ability to alternate between and thus selectively activate specific neural networks is also disrupted, such that patients have difficulty shifting from one train of thought to another. That is, they may tend to become stuck in-set and to engage in recurrent perseveration (Fuster 2008; Joseph, 1986a, 2016a; Vikki, 2007) such that the same speech patterns or "memories" may be repeated unless something occurs to arrest and shift their attention.

Hence, with frontal-thalamic damage, retrieval is impaired as is the ability to selectively recall of shift between old versus recent memories, and to keep track of the order in which they may have been formed e.g. morning, evening, yesterday, last week, five years ago and so on (see Graff-Radford, et al. 1990; Squire, 1992; Talland, 1961). Therefore, a patient may deny possessing a certain memory of an event which occurred five weeks ago, because he is searching his memory store for events which were experienced five years ago or five days ago.

For example, one patient with severe frontal lobe damage claimed to have never been married and laughingly indicated that he never wanted to get married and that marriage was a bad idea. When pressed as to why, he exclaimed that "the wife may just up and die on you," and then began to laugh quite loudly and then just as suddenly began to sob and cry. When asked why he was crying, he claimed not to know why. However, when he was reminded that he had been married, he was suddenly able to recall that his wife (of two years) had been killed in the same accident that resulted in his injuries.

Another patient with anterior and dorsal medial thalamic damage erroneously stated that the president was Lyndon Johnson. However, when told the correct date ("1982") she correctly named Ronald Regan (Graff-Radford, et al. 1990).

Thus "time sense" and capacity to selectively search memory may be disrupted with frontal-dorsal medial dysfunction; a condition which is also characteristic of Korsakoff's syndrome. For example, Talland (1961, p. 375) described one woman with Korsakoff's disease who "after ten year's hospitalization continually maintained that she has been brought in the previous day for observation." When questioned she also argued that she still lived with her husband in a fancy hotel, where she had lived "the life of a well-to-do lady of leisure. She seemed unaware that the conditions of that very agreeable life had long since ceased to operate."

Individuals suffering from Korsakoff's syndrome demonstrate profound disturbances of memory, including a dense verbal and visual anterograde amnesia (Aggleton & Mishkin, 2003; Graff-Radford, Tranel, Van Hoesen & Brandt, 1990; Victor et al. 2007; von Cramon et al. 2005) and in some cases a more temporally graded memory loss for the remote past (Squire, 1992) --although the hippocampus is intact. Rather, in Korsakoff's syndrome, damage typically involves the dosal medial nucleus of the thalamus and atrophy of the frontal lobes (Aggleton & Mishkin, 2003; Graff-Radford, et al, 1990; Lishman, 1981; Mair et al., 1979; Victor et al. 2007; von Cramon et al. 2005; Wilkinson & Carlen, 1982) as well as the mammillary bodies (Victor & Adams, 1993; Victor et al., 1971); i.e. "diencephalic amnesia". Nevertheless, recognition memory may be partially intact, and with selective reminders and reorientation, the retrieval deficits associated with frontal/dorsal medial damage can sometimes be partly overcome (Graff-Radford, et al. 1990).

As noted, the mammillary bodies are interconnected with the hippocampus also maintains interconnections with this tissue (Guillary, 1956; Nauta, 1958), as well as to the hypothalamus and brainstem reticular formation, and are relayed to the septal nucleus--which is also implicated in memory (Gage et al., 2003; Olton, 1990). Injury to the mammillary bodies is typically associated with "diencephalic" amnesia (Victor & Adams, 2010; Victor et al., 1971).

HIPPOCAMPUS AND DORSAL MEDIAL NUCLEUS

In addition, the hippocampus interacts with the DMT, and on the orbital frontal lobes, and via the entorhinal cortex on the neocortex. Thus the hippocampus can transmit to and keep track of where memories are stored, while simultaneously acting to store them in select neocortical regions. This is accomplished by simultaneously exerting influences on the DMT while sharing reciprocal influences with the orbital frontal lobe which also projects to the DMT.

Specifically, layer 2 of the hippocampus consists of pyramidal neurons which provide excitatory output and thus act to activate and arouse target tissues; via the transmitters glutamate and aspartic acid. In addition, the entorhinal cortex provides excitatory input into the hippocampus--input which is derived from the neocortex; using again, aspartic and glutamate acid (Gloor, 1997). It thus appears that the hippocampus can interact with the neocortex is regard to arousal and memory storage via the dorsal medial nucleus of the thalamus and the entorhinal cortex, and can excite, for example, inhibitory circuits in the DMT (in conjunction with the frontal lobe) so as to direct neocortical activity, and perhaps coordinate this activity in regard to memory storage. In other words, these structures interact to insure that a certain neocortical area is selected for memory storage (via excitation), while simultaneously inhibiting and preventing information access in other areas. Memories can be stored and the hippocampus and frontal lobes, via the DMT, can keep track of where they are stored.

HIPPOCAMPUS & NEOCORTICAL AROUSAL

The frontal lobes, DMT, amygdala, hippocampus, entorhinal cortex, and the neocortex of the overlying temporal lobe all appear to interact in concert during various aspects of memory storage and retrieval as well as in the temporal placement of events in regard to time and even place (Brewer et al., 1998; Gloor, 1997; Graff-Radford et al. 1990; Talland, 1961; Wagner et al., 1998). This is why retrieval and even memory storage may become abnormal with damage to any of these nuclei.

There are reciprocal connections between the DMT and the amygdala, and temporal allocortex and mesocortex including the entorhinal cortex, as well as the lateral and orbital frontal lobes. This relationship suggests that the DMT upon receiving converging input, processes this material, and then at the behest of the frontal lobes, amygdala, and entorhinal cortex/hippocampus, stores this material in select areas of the neocortex such as the temporal lobe.

The hippocampus exerts desynchronizing or synchronizing influences on various thalamic nuclei which in turn augments or decreases thalamic and neocortical activity (Green & Adey, 1956; Guillary, 1955; Joseph 1996, 2016; Nauta, 1956, 1958). As the thalamus is the major relay nucleus to the neocortex and is richly interconnected with the frontal lobes and amygdala, the hippocampus therefore appears able to act in concert with these nuclei so as to block or enhance information transfer to various neocortical areas where memories and perceptual experiences are presumably stored.

For example, when the neocortex becomes desynchronized (indicating cortical arousal), the hippocampus often (but not always) develops slow wave, synchronous theta activity (Grastyan et al. 1959; Green & Arduni, 1954; Vertes 2005) such that it appears to be functioning at a much lower level of arousal--at least in lower mammals. Conversely, when cortical arousal is reduced to a low level (indicated by EEG synchrony), the hippocampal EEG often becomes desynchronized and thus highly aroused (Grastyan et al., 1959; Green & Arduni, 1954). However, when this occurs, theta activity disappears and learning and memory are also disrupted--at least in lower mammals.

With the exception of the orbital frontal lobe, neocortical interconnections with the hippocampus are indirect and relayed by the entorhinal cortex,. Nevertheless, these interconnections (coupled with those of the DMT) enable the hippocampus to not only activate select regions--as its pyramidal projection system and that of the entorhinal cortex is excitatory (Gloor, 1997)--but to sample information after it has been partially processed. This is accomplished via the entorhinal cortex which projects back and forth from the association areas to the hippocampus. In this manner the hippocampus can also influence the processing that takes place via the DMT/Entorhinal cortex, and keep tract of what takes place as well.

The hippocampus consists of 3 layers, layer 2 consisting of pyramidal neurons which provide excitatory output. The hippocampus can act to activate and arouse target tissues; via the transmitters glutamate and aspartic acid. In addition, the entorhinal cortex provides excitatory input into the hippocampus--input which is derived from the neocortex; using again, aspartic and glutamate acid. The hippocampus can therefore exert significant activating influences on target tissues.

Specifically, it appears that the hippocampus interacts with the neocortex is regard to arousal via the orbital frontal lobe, dorsal medial nucleus of the thalamus, the septal nuclei, the hypothalamus, amygdala and brainstem--structures with which it maintains direct interconnections. As per the neocortex, this sheet of tissue is also innervated by these same limbic, thalamic, and brainstem structures, and by the entorhinal cortex. Hence, the hippocampus serves as a major component of an excitatory interface and can be aroused by neocortical activity (via orbital frontal lobes, and aroused by the entorhinal cortex which provides excitatory input to the hippocampus). And the hippocampus can provide excitatory input directly to subcortical structures and indirectly to the neocortex (via the entorhinal cortex and dorsal medial nucleus) as well as directly influences the orbital frontal lobes and DMT.

Again, presumably these reciprocal interconnections may enable the hippocampus to keep track of this activity so as to form conjunctions between different brain regions which process associated memories. By sampling the activity occurring in different regions and via its rich, indirect interconnections with these neocortical areas, the hippocampus (or entorhinal cortex) may also be able to determine which perceptions are the most relevant and which should be stored vs inhibited so that relevant memories need not compete with irrelevant sense data (Joseph, 1992a; Rolls, 1990a).

Presumably the hippocampus acts to aid in the creation of these networks and to thus protect memory and the encoding of new information during the storage and consolidation phase, by the gating of afferent streams of information and the filtering/exclusion (or dampening) of irrelevant and interfering stimuli; i.e. by reducing or increasing arousal in select regions and via inhibitory and excitatory influences on the DMT.

In consequence, if the hippocampus is damaged or is overwhelmed, there may be input overload, the neuroaxis may be also overwhelmed, and the consolidation phase of hippocampal memory formation is disrupted such that cognitively relevant information is not properly stored or even attended to (Joseph, 1998b, 2016d; Squire, 1992). Consequently, the ability to form non-emotional associations (e.g. between stimulus and response) and to create new neural networks, or to alter preexisting cognitive schemas and neural circuits is attenuated. These individuals appear to be amnesic.

Again, however, this is a role the hippocampus also shares with the frontal lobes, which, in humans, is clearly dominant over the hippocampus in this regard. That is, the frontal lobes have taken over many functions that the hippocampus mediates in lower mammals.

EXCESSIVE HIPPOCAMPAL AROUSAL & MEMORY LOSS

When lower mammals are exposed to novel stimuli or when engaged in active searching of the environment, hippocampal theta appears (Adey, et al. 1960;Vertes 2005) as does LTP (Lynch, 1986). There is thus a direct correlation between hippocampal theta and the development of hippocampal LTP (Lynch et al. 1990; Vertes 2005)--at least in lower mammals. However, with repeated presentations of a novel stimulus or when familiar stimuli are presented, the hippocampus habituates and theta disappears (Adey et al., 1960; Vertes 2005). Possibly, the reason the hippocampus and other brain structures appear to respond preferentially to novel stimuli and to then cease, at least during learning tasks, is because the continual processing of familiar stimuli in short-term memory is a waste of energy and attentional space.

As noted above, when the neocortex is highly stimulated, the hippocampus (in order to monitor what is being received and processed), functions at a lower arousal level in order not to become overwhelmed. However, at extremely high levels of arousal, what is being experienced may not be learned, or it will be learned independent of the hippocampus due to diminished hippocampal activity.

In situations where both the neocortex and the hippocampus become highly aroused and desynchronized, there results distractibility and hyper responsiveness such that the subject becomes overwhelmed, confused, and may orient to and approach several stimuli (Grastyan et al., 1959); a condition that also occurs following hippocampal lesions (Clark & Issacson 1965; Douglas, 2007; Ellen et al. 1964)--at least in non-humans. Under conditions of abnormal or incoherent cortical arousal, the ability to think or respond coherently may be disrupted as is attention, learning, and memory functioning, i.e. memories are stored haphazardly, incompletely, or not at all.

Situations inducing high levels of arousal, perceptual disorganization, and memory loss sometimes also occur when individuals are highly anxious, frightened, or emotionally upset and traumatized, e.g. during a prolonged and brutal rape or physical assault, or during horrendous battle field conditions -in which case hippocampal participation in memory formation dramatically decreases as neocortical and limbic arousal increases (Joseph, 1998b, 2016d, 2003). If the hippocampus is overwhelmed and deactivated, the victim will experience amnesia.

For example, in cases of transient global amnesia there is evidence for temporary mesial temporal inactivation (Hodges & Warlow, 1990), including bilateral hypofusion of the hippocampus (Evans et al., 1993). These structures also become inactivated following the seizure- or electrode induced- postictal anterograde amnesia (Brazier, 1966; Chapman et al. 2007; Halgren, et al., 1991). However, these memory deficits may shrink over time (Brazier, 1966; Squire

1992), as do those following mild or moderate head injuries up to the moment of impact.

Under emotionally traumatic or stressful conditions the hippocampus may also become highly and over activated and it may in fact be injured (Joseph 1998, 2016, 2003; Lupien & McEwen, 1997; Sapolsky, 1996). Hence, it is not at all unusual for victims to profess a complete or partial amnesia for the event. However, because the amygdala may continue to function normally the victim may later experience flashbacks, heightened startle reactions, and intrusive emotional images. In these instances of extreme emotional stress, other brain structures, such as the amygdala probably play a more important role in memory and learning.

AMYGDALA & EMOTIONAL NEURAL NETWORKS

It is noteworthy, however, that the amygdala appears to act on the anterior hippocampus in order to emotionally reinforce as well as modulate its functional activity (Gloor, 1992, 1997; Halgren, 1992), and LTP occurs in both nuclei.

The amygdala (although dependent on the hypothalamus) is preeminent in the control and mediation of most higher order emotional and motivational activities including the formation of emotional memories (Davis et al., 1997; Gloor, 1992, 1997; Halgren, 1992; Kensinger et al., 2011; LeDoux, 1992, 1996; Pessoa & Adolphs 2010; Rolls, 1992; Whalen & Phelps, 2009) and the recall of trauma-related memories and stimuli (Gloor, 1992, 1997; Halgren, 1992; Poulos et al., 2009; Rauch et al., 1996; Roozendaal et al., 2009; Shin et al., 1997). Amygdaloid neuron are able to monitor and abstract from the sensory array stimuli that are of motivational significance to the organism (Gloor, 1992, 1997; Ono & Nishijo, 1992; Rolls, 1992; Steklis & Kling, 2005) as well as add emotional attributes to perceptual and cognitive activities. This includes the ability to discern and express even subtle social-emotional nuances such as friendliness, fear, love, affection, distrust, anger, etc., and at a more basic level, determine if something might be good to eat (Blackford et al., 2009; Fukuda et al., 1987; O'Keefe & Bouma, 1969; Ono & Nishijo, 1992; Ono et al., 1980; Zhang et al., 2011). The lateral amygdala also has high concentrations of acetylcholine (Woolf & Butcher, 1982) as does the hippocampus (Kuhar, 2015) and acetylcholine (ACh) activity within the amygdala as well as hippocampus is correlated with learning and memory (Todd & Kesner, 2014). Indeed, a portion of the "extended amygdala"; i.e. the substantia innominata (of the limbic striatum) is a major source of neocortical ACh, and is therefore exceedingly important in memory. Alzheimer's disease is associated with degeneration in the substantia innominata, as well as a host of other abnormalities.

Apparently the amygdala acts on neocortical arousal in a very widespread manner via its direct projections to all areas of the neocortex and through its influences on substantia innominata and brainstem ACh containing neurons. These latter structures and neurons also project to the thalamus and onto the widespread areas of neocortex (Davis, 1992; Kapp et al. 1992; Steriade, et al. 1990). The amygdala and its satellite structures can therefore influence the receptivity of the neocortex when processing specific types of sensory information (Steriade, et al. 1990). Amygdala activation, for example, may also lead to a state of vigilance, attention, or emotional arousal such as fear.

Single amygdaloid neurons receive a considerable degree of topographic input, and are predominantly polymodal, responding to a variety of stimuli from different modalities simultaneously (O'Keefe & Bouma, 1969; Perryman et al. 1987; Sawa & Delgado, 1963; Schutze et al. 1987; Turner et al. 1980; Ursin & Kaada, 1960; Van Hoesen, 1981). Hence, multi-modal integration and assimilation occurs within single amygdala neurons. Amygdala neurons are also involved in recognition memory, and the detection of faces, facial expressions, and visual stimuli involving context (Blackford et al., 2009; Gloor, 1992; Murray, 1992; Rolls, 1992; Rule et al., 2010).

The amygdala, therefore is also capable of forming cross modal associations such that a neutral stimulus can come to be endowed with emotional attributes (Gaffan & Harrison, 1987; LeDoux, 1992, 1996; Rolls, 1992). This includes forming associations between primary as well as secondary reinforcers (Everitt et al. 1991; Gaffan & Harrison, 1987). In addition, there are single neurons in the amygdala which discriminate between stimuli which are rewarding or punishing (Rolls, 1992).

The amygdala is functionally related and richly (and reciprocally) interconnected with the hippocampus, inferior temporal lobe, and a variety of other limbic, brainstem, and neocortical regions that are important in memory functioning. It also projects to all areas of the neocortex and receives highly processed visual, somesthetic, auditory, as well as olfactory input and is especially responsive to faces, when making eye contact, and can discriminate between males and females, strangers and those who are familiar, and can determine if someone is staring or looking away.

Because of its involvement in all aspects of social-emotional and motivational functioning, activation of the amygdala therefore, can evoke highly personal and emotional memories as it is highly involved in remembering emotionally charged experiences (Gloor, 1992, 1997; Halgren, 1981, 1992; Halgren, et al. 2014; Rolls, 1992; Sarter & Markowtisch, 2005). In fact, the amygdala becomes particularly active when recalling personal and emotional memories (Halgren, 1992; Heath, 1964; Penfield & Perot, 1963), and in response to cognitive and context determined stimuli regardless of their specific emotional qualities (Halgren, 1992). Moreover, depth electrode activation of the amygdala can even evoke memories of sexual intercourse, and traumatic memories that had long ago been forgotten.

Consider, for example, a case described by Gloor (1997, pp. 7-9) in which the right amygdala of a 21 year old patient "was briefly stimulated for 2.8 seconds at a low intensity. Immediately upon its onset" the patient reported "a feeling like falling into the water. When he was asked to elaborate, he replied that it was as if something had covered his eyes, nose, and mouth." Again the stimulation was applied and the patient excitedly asked: "Could you do it again, Doctor? When asked why, he said he had the words on his lips to describe the feeling, but then could not." The stimulation was then applied without warning for 4.4 seconds. The patient "opened his mouth, with an astonished look on his face," for a terrifying memory had suddenly come back to him. It was when he was eight years old and had been at a picnic when "A kid was coming up to me to push me into the water.... I was pushed by somebody stronger than me... a big fellow..." who pushed him under the water and had kept his head under the water so that he couldn't breath.

As pondered by Gloor (1997, p. 9): "why did the first two stimulations elicit only a quasi-affective response, vaguely evocative of a past event, whereas the third brought out the reenactment or recollection of the specific event? One possibility is that because the third stimulation was 30% to 50% longer than the first two, more time was provided for initiating the activation of the neural systems encoding the experience. A second possibility is that the stimulations that were carried out a few minutes apart left in their wake some residual long-lasting neural facilitation."

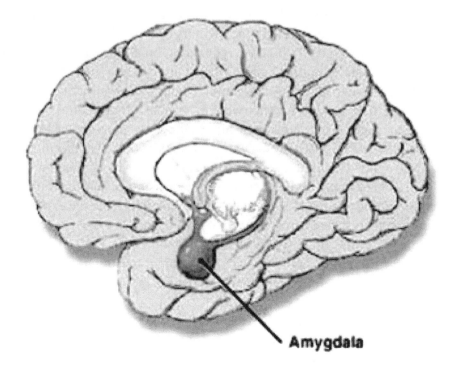

Amygdala

Under conditions of prolonged fear and traumatic stress, the amygdala may process and store emotional experiences in memory in the absence of significant hippocampal participation (Joseph 1996, 1998, 2016). In consequence, the victim may become amnesic, though they may later experience a shrinking amnesia, and/or when presented with trauma-related cues, they may begin to remember, in bits and pieces, the original traumatic experience in a manner identical to that described by Gloor (1997).

FEAR, ANXIETY, STARTLE, & TRAUMATIC STRESS

The amygdala is the major site where conditioned fear, startle and autonomic reactions occur (Davis, 1992; Davis et al., 1997; Hitchcock & Davis, 1991; Nitschke et al. 2009; Pope & Pare 2010; Poulos et al., 2009; Roozendaal et al. 2009) -reactions which may be stored in memory. Moreover, when recalling traumatic memories or when presented with traumatic-stimuli, the amygdala becomes highly active and subjects display all the signs of heightened autonomic activity (Rauch et al., 1996; Shin et al., 1997). Hence, in response to a certain stimulus that has been repeatedly associated with positive or negative outcomes, autonomic changes are triggered which may be accompanied by fear as well as memory recall. That is, although an emotional event may be seemingly forgotten, associated cues may trigger the remembrance of things past, including memories that may have been seemingly forgotten and "repressed." However, if the memory is not completely remembered, the patient may reexperience feelings and autonomic changes associated with the memory (Gloor 1998).

For example, the amygdala directly influences breathing and heart rate in response to emotional stimuli. It may in fact may create a circuit or neural network that triggers heart rate and autonomic changes, as well as neocortical desynchronization (low voltage fast activity) in response to a neutral stimulus that has been repeatedly associated with highly arousing pleasant or aversive emotional outcomes (Kapp et al. 1992; Ursin & Kaada, 1960). That is, emotional learning of a well defined conditioned response occurs within the amygdala which in turn influences autonomic activity such that both classical and instrumental emotional conditioning occurs. However, this also makes possible the experience of anxiety and anticipatory fear in response to cues which might trigger the original emotional memory. Even if the original memory is not recalled, the victim may still experience the emotional and associated autonomic reactions--all of which may contribute to the development and maintenance of post-traumatic stress disorder (Joseph 1996).

In these particular instances, however, the more the cue is linked and associated with the original traumatic event, the more severe might be the reaction, and the more upsetting the recalled memory. Kolb (1986, p. 172), for example, in his discussion in the persistence of startle reaction in combat soldiers, noted that "it was remarkable 10, 15, or 20 years after the combat event to hear men tell about suddenly hearing a loud noise reminding them of battle sounds and then being in a panic state."

Kolb (1986, p. 172) also reports that when they "played a tape consisting of combat sounds, including those of helicopters, mortars, and screaming wounded... the patients immediately returned to a critical event in the battlefield. Many then experienced and reenacted scenes of fight, flight, or rage." For most of these individuals, reexperiencing the traumatic memory is, in itself extremely traumatic and they avoid all forms of stimulation that can reawaken these memories.

Hence, an individual may become severely stressed or repeatedly frightened, and later experience an increase in heart rate, changes in breathing patterns, and other autonomic alterations, in anticipation or in response to associated emotional and contextual cues, which in turn may activate the neural network in which the original emotional memory is stored. However, at least in regard to heart rate changes, this circuitry is in part hard wired and involves a projection into the midbrain periaqueductal gray (as well as the basal ganglia) and then on to the lower brainstem into the vagal nucleus (Kapp et al. 1992).

According to Davis (1992, p. 283), "much of the complex behavioral pattern seen during fear conditioning has already been hard wired during evolution. In order for a formerly neutral stimulus to produce the constellation of behavioral effects used to define a state of fear or anxiety, it is only necessary for that stimulus to now activate the amygdala, which in turn will produce the complex pattern of behavioral changes by virtue of its innate connections to different brain target sites." Hence, the amygdala need only learn what stimuli are the most arousing, threatening, fearful, pleasurable and so on, and can then automatically trigger autonomic and behavioral responses which are already hard wired into the nervous system.

Amygdala activation will also increase the frequency of respiration and will trigger behavioral freezing and an arrest of ongoing behavior (Kapp et al. 1992; Ursin & Kaada, 1960). The amygdala may also contribute to the frozen states common among those with Parkinson's disease (Joseph 1996).

Initially, however, freezing behavior is part of the attention response, which in turn may be followed by an orienting reaction, sometimes with anxious glancing about, and/or with an approach or withdrawal reaction (Gloor, 1960; Ursin & Kaada, 1960). If amygdala stimulation continues fear and/or rage reactions are elicited (Ursin & Kaada, 1960).

In general, the right amygdala is more involved than the left in the production of fear and anxiety (Davis, 1987), particularly free floating fears , and the right hemisphere is more greatly involved in the fear potentiated startle response (Lang et al. 1990), as well as emotion in general .

FEAR, ANTICIPATION, & REPRESSION

As noted, the amygdala can make fine discrimination between stimuli that are closely vs not so closely associated with fear, so that startle and fear reactions are elicited to stimuli which most closely match (Davis, 1992; Lang et al., 2009; Nitschke et al. 2009). The amygdala, therefore, can also anticipate fearful stimuli based on only fragmentary cues or sensory stimuli, some of which might trigger startle reactions (Davis, 1992; Davis et al., 1997; Kurtz & Siegel, 1966; LeDoux, 1996) or memory recall.

The amygdala is thus very important in the production of anticipatory anxiety (Davis, 1992; Nitschke et al. 2009) as well as emotional memory (Gloor, 1997, Halgren, 1993; Pape & Pare 2010; Poulos et al., 2009; Rauch et al., 1996; Shin et al., 1997). Because it can anticipate based merely on fragmentary cues, individuals may come to feel upset, angry, frightened, and yet not know why or what might have triggered these emotions. This often occurs among individuals suffering from post traumatic stress disorder, as well as among those with repressed memories; i.e. a consequence of a single cue triggering a complex emotional memory or associated feelings of anxiety.

In some respects this is a very adaptive arrangement, for if the individual were unable to inhibit or forget emotionally upsetting memories, their intrusion would crippled his or her ability to function. That is, perhaps it makes little evolutionary sense for an individual to be able to recall and act on extremely arousing and emotionally upsetting memories except when in a highly aroused state. For these memories to seep or burst into consciousness at other times may exert a deleterious effect on functioning --which appears to be the case in post-traumatic stress disorder.

Perhaps it is adaptive for the hippocampus to sometimes cease to participate in memory formation under extremely distressful conditions, and why only fragments of the emotional trauma may appear in consciousness under certain similar circumstances and conditions. From the standpoint of survival it makes sense for these memories to be forgotten but then recalled when in a similar state of high arousal or when presented with similar emotional cues. However, even under these conditions the forgotten memory may remain "repressed," and this too may be made possible via the amygdala (as well as the frontal lobes).

For example, the amygdala in response to a partial cues may respond with feelings of anxiety and fear before the actual memory or associated neural network can be fully activated (Gloor, 1997). In instances such as these, the actual memory might come to be inhibited, or repressed, in response to the anxiety that was triggered in advance.

FEAR, EMOTIONAL TRAUMA, HIPPOCAMPAL DEACTIVATION & MEMORY LOSS

Rhythmic slow activity (theta), is generated by both the hippocampus and entorhinal cortex (Alonso & Garcia-Austt, 1987; Vertes 2005) and theta has been found in the hippocampus of most species studied, including monkeys (Stewart & Fox, 1990) and humans (Sano et al., 1970); though in primates it seems to differ from the theta rhythm of non-primates (see Gloor, 1997). Theta is an indication of hippocampal arousal (Green & Arduini, 1954; Petsche et al., 1965; Vanderwolf, 1992) and is associated with learning and memory (O'Keefe & Nadel, 2014). Moreover, LTP is generated in those neurons demonstrating theta or activity that is at the "theta frequency" (Staubli & Lynch, 1987; Vertes 2005).

Neurons of the septal nucleus which innervate the hippocampus fluctuate in activity in parallel with changes in the theta rhythm (Petsche et al., 1965). The septal nucleus, in fact, acts as an interface between the reticular formation and the hippocampus (Petsche et al., 1965) and thus appears to contribute to the development of theta by modulating hippocampal arousal thus promoting learning and memory. Hence, if the septal nucleus is lesioned hippocampal theta is abolished (Green & Arduini, 1954) and significant memory deficits are produced. Moreover, the septal nuclei is directly implicated in the stress response and can be injured by prolonged stress (Joseph 1998, 2016); conditions which also result in the loss of theta and LTP.

In response to continued, ongoing fear, emotional stress, and anxiety, the amygdala (as well as the HPA axis) begins to secrete large amounts of the amino peptide, corticotropin-releasing factor (CRF) which in turn potentiates the behavioral and autonomic reaction to fear and stress. Cortisone levels also increase dramatically when stressed by restraint (Davis, 1992) and amygdala activity will increase as well (Henke 1992). Moreover, high levels of cortisone exerts an inhibitory influence on the hippocampus and eliminates hippocampal theta by attacking hippocampal pyramidal cells (Joseph, 1998d, Spoont, 1992) which normally provide excitatory output. In consequence, memory begins to decline (Lupien & McEwen, 1997; Sapolsky, 2006).

When fear follows the attention response, the pupils dilate and the subject will cringe, withdraw, and cower -which is associated with high levels of amygdaloid activity. This cowering reaction in turn may give way to extreme fear and/or panic and the animal will attempt to take flight. This may be accomplished via amygdala activation of the locus coeruleus which would release norepinephrine (NE), and activation of the raphe nucleus which would release serotonin (Magnuson & Gray, 1990), both of which facilitate motor responsiveness (White & Neuman, 1980). However, if arousal levels continue to increase, the hippocampus may cease to participate in memory functioning such that whatever is experienced and learned may subsequently appear repressed due to hippocampal deactivation

(Joseph 1996, 2016).

Among humans, the fear response is one of the most common manifestations of amygdaloid electrical stimulation (Gloor, 1990; Halgren, 1992; Williams, 1956). Moreover, unlike hypothalamic on/off emotional responses, attention and fear reactions can last up to several minutes after the stimulation is withdrawn. Apparently this is associated with the development of LTP within amygdala neurons which thus continue to reverberate even when the subject is frightened or in pain.

In addition, when the (human) amygdala is abnormally or highly activated, it is able to possibly deactivate the anterior hippocampus as well as overwhelm the neocortex and the rest of the brain so that the person not only forms emotional ideas (that later cannot be fully remembered) but responds to them in an abnormal manner.

In fact, during periods of extreme fear, such as when a subject freezes, hippocampal theta disappears and is replaced by irregular electrophysiological activity (Vanderwolf & Leung, 2003). Prolonged stress also inhibits long term potentiation in the hippocampus (Shors et al. 2007). Theta also disappears if a subject is placed in a situation where they are completely hopelessly surrounded by painful physical threat, such as an electrified grid floor (Vanderwolf & Leung, 2003). Similarly, under conditions of stress or when the body has been anesthetized (Green & Arduini, 1954), hippocampal theta disappears, as does LTP (Shors et al. 2007) and the threshold for hippocampal responding is significantly raised. In part it is overwhelmed and inhibited by the amygdala and the reticular activating system, which in turn reduces its participation in learning and memory.

The hippocampus maintains a reciprocal relationship with the reticular formation in regard to the modulation of neocortical activity except under conditions of high arousal in which case it can be inhibited by the reticular activating system (Adey, et al. 1957; Green & Arduini, 1954; Redding, 2007). This may occur in situations involving high levels of arousal and with repetitive stimulation (Redding, 2007) in which case theta and LTP may be prevented. Indeed, with persistent and repeated stimulation, instead of excitation there is synaptic depression with no evidence of LTP even under neutral and non-emotional conditions (Lynch, 1986). Presumably this is related to rapid calcium depletion, for LTP and synaptic plasticity are effected by calcium levels.

This loss of hippocampal theta and LTP under repetitive, stressful, painful, or fearful conditions is not a function of lack of whole body movement, however. For example, theta appears when human subjects are sitting motionless but are mentally engaged in problem solving or learning tasks (Meador et al. 1991) and when the median raphe nucleus (which suppresses hippocampal theta and induces high states of arousal) is destroyed and subjects are immobilized (Vertes, 1981, 2005). Rather this loss of theta activity is a function of overwhelming fear and high levels of arousal, for although seemingly alert, the hippocampus is desychronized, and the subject may seem frozen and will be unable to respond to environmental stimuli, be it threat or painful stimuli (Redding, 2007). In consequence they are unable to recall what occurred as this data was stored by the amygdala in the absence of hippocampal participation.

Later, hippocampal retrieval mechanisms are unable to find the memory. The patient will appear amnesic when they are in fact relying on the wrong (albeit "normal") retrieval mechanisms; i.e. the hippocampus.

Indeed, under conditions of high hippocampal arousal or inhibition (Evans et al., 1993; Halgren, et al., 1991; Hodges & Warlow, 1990), or due to direct hippocampal stimulation, verbal amnesia results (Brazier, 1966; Chapman et al. 2007) and there is a loss or significant reduction in theta (Redding, 2007). This occurs even when there has been no loss of consciousness, and while the subject seems fully alert with no evidence of confusion.

Normally, as described by Squire (1992, p. 224, 208), "the possibility of later retrieval is provided by the hippocampal system because it has bound together the relevant cortical sites. A partial cue that is later processed through the hippocampus is able to reactivate all of the site and thereby accomplish retrieval of the whole memory... In the absence of the hippocampus, representations that had been established in short-term memory are literally lost, become disorganized, or achieve some abnormal fate."

Memories formed by the amygdala in the absence of hippocampal participation, such as in instances of extreme emotional stress and neocortical arousal, may appear to be forgotten as they cannot be accessed via normal hippocampal retrieval mechanisms. However, even when the hippocampus has been destroyed, this amnesia does not extend to fear or pain related stimuli (Seldon et al. 1991). In fact, aversive conditioning is completely unaffected (Seldon et al. 1991), particularly when the conditions are highly aversive and painful or highly emotional as this form of learning is mediated by the amygdala (Cahill & McGaugh, 1990; Hitchcock & Davis, 1987; Kesner & DiMattia, 1987) as well as the hypothalamus. Rather, what may be forgotten is the place and the circumstances around which the pain was experienced (Seldon, et al. 1991).

However, although the hippocampal amnesia may extend backward in time from minutes to days and even weeks, the amnesia may shrink over the course of the next several hours such that only those events which took place just prior and during the period of abnormal hippocampal excitation are seemingly forgotten (Brazier, 1966; Chapman et al. 2007). Nevertheless, when specific cues are provided, recall and memory recovery occurs (Seldon, et al. 1991). Recognition memory is activated and what was forgotten is suddenly recalled -sometimes to the disbelief of family or treating physicians.

MEMORY LOSS & AMYGDALA DYSFUNCTION

The amygdala appears to be involved in all aspects of social-emotional memory functioning (Joseph 1982, 1992, 2014, 1998, 2016). Hence, destruction of the amygdala makes it exceedingly difficult to form associations between reinforcing stimuli, regardless of their being positive or negative (Jones & Mishkin, 1972; LeDoux, 2012; Rolls, 2002; Weiskrantz, 1956), and results in a dense social-emotional agnosia and amnesia such that even loved one's are no longer recognized. Similarly emotional learning becomes very limited, primitive and dependent on the hypothalamus .

For example, animals who have been amygdalectomized often demonstrate very poor performance on emotional learning and attention tasks (Kesner, 1992; Murray, 1992; Sarter & Markowitsch, 2005) as they are unable to assign emotional attributes to what they perceive. They also cannot learn associations between primary reinforcers and rewarded stimuli, including those where the subject has to approach or avoid stimuli which has either been rewarded or punished (Kesner, 1992; Murray & Mishkin, 2005; Rolls, 2005, 2012).

Neurosurgical removal of the right or left amygdala also results in significant memory disturbances, particularly in the realm of information retrieval and social-emotional perception and contextual information storage (Andersen, 2014; Gloor, 1992; Rolls, 1992; Sarter & Markowtisch, 2005). Moreover, a complete amnesia can result following electrical stimulation of the amygdala (Chapman, 1958; Jasper & Rasmussen, 1958), and difficulty recognizing people and objects has been repeatedly noted following amygdalectomy in humans.

Moreover, Alzheimer's disease as well as other dementias and encephalitic conditions not only result in severe memory loss, but often attack the amygdala and the anterior commissure (which links the right and left amygdala) creating both neurofibrillary changes and senile plaques. With normal aging there is also a progressive memory loss and a significant drop out of neurons in the amygdala (Herzog & Kemper, 1980), as well as in other structures, particularly the substantia innominata which is part of the "extended amygdala" and which is directly implicated in the genesis of Alzheimer's disease.

AMYGDALA, HIPPOCAMPUS & DORSAL MEDIAL NUCLEUS

Both the hippocampus and amygdala maintain rich interconnections with the anterior thalamus (Ammaral et al. 1992; Krettek & Price, 1977; Nauta, 1971; Graff-Radford, et al. 1990). However, these two limbic pathways remain distinct and terminate in separate, albeit adjacent thalamic areas (Graff-Radford, et al. 1990). A similar pattern of parallel organization characterizes amygdala and hippocampal input into the basal ganglia and other limbic and brainstem nuclei. This suggests that the influences and contributions of the amygdala and hippocampal to memory, motor, and perceptual activity remain distinct within the brainstem, basal ganglia, and the neocortex such that perhaps two separate, albeit closely aligned neural circuits are created in parallel; one concerning the emotional the other the cognitive attributes of what has been attended to, learned, and stored in memory.

It is also noteworthy that although destruction of the anterior and dorsal medial thalamus can induce severe verbal and visual amnesic disorders, it appears that both the amygdala and hippocampal pathways must be destroyed (Graff-Radford et al. 1990). Presumably this is because the amygdala and hippocampus interact at the level of the limbic system, and again within the thalamus, and probably again within the neocortex to insure that certain memories are formed. Hence, damage to the DMT may result in a disconnection syndrome. That is, the interacting influences of the hippocampus and amygdala is no longer possible within the DMT which negatively impacts memory formation within the neocortex.

In contrast, thalamic lesions which are more caudally located and which spare these limbic pathways, do not induce amnesia (see Graff-Radford et al. 1990; von Cramon et al. 2005). Because these limbic-thalamic pathways have been spared, the hippocampus and amygdala are able to continue to exert tremendous influences on neocortical information processing, including the gating of perceptual activity and neocortical arousal and the filtering vs selective attention to events which are emotionally, motivationally and cognitively significant.

These distinct, albeit codependent (emotional vs cognitive) memory traces are also probably mutually reinforcing and linked to some degree. However, because they are separate, it is possible to recall the cognitive attributes of an experience in the absence of its emotional significance, or conversely, to recall the emotional features of an event in the absence of memory for the event; e.g., an individual may recall having a horrible argument but be unable to remember what was said. In severe cases they may become severely amnesic.

OVERVIEW: THE HIPPOCAMPUS, AMGYDALA & MEMORY

There is considerable evidence which strongly suggests that the hippocampus plays an interdependent role with the amygdala (and the frontal-thalamic system) in regard to many aspects of memory (e.g. visual, verbal, spatial), and that the amygdala plays a primary role in regard to all aspects of emotional memory. That is, the amygdala (in conjunction with the hypothalamus) extracts and stores the emotional attributes as well as mediating the emotional reactions and feelings triggered by particular events. It also acts on the anterior hippocampus and dorsal medial thalamus so that motivationally and emotionally significant information is attended to and stored via the creation of appropriate neural networks. The hippocampus performs likewise with verbal, visual-spatial, and cognitive material. Thus, these two nuclei work in concert.

The amygdala seems to reinforce and maintain hippocampal activity via the identification of social-emotional and motivationally significant information and the generation of pleasurable rewards -through interaction with the lateral hypothalamus and by "rewarding" the anterior hippocampus . That is, reward increases the probability of attention being paid to a particular stimulus or consequence as a function of its association with reinforcement (Douglas, 2007; Kesner & Andrus, 1982).

The same is true when an experience is personally significant and moderately emotionally arousing. It is perhaps for this reason that personal emotional events are often better recalled than those which are neutral and why learning and memory improves when rewarded; i.e. amygdala-hippocampal interactions are enhanced which leads to the establishment of cognitive-emotional neural networks and thus long term memory. Conversely, when both the amygdala and hippocampus are damaged, striking and profound disturbances in memory functioning result (Kesner & Andrus, 1982; Mishkin, 2014, 1990).

There is also evidence which indicates that these emotional and cognitive memories may be stored in separate, albeit aligned neural networks. As noted, the pathways leading from the amygdala and hippocampus to the anterior and dorsal medial thalamus terminate in separate, albeit adjoining thalamic neurons (Graff-Radford, et al. 1990) as well as in adjacent basal ganglia and brainstem neurons. Thus these two networks of emotional vs cognitive "memories" and associated neural pathways remain separate and may terminate on different dendrites and neurons. Hence, cognitive and associated emotional memories are maintained by semi-independent neural networks which might be activated or inhibited separately, partially, sequentially or in parallel, and conjointly. Also, as noted, the amygdala and hippocampus act differentially in regard to the effects of positive vs. negative reinforcement. For example, whereas the hippocampus produces theta in response to noxious stimuli it soon ceases to participate in memory formation when negative conditions are continuous and ongoing, i.e., theta disappears (Vanderwolf & Leung, 2003) as does hippocampal LTP (Lupien & McEwen, 1997; Shors et al. 2007). Similarly, Heath (1977) reports that high emotional states, including fear, and rage, are associated with high amplitude spindle EEG wave forms within the hippocampus. In contrast, the amygdala increases its activity following the reception of a reward and in response to stressful stimuli (see Gaffan, 1992; Halgren, 1992; Rolls, 1992; Roozendaal et al. 2009). It also develops LTP under these conditions.

The amygdala also mediates behavioral responsiveness under conditions of high arousal, so as to maintain attention, or to attack in anger (or hunger) or run away in fear. Hence, whereas the hippocampus diminishes its contribution under these highly arousing conditions, the amygdala continues to subserve perceptual and behavioral activity, and continues to monitor and store the emotional attributes in memory, even in the absence of hippocampal participation. From the standpoint of survival, this makes evolutionary sense. Consequently, later this information may not be accessible via normal "hippocampal retrieval strategies" and may appear to be forgotten or repressed.

This neurological relationship is quite adaptive for in some life threatening situations an immediate emotional reaction is called for and the recall and consideration of cognitively based alternatives might result in death. Hence, the hippocampus ceases to participate. Moreover, for much of limbic system and human evolution, under highly stressful and emotionally arousing conditions, the expression, consideration and storage of thought patterns and other cognitive processes may have been irrelevant and might even have interfered with the retrieval of survival related information. Consequently, irrelevant information is not stored in memory, whereas when highly emotionally aroused, relevant memories might be suddenly recalled.

In fact, as individuals may not be capable of (verbally)-thinking too clearly under certain highly stressful and fearful conditions, the generation and storage of these thoughts might result in their latter recollection when in a similar situation (which, for almost all of our ancestry was probably likely), thus disrupting the ability to engage in effective action (such as fleeing or fighting) or to recall the last successful strategy.

However, these emotional memories may be suddenly recalled if the person is later confronted with similar emotional and contextual cues; which enables them to act in the same manner which previously saved their life. This may also account for the effect of certain contextual cues in the elicitation of traumatic stress reaction; i.e. hearing a car backfire and suddenly dropping to the floor in response to a "flashback" of being in battle. That is, the amygdala responds to associated cues to trigger the recollection of associated emotional memories and relevant (and life saving) behaviors.

It is presumably due to these separate neural networks and the differential contributions of the amygdala and hippocampus, that a cognitive memory might be retrieved or recalled stripped of its original emotional attributes (which may be too troubling and upsetting to remember), or why emotional memories might be triggered in the absence of concrete auditory and visual cognitive cues. As such, an individual may feel exceedingly upset, anxious, angry, and so on, and not know why, or conversely verbally recall certain traumatic or negative events which are expressed and verbally described in neutral or even positive terms, though the memory is actually quite negative if not traumatic. However, in some cases the individual may "recall" nothing at all and may not even be aware that something unpleasant has been repressed.

Again, this is very "adaptive" for otherwise an individual may be plagued by memories that may best be forgotten. Indeed, although resulting in modern day "neurosis" and brain damaged induced amnesias, it is presumably this dual amygdala-hippocampal relationship and the capacity to separately store and selectively recall emotional vs cognitive information which has promoted not just learning and memory, but individual and species survival (if not sanity) for much of human history.

REFERENCES

Alberini, C. M. (2008). Transcription Factors in Long-Term Memory and Synaptic Plasticity. Physiological Reviews, 89. 121-145.

Aggleton, J. P. (1992). The amygdala. New York: Wiley-Liss.

Aggleton, J. P., Burton, M. J., & Passingham, R. E. (1980). Cortical and subcortical afferents to the amygdala of the rhesus monkey. Brain Research, 190, 347-368.

Aggleton, J. P.,& Mishkin, M. (2003). Visual recognition impairment following thalamic lesions in monkeys. Neuropsychologia, 21, 189-197.

Ahmad, S. S., & Harvey, J. A. (1968). Long-term effect of spetal lesions and social experience on shock elicited fighting in rats. Journal of comparative and Physiological Psychology, 66, 596-602.

Aich, H., Moos-Heilen, R., & Zimmerman, E. (1990). Vocalization of adult gelada baboons (T heropithecus gelada): Acoustic structure and behavioral context. Folia Primatoligica, 55: 109-132.

Ainsworth, M. D. S. (1973). The development of infant-mother attachment. In B. Caldwell & H. Ricciuti (Eds.), Review of child development research, Vol. 3, (pp. 173-196). Chicago: University of Chicago Press.

Ainsworth, M. D. S., & Witig, B. A. (1969). Attachment and exploratory behavior of one year olds in a strange situation. Lawrence Erlbaum. N. J.

Aitchison, J. (1987). Words in the mind: An introduction to the mental lexicon. Oxford: Blackwell.

Aitkin, L. (1986). The auditory midbrain. New Jersey: Humana Press.

Amaral, D. G., Insausti, R., & Cowan, W. M. (2003). Evidence for a direct projection from the superior temporal gyrus to the entorhinal cortex in the monkey Brain Research, 275, 263-277.

Amaral, D. G., & Kurtz, J. (2005). An analysis of the origins of the cholinergic and non-cholinergic septal projections to the hippocampal formation of the rat. Journal of Comparative Neurology , 24, 37-59.

Amaral, D. G.,& Price, J. L. (1984). Amygdalo-cortical projections in teH monkey (Macaca fascicularis). Jouranl of Comparative Neurology, 230, 465-496.

Amaral, D. G., et al. (1992). Anatomical organization of the primate amygdaloid complex. In J. P. Aggleton (Ed.). The Amygdala. (Wiley. New York.

Anand, B. K., & Brobeck, J. R. (1951). Hypothalamic control of food intake in rats and cats. Yale Journal of Biology & Medicine, 24, 123-140.

Anand, B.K., & Dua, S. (1956).Electrical stimulation in the limbic system of brain ("visceral brain") in the waking animal. Indian Journal of Medical Research, 44, 107-119.

Anand, B.K., Dua, S., & China, G.S. (1958).Higher nervous control over food intake.Indian Journal of Medical Research.46, 277-287.

Anand, B. K., Malhortra, C. L., Singh, V., & Dua. S. (1959). Cerebellar projections to limbic system. Journal of Neurophysiology, 22, 451-457.

Andersen, P. et al. (2006). The hippocampus book. Oxford University Press.

Bailey CH , Kandel ER , Si K (2004) The persistence of long-term memory: A molecular approach to self-sustaining changes in learning-induced synaptic growth. Neuron 44:49–57.

Bao, A-M, & Swaab, D. F. (2010). Corticotropin-Releasing Hormone and Arginine Vasopressin in Depression: Focus on the Human Postmortem Hypothalamus. Vitamins & Hormones, 82, 339-365.

Barbey, A. K., et al., (2011). Orbitofrontal Contributions to Human Working Memory. Cerebral Cortex, 21, 789-795.

Barnet A, Bazelon M, Zapella M. Visual and auditory function in an hydranencephalic infant. Brain Res. 1966;2:351–360.

Barrett, M. (1996). Early lexical development. In P. Fletcher & B. MacWhinney (Eds.), The handbook of child language, (pp. 363-392). New York: Blackwell.

Bartels A, Zeki S. The neural correlates of maternal and romantic love. Neuroimage. Mar 2004. 21(3)1155–1166.

Bashir, Z. I., Alford, S., Davies, S. N., et al., (1991). Long-term potentiation of NMDA receptor-mediated synaptic transmission in the hippocampus. Nature, 349, 156-158.

Bauman MD, Lavenex P, Mason WA, Capitanio JP, Amaral DG. The development of mother-infant interactions after neonatal amygdala lesions in rhesus monkeys. J Neurosci. 2004;24:711–721.

Bearer, E, L. et al., (2007). Live imaging of neuronal connections by magnetic resonance: Robust transport in the hippocampal–septal memory circuit in a mouse model of Down syndrome. NeuroImage, 37, 230-242.

Bekinschtein P , et al. (2007) Persistence of long-term memory storage requires a late protein synthesis- and BDNF-dependent phase in the hippocampus. Neuron 53:261–277.

Bird, C. M., & Burgess, N. (2008). The hippocampus and memory: insights from spatial processing. Nature Reviews Neuroscience 9, 182-194

Blackford, J. U., et al., (2009). Amygdala temporal dynamics: temperamental differences in the timing of amygdala response to familiar and novel faces. BMC Neuroscience 2009, 10:145.

Blair, R. J. R. (2003). "Facial expressions, their communicatory functions and neuro-cognitive substrates." Philosophical Transactions of the Royal Society of London Series B- Biological Sciences 358(1431): 561-572.

Blouet, C. et al., (2009). Mediobasal Hypothalamic Leucine Sensing Regulates Food Intake through Activation of a Hypothalamus–Brainstem Circuit.

he Journal of Neuroscience, 29, 8302-8311.

Borszcz, G. S. & Spuz, C. A. (2010). Hypothalamic control of pain vocalization and affective dimension of pain signaling. Handbook of Behavioral Neuroscience, 19, 281-291

Bowlby, J. (1940). The influence of early environment in the develpment of neurosis and neurotic charcter,"International Journal of Psycho-Analysis. 21, 154-178;

Bowlby, J. (1951). Maternal care and mental health, Geneva, WHO.

Bowlby, J. (1960). Separation Anxiety," International Journal of Psychoanalysis, 412, 1-25.

Bowlby J.(1982). Attachment and Loss. New York: Basic Books.

Braak, H.,& Braak, E. (2003). Neuronal types in the basolateral amygdaloid nuclei of man. Brain Research Bulletin, 11, 349-396.

Braak, H.,& Braak, E. (1992). The human entorhinal cortex. Neuroscience Research, 15, 6-31.

Bracke-Tolkmitt, R., Linden, A., Canavan, A.G. M., et al. (1989). The cerebellum contributes to mental skills. Behavioral Neuroscience, 103, 442-446.

Bradbury, A. J., Costall, B., Domeney, A. M., & Naylor, R. J. (2005). Laterality of dopamine function and neuroleptic action in the amygdala of the rat. Neuropharmacology, 24, 1163-1170.

Bradbury, Costall, Domeney, & Naylor, 2005). Laterality of dopamine function and neuroleptic action in the amygdala in the rat. Neuropharmacology, 24, 1163-1170.

Brazier, W.A.B. (1966). Stimulation of the hippocampus in man using implanted electrodes. In M.A. B. Brazier (Ed). RNA and Brain Function, Memory and Learning. Berkeley, U. California.

Bremner, J. G. & Slater, A. (2003). Theories of Infant Development. Wiley-Blackwell

Brown MW, Aggleton JP (2001) Recognition memory: what are the roles of the perirhinal cortex and hippocampus? Nat Rev Neurosci 2:51–61.

Brisch, R. et al., (2010). A morphometric analysis of the septal nuclei in schizophrenia and affective disorders: reduced neuronal density in the lateral septal nucleus in bipolar disorder. European Arch,. of Neurosceience 261m 47-58.

Brosch, T. (2007). "That baby caught my eye... attention capture by infant faces." Emotion 7(3): 685.

Bruel-Jungerman, E. et al., (2005). New neurons in the dentate gyrus are involved in the expression of enhanced long-term memory following environmental enrichment. European Journal of Neuroscience, 21, 5130521.

Brun, V. H., et al., (2008). Impaired Spatial Representation in CA1 after Lesion of Direct Input from Entorhinal Cortex. Neuron, 57, 290-302.

Cahill, L., & McGaugh, J. L. (1990). Amygdaloid complex lesions differentially affect retention of tasks using appetitive and aversive reinforcement. Behavioral Neuroscience, 104, 532-543.

Caligiuri, M. P., Heindel, W. C., & Lohr, J. B. (1992). Sensorimotor disinhibition in Parkinson's Disease: Effects of Levodopa. Annals of Neurology, 31, 53-58.

Cain, D. P. (1992). Kindling and the amygdala. In J. P. Aggleton (ed). The amygdala. New York, Wiley.

Cairns, R.B. (2007). The attachment behavior of mammals. Psychological Review, 73, 409-426.

Cajal, S. Ramon y. (1911). Histoligie du Systeme Nerveux de L'Homme et des Vertebres. Maloine, Paris (1955).

Cajal, S. Ramon y. (1954). Neuron theory or reticular theory (translated by W. U. Purkiss & C.a. Fox). Madrid.

Cao, H., et al., 2009). Activation of Extracellular Signal-Regulated Kinase in the Anterior Cingulate Cortex Contributes to the Induction and Expression of Affective Pain. The Journal of Neuroscience,29,

3307-3321

Cazakoff, B. N & Howland, J. G. (2010). Acute stress disrupts paired pulse facilitation and long-term potentiation in rat dorsal hippocampus through activation of glucocorticoid receptors. Hippocampus, 20, 1327-1331.

Cendes, F., Andermann, F., Gloor, P., et al. (2014). Relationship between atrophy of the amygdala and ictal fear in temporal lobe epilepsy. Brain, 117, 739-736.

Chadwick, M.J., et al., (2010). Decoding Individual Episodic Memory Traces in the Human Hippocampus. Current Biology, 20, 544-547.

Chang, C-C, et al., (2007). Right Anterior Cingulate Cortex Infarction and Transient Speech Aspontaneity
Archives of Neurology, 64, 442-446.

Chandler, S. H. G., Chase, M. H., & Nakamura, Y. (1980). Intracellular analysis of synaptic mechanisms controlling trigeminal motorneurons activity during sleep and wakefulness. Journal of Neurophysiology, 44, 359-371.

Chaouloff, F. (1993). Physiopharmacological interactions between stress hormones and central serotonergic systems. Brain Research Reviews, 18, 1-32.

Chapman, J. (1966). The early symptoms of schizophrenia. British Journal of Psychiatry, 12, 225-251.

Chapman, L. F., Markham, C. H., Rand, R. W., & Crandall, P. H. (2007). Memory changes induced by stimulation of the hippocampus or amygdala in epilepsy patients implanted with electrodes. Transactions of the American Neurological Association, 92, 50-56.

Chapman, L. F., & Walter, R. D. (1965). Actions of lysergic acid dienthalamid on averaged human cortical evoked rsposnes to light flash. Recent Advances in Biological Psychiatry, 7, 23-36.

Chapman, L. F., Walter, R. D., Ross, W., et al. (1963). Altered electrical activity of human hippocampus and amygdala induced by LSD-25. Physiologist, 5, 118.

Chapman, P. F., Kairiss, E. W., Keenan, C. L., & Brown, T. H. (1990). Long-term synaptic potentiation in the amygdala. Synapse, 6, 271-278.

Chapman, W. P. (1958). Studies of the periamygdaloid area in relation to human behavior. Proceedings of the Association for Research in Nervous and Mental Disease, 36, 258-277.

Chapman, W. P. (1960). Depth electrode studies in patients with temporal lobe epilepsy. In E. R. Ramey & D. S. O'Doherty (Eds.), Electrical studies on the unanesthetized brain.(pp. 334-350). New York: Hoeber.

Chapman, W.P., Livingston, R., & Livingston, K.E. (1950). The effects of lobotomy and of electrical stimulation of the orbital surface of the frontal lobe upon respiration and blood pressure in man. In M. Greenblatt, R. Arnot, & H.C. Solomon (Eds.), Studies in lobotomy. New York: Grune & Stratton.

Chapman, W.P., Schroeder, H.R., Geyer, G., Brazier, M.A. B., Fager, C., Poppen, T.L., Soloman, H.C., & Yakovlev, P.I. (1954). Physiological evidence concerning importance of the amygdaloid nuclear region in the integration of circulatory functioning and emotion and man. Science, 177, 949-951.

Charney, D., Deutch, A., Krystal, J., et al. (1993). Psychobiological mechanisms of posttraumatic stress disorder. Archives of General Psychiatry, 50, 294-305.

Charrier I, Mathevon M, Jouventin P. Vocal signature recognition of mothers by fur seal pups. Anim Behav. 2003;65:543–550.

Clugnet, M. C., & LeDoux, J. E. (1990). Synaptic plasticity in fear conditioning circuits: Induction of LTP in the lateral nucleus of the amygdala by stimulation of the medial geniculate body. Journal of Neuroscience, 10, 2818-2824.

Collingridge GL. (2003). The induction of N-methyl-D-aspartate receptor-dependent long-term potentiation. Philos Trans R Soc Lond B Biol Sci. 2003 Apr 29;358(1432):635-41.

Cushing, H. (1932). Papers relating to the pituitary body, hypothalamus, and parasympathetic nervous system. Springfield, Thomas.

Davis, M. (1984). The mammalian startle response. In R. C. Eaton (Ed)., Neural Mechanisms of Startle Behavior. New York, Plenum.

Davis, M. (1992). The amygdala and conditioned fear. In J. P. Aggleton (Ed). The Amygdala. New York, Wiley-Lis.

Davis, P. J. (1990). Repression and the inaccessibility of emotional memories. In J. L. Singer (Ed.,) Repression and Dissociaiton. Chicago. Chicago U. Press.

Davis, P.G., McEwen B.S., Pfaff, D.W. (1979). Localized behavioral effects of tritiated estradiol implants in the ventromedial hypothalamus of female rats. Endocrinology, 104, 898-903

Davis, P. H., Dambrosia, J. M., Schoenberg, B. S., et al. (1987). Annals of Neurolgoy, 22, 319-327.

Davis, J. A., & Smith, T. W. (2014). General social surveys, 1972-2014). Cumulative Code Book. Chicago, National Opinion Research Center.

Davis, M., Walker, D. L., & Lee, Y. (1997). Amygdala and bed nucleus of the stria terminalis: Differential roles in fear and anxiety measured with acoustic startle reflex. Annals of the New York Academy of Sciences, 821, 305-331.

Davison, C., & Kelman, H. (1939). Pathological laughing and crying. Archives of Neurology and Psychiatry, 42, 595-643.

DeKosky, S. T., Heilman, K. M., Bowers, D., & Valenstein, E. (1980). Recognition and discrimination of emotional faces and pictures. Brain and Language, 9, 206-214.

Delaney, R. C., Rosen, A. J., Mattson, R. H., & Novelly, R. A. (1980). Memory function in focal epilepsy: A comparison of non-surgical unilateral temporal lobe and frontal lobe samples. Cortex, 16, 103-117.

Delgado, J. (1955). Cerebral structures involved in transmission and elaboration of noxious stimulation. Journal of Neurophysiology, 18, 261-275.

Delego, J. M.R., & Anand, B. K. (1953). Increased food intake induced by electrical stimulation of the lateral hypothalamus. American Journal of Physiology, 172, 162-168.

Delgado, J.M.R., & Livingston, R.B. (1948). Some respiratory, vascular, and thermal responses from stimulation of the orbital surface of frontal lobe. Journal of Neurophysiology, 11, 39-55.

Delgado, P. L., Price, L. H., Miller, H. L., et al. (2014). Serotonin and the neurobiology of depression. Archives of General Psychiatry, 51, 865-874.

d'Elia, G., & Perris, C. (1974). Cerebral functional dominance and memory functioning. Acta Psychiatrica Scandinavica, 255, 143-157.

Delis, D. C., Robertson, L. C., & Efron, R. (1986). Hemispheric specialization of memory for visual hierarchical stimuli. Neuropsychologia, 24, 410-433.

DeLisis, L. E., Hoff, A. L., Schwartz, J. e., et al. (1991). Brain morphology in first-episode schizophrenic-like psychotic patients. Biological Psychiatry, 29, 159-175.

Deloche, G., Serion, X., Scius, G., & Segui, J. (1987). Right hemisphere language processing: Lateral difference with imageable and nonimageable ambiguous words. Brain and Language, 30, 197-205.

Douglas, R. J. (2007). The hippocampus and behavior. Psychological Bulletin, 67, 416-442.

Dudai, Y. (2004). The neurobiology of consolidations, or, how stable is the engram?. Annu. Rev. Psychol., 55 . 51–86.

Dudai Y , Eisenberg M (2004) Rites of passage of the engram: Reconsolidation and the lingering consolidation hypothesis. Neuron 44:93–100.

Dutar, P., & Nicoll, R. A. (1988). Classification of muscarinic responses in hippocampus. Journal of Neuroscience, 8, 4214-4224.

Duvernoy, H. M. et al., (2005) The Human Hippocampus: Functional Anatomy, Vascularization and Serial Sections with MRI. Springer.

Egger M.D., & Flynn, J.P. (1963). Effect of electrical stimulation of the amygdala on hypothalamically elicited attach behavior. Journal of Neurophysiology, 26, 705-720.

Ehrhardt A. K. & Baker, W. W. (1974). Fetal angrodgens, Human central nervous system differentation and behavior sex differences. In Freidman R.C. et al. (eds.), Sex differences in Behavior. New York, Wiley.

Ehrlichman, H. M., Antrobus, J. S., & Wiener, M. (2005). EEG assymetry and sleep mentation during REM and NREM. Brain and Cognition, 4, 477-485.

Ehrlichman, H., & Barrett, J. (2003). Right hemisphere specialization for mental imagery: A review of the evidence. Brain and Cognition, 2, 55-76.

Eibl-Eibesfeldt, I. (2007). Human Ethology. New York, Holt.

Eich, E. (1980). the cue-dependent nature of state-dependent memory. Memory & Cognition, 8, 157-173.

Eich, E. (1987). Theoretical issues in state-dependent memory. In Roediger, H. L., & Craik, F.I. M. (eds). Varies of Memory and Consciousness. Papers presented in honor of Endel Tulving. Erlbaum. New Jersey.

Eich, E., & Metcalfe, J. (1989). Mood dependent memory for internal versus external events. Journal of Experimental Psychology: Learning, Memory, & Cognition, 15, 443-455.

Eichenbaum. H., Otto, T., & Cohen, N. J. (2014). Two functional components of the hippocampal memory system. Behavioral & Brain Sciences, 17, 449-518.

Eimas, P. (2005). The perception of speech in early infancy. Scientific American, 252: 46-53.

Eisele, J. A., & Aram, D. M. (2014). Comprehension and imitation of syntax following early hemisphere damage. Brain and Language, 46, 212-231.

Eisenberg, N., Fabes, R. A., Miller, P. A., et al. (1989). Relation of sympathy and personal distress to prosocial behavior. Journal of Personality & Social Psychology, 57, 55-66.

Ekerot, C.-F., & Kano, M. (2005). Long-term depression of parallel fibre synapses following stimulation of climbing fibres. Brain Research, 342, 357-360.

Enoki, R., et al. (2009). Expression of Long-Term Plasticity at Individual Synapses in Hippocampus Is Graded, Bidirectional, and Mainly Presynaptic: Optical Quantal Analysis. Neuron, 62, 242-253.

Eto, K. et al., (2011). Inter-regional Contribution of Enhanced Activity of the Primary Somatosensory Cortex to the Anterior Cingulate Cortex Accelerates Chronic Pain Behavior. The Journal of Neuroscience, 31, 7631-7636.

Everitt, B. J., Morris, K. A., O'Brien, A., & Robbins, T. W. (1991). The basolateral amygdala-ventral striatal system and conditioned place preference: Further evidence of limbic striatal interactions underlying reward-related processes. Neuroscience, 42, 1-18.

Falkai, & Bogerts, B. (1986). Cell loss in hippocampus of schizophrenics. Europen Archives of Psychiatry & Neurological Science, 236, 154-161.

Fallon, J. (1981). Histochemical characterization of dopaminergic, noradrenergic and serotonergic projections to the amgydala. In Y. Ben-Ari (Ed.), the Amygdaloid Complex, pp. 175-184. Amersterdam, Elsevier.

Fallon, J., & Ceiofi, P. (1992). Distribution of monoamines within the amygdala. In J. P. Aggleton (Ed). The Amygdala. New York, Wiley-Lis.

Foley, P., & Kirschbaum, C. (2010). Human hypothalamus–pituitary–adrenal axis responses to acute psychosocial stress in laboratory settings. Neuroscience & Biobehavioral Reviews, 35, 91-96.

Foreman, N., & Stevens, R. (1987). Relationship between the superior colliculus and hippocampus. Neural and behavioral considerations. Behavioral and Brain Sciences, 10, 101-152.

Frankland, P.W. & Bontempi, B. (2005). The organization of recent and remote memories. Nat. Rev. Neurosci., 6, 119–130.

Friedman, D. P., & Murray, E. A. (1986). Thalamic connectivity of the second somatosensory area and neighboring somatosensory fields of the lateral sulcus of macaques. Journal of Comparative Neurology, 252, 348-373.

Friedman, R. C., et al. (1974). Sex differences in behavior. New York, Wiley.

Frisch, R. E. (1988). Fatness and fertility. Scientific American, 258, 70-77.

Frisk F. & Milner B. (1990). The role of the left hippocampal region in the acquistion and retention of story content. Neuropsychologia, 28, 349-359.

Frodi, A. M., & Lamb, M E. (2014). Sex differences n responsiveness to infants. Child Development, 49, 1182-1188.

Frodi, A. M., Lamb, M. E., Hwang, C. P., & Frodi, M. (1982). Father-mother-infant interaction in traditional and nontraditional Swedish families. Alternative Lifestyles, 4, 6-13.

Frost, D. O. (1990). Sensory processing by novel experimentally induced cross-modal circuits. Annal of the New York Academy of Sciences, 608, 92-112.

Frost, J. A., Binder, J. R., Springer, J. A., et al., (2016). Language processing is strongly left lateralized in both sexes. Evidence from functional MRI. Brain, 122, 199-208.

Fuchs, D., & Thelen, M. H. (1988). Children's expected interpersonal consequences of communicating their affective state and reported likelihood of expression. Child Development, 59, 1314-1322.

Fugjiwara, E. et al., (2008). Functional retrograde amnesia: A multiple case study. Cortex 2008.

Fujii, T., Fukatsu, R., Watabe, S., et al., (1990). Auditory sound agnosia without aphasia following a right temporal lobe lesion. Cortex, 26, 263-268,

Fukuda, M., Ono, T., & Nakamura, K. (1987). Functional relation among inferiotemporal cortex, amygdala and lateral hypothalamus in monkey operant feeding behavior. Journal of Neurophysiology, 57, 1060-1077.

Fukuda, M., Ono, T., & Nakamura, K. (1987). Functional relation among inferiotemporal cortex, amygdala and lateral hypothalamus in monkey operant feeding behavior. Journal of Neurophysiology, 57, 1060-1077.

Fuld, P. A., & Fisher, P. (1977). Recovery of intellectual ability after closed head injury, Developmental Medicine and Child Neurology, 19, 495-502.

Fuller, J. L. Rosvold H. E. & Pribram, K. H. (1957). Effects on affective and cognitive behavior in the dog after lesions of the pyriform-amygdaloid- hippocampal complex. Journal of Comparative and Physiological Psychology, 50, 89-96.

Fuster, J. (2008) The Prefrontal Cortex. Academic Press.

Fuster, J.M. (1980). The prefrontal cortex. Anatomy, physiology, and neuropsychology of the frontal lobes. New York: Ravens Press.

Fuster, J. M. (1995). Neuropsychiatry of frontal lobe lesions. In B.S. Fogel & R. B. Schiffer (Eds). Neuropsychiatry. Baltimore, Williams & Wilkins.

Fuster, J.M., Bauer, R.H. & Jervey, J.P. (1982). Cellular discharge in the dorsolateral prefrontal cortex of the monkey in cognitive tasks. Experimental Neurology, 77, 679-694.

Fuster, J. M., & Jevey, J. P. (1981). Inferotemporal neurons distinguish and etain behaviourally relevant features of visual stimuli, Science, 212, 952-955.

Fuxe, K. (1965). Distribution of monoamine nerve terminals in the central nervous system. Acta Physiologica Scandinavica, 64, 39-85.

Fyhn, M. et al., (2007). Hippocampal remapping and grid realignment in entorhinal cortex. Nature, 446, 190-207.

Gabriel, M., Poremba, A. L., Ellison-Perrine, C., & Miller, J. D. (1990). Brainstem mediation of learning and memory. In W. R. Klemm, & R. P. Vertes (Eds.). Brainstem mechanisms of behavior. Wiley. New York.

Gabrieli, J. D.E., Cohen, N. J., & Corkin, S. (1988). The impaired learning of semantic knowledge following bilateral medial temporal-lobe resection. Brain & Cognition, 7, 157-177.

Gabrielli, J. D., E., Desmond, J. E., Demb, J. B., et al., (1996). Functional magnetic resonance imaging of semantic memory processes in frontal lobes. Psychological Science, 7, 278-283.

Gaffan, D. (1992). Amygdala and the memory of reward. In J. P. Aggleton (ed.). The Amygdala. New York. Wiley.

Gaffan, D., & Harrison, S. (1987). Amygdalectomy and disconnection in visual learning for auditory secondary reinforcement in monkeys. Journal of Neuroscience, 7, 2285-2292.

Gaffan D., Parker A. (2000). Mediodorsal thalamic function in scene memory in rhesus monkeys. Brain 123(Pt 4), 816–827. doi: 10.1093/brain/123.4.816.

Gahwiler, B. H. (2003). The action of neuropeptides on the bioelectric activity of hippocampal neurons. In W. Seifert (Ed). Neurobiology of the Hippocampus. San Diego, Academic Press.

Gartner, A. & Frantz, D. (2010). Hippocampus: Anatomy, Functions and Neurobiology. Nova Science Pub Inc.

Gloor, P. (1955). Electrophysiological studies on the connections of the amygdaloid nucleus of the cat. I & II. Electroencephalography and Clinical Neurophysiology, 7, 223-262.

Gloor, P. (1960). Amygdala. In J. Field (Ed.), Handbook of physiology (pp. 300-370). Washington, D. C. American Physiological Society.

Gloor, P. (1972). Temporal lobe epilepsy. In B. E. Elftheriou (Ed.), The neurobiology of the amygdala. New York: Plenum.

Gloor, P. (1986). The role of the human limbic system in in perception, memory, and affect. Lessons from temporal lobe epilepsy. In B. K. Doane, & K. E. Livingston (Eds.). The Limbic System: Functional organization and Clinical Disorder. New York, Raven Press.

Gloor, P. (1990). Experiential phenomena of temporal lobe epilepsy. Brain, 113, 1673-1694.

Gloor, P. (1992). Role of the amygdala in temporal lobe epilepsy. In J. P. Aggleton (Ed.). The Amygdala. New York, Wiley-Liss.

Gloor, P. (1997). The Temporal Lobes and Limbic System. Oxford University Press. New York.

Gloor, P., Olivier, A., Quesney, L. F., et al. (1982). The role of the limbic system in experimental phenomena of temporal lobe epilepsy. Annals of Neurology, 12, 129-144.

Gonzalez-Lima, F. (2010). Responses of limbic, midbrain and brainstem structures to electrically-induced vocalizations. Handbook of Behavioral Neuroscience, 19, 293-301.

Hage, S. R. (2010). Neuronal networks involved in the generation of vocalization. Handbook of Behavioral Neuroscience, 19, 339-349.

Hales, J. B. & Brewer, J. B. (2011). The timing of associative memory formation: frontal lobe and anterior medial temporal lobe activity at associative binding predicts memory. Journal of Neurophysiology, 105, 1454-1463.

Halgren, E. (1981). The amygdala contribution to emotion and memory. In Y. Ben-Ari (ed.), The Amygdaloid Complex. Amsterdam, Elsevier.

Halgren, E. (1992). Emotional neurophysiology of the amygdala within the context of human cognition. In J. P. Aggleton (Ed.). The Amygdala. New York, Wiley-Liss.

Halgren, E., et al. (2014). Activity of human hippocampal formation and amygdala neurons during memory tests. Electroencephalography and Clinical Neurophysiology, 45, 585-601.

Halgren, E., Walter, R. D., Cherlow, D. G., & Crandal, P. H. (2014). Mental phenomenoa evoked by electrical stimualtion of the human hippocampal formation and amygdala, Brain, 101, 83-117.

Hall, G. S. (1899) Note on early memories. Pedagogical Seminary, 6, 485-512.

Hall, J. (2014). Gender effects in decoding nonverbal cues. Psychological Review, 85, 845-857.

Hallett, T., & Proctor, A. (1996). Maturation of the central nervous system as related to communication and cognitive development. Infants & Young Children, 8, 1-15.

Hardt, O. et al., (2010). PKMζ maintains 1-day- and 6-day-old long-term object location but not object identity memory in dorsal hippocampus. Hippocampus, 20, 691-695.

Hartley, T. et al., (2007). The hippocampus is required for short-term topographical memory in humans. Hippocampus, 17, 34-48.

Heath, R. (1954). Studies in schizophrenia. Cambridge. Harvard University Press.

Heath, R. G. (1964). Pleasure response of human subjects to direct stimulation of the brain. In R. G. Heath (Ed.). The Role of Pleasure in Behavior. New York, Harper.

Heath, R. G. (1972). Physiological basis of emotional expression. Biological Psychiatry, 5, 172-184.

Heath, R. G. (1976). Brain function in epilepsy: Midbrain, medullary and cerebral interaction with the rostral forebrain. Journal of Neurology, Neurosurgery, and Psychiatry, 39, 1037-1051.

Heath, R. G. (1977). Modulation of emotion with a brain pacemaker. Journal of Nervous and Mental Disease, 165, 300-317.

Heath, R. G., Franklin, D. E., Walker, C. F., & Keating, J. W. (1982). Cerebellar vermal atrophy in psychiatric patients. Biological Psychiatry, 17, 569-583.

Heath, R. G., & Harper, J. W. (1974). Ascending projections of the cerebellar fastigial nucleus to the hippocampus, amygdala, and other temporal lobe sites. Experimental Neurology, 45, 268-287.

Heath, R. G., Monroe, R., & Mickle, W. (1955). Stimulation of the amygdaloid nucleus in schizophrenic patients. American Journal of Psychiatry, 111, 862-863.

Hebb. D. O. (1949). The organization of behavior. New York. Wiley.

Herrick, C.J. (1925). The amphibian forebrain. Journal of Comparative Neurology, 39, 400-489.

Herschkowitz, N., Kagan, J., & Zilles, K. (1997). Neurobiological bases of behavioral development in the first year. Neuropediatrics, 28, 296-306.

Herzog, A. G., & Kemper, T. L. (1980). Amygdaloid changes in aging and dementia. Archives of Neurology, 37, 625-629.

Herzog, A. G., & Van Hoesen, G. W. (1976). Temporal neocortical afferent connections in the amygdala in the rhesus monkey. Brain Research, 115, 57-59.

Herzog, M. & Hopf, S. (1984). Behavioral response to species-specific warning calls in infant squirrel monkeys reared in social isolation. American Journal of Primatology, 7, 99-106.

Hess, E. H. (1959). Imprintng an effect of early experience. Science, 130, 1959, 133-141.

Hetherington, A. W., & Ranson, S. W. (1940). Hypothalamic lesions and adiposity in the rat. Anatomical Record. 78. 149-172.

Hitchcock, J., & Davis, M. (1987). Fear-potentiated startle using an auditory conditioned stimulus: Effect of lesions on the amygdala. Physiology & Behavior, 10, 403-408.

Hitchcock, J. M., & Davis, M. (1991). Efferent pathway of the amygdala involved in conditioned fear as measured with the fear-potentiated startle paradim. Behavioral Neuroscience, 105, 826-842.

Hoff, E. & Shatz, M. (2009). Blackwell Handbook of Language Development. Wiley-Blackwell.

Humphrey, T. (1972). The development of the human amygdaloid complex. In B.E. Elefterhiou (Ed.) The neurobiology of the amygdala. New York: Plenum Press.

Jonides J, Lewis RL, Nee DE, Lustig CA, Berman MG, Moore KS (2008) The mind and brain of short-term memory. Annu Rev Psychol 59:193–224.

Joseph, R., Hess, S., & Birecree, E. (2014). Effects of sex hormone manipulations on exploration and sex differences in maze learning. Behavioral Biology, 24, 364-377,

Joseph, R., & Casagrande, V. A. (2014). Visual field defects and morphological changes resulting from monocular deprivation in primates. Proceedings of the Society for Neuroscience, 4, 1982, 2021.

Joseph, R. (1979). Effects of rearing environment and sex on learning, memory, and competitive exploration. Journal of Psychology, 101, 37-43.

Joseph, R. & Casagrande, V. A. (2014). Visual field defects and recovery following lid closure in a prosimian primate. Behavioral Brain Research, 1, 150-178.

Joseph, R., & Gallagher, R. E. (1980). Gender and early environmental influences on learning, memory, activity, overresponsiveness, and exploration. journal of Developmental Psychobiology, 13, 527-544.

Joseph, R., Forrest, N., Fiducia, N., Como, P., & Siegel, J. (1980). Electrophysiological and behavioral correlates of arousal. Physiological Psychology, 9, 90-95.

Joseph, R. (1982). The Neuropsychology of Development. Hemispheric Laterality, Limbic Language, the Origin of Thought. Journal of Clinical Psychology, 44 4-33.

Joseph, R. (1984). La Neuropsiciologia Del Desarrollo: Lateralidad, Hemisferica, Lenguaje Limbico, y el Origen del pensamiento. Archives of Psychiatry and Neurology, Venezolanos, 30, 25-52.

Joseph, R., Gallagher, R., E., Holloway, J., & Kahn, J. (1984). Two brains, one child: Interhemispheric transfer and confabulation in children aged 4, 7, 10. Cortex, 20, 317-331.

Joseph, R., & Gallagher, R. E. (2005). Interhemispheric transfer and the completion of reversible operations in non-conserving children. Journal of Clinical Psychology, 41, 796-800.

Joseph, R. (1986). Reversal of language and emotion in a corpus callosotomy patient. Journal of Neurology, Neurosurgery, & Psychiatry, 49, 628-634.

Joseph, R. (1986). Confabulation and delusional denial: Frontal lobe and lateralized influences. Journal of Clinical Psychology, 42, 845-860.

Joseph, R. (1988) The Right Cerebral Hemisphere: Emotion, Music, Visual-Spatial Skills, Body Image, Dreams, and Awareness. Journal of Clinical Psychology, 44, 630-673.

Joseph, R. (1988). Dual mental functioning in a split-brain patient. Journal of Clinical Psychology, 44, 770-779.

Joseph, R. (1990). Neuropsychology, Neuropsychiatry, Behavioral Neurology, Plenum, New York.

Joseph, R. (1990). The right cerebral hemisphere. Emotion, music, visual-spatial skills, body image, dreams, awareness. In A. E. Puente and C. R. Reynolds (series editors). Critical Issues in Neuropsychology. Neuropsychology, Neuropsychiatry, Behavioral Neurology. Plenum, New York.

Joseph, R. (1990). The left cerebral hemisphere. Aphasia, alexia, agraphia, agnosia, apraxia, language and thought. In A. E. Puente and C. R. Reynolds (series editors). Critical Issues in Neuropsychology. Neuropsychology, Neuropsychiatry, Behavioral Neurology. Plenum, New York.

Joseph, R. (1990). The limbic system. Emotion, laterality, unconscious mind. In A. E. Puente and C. R. Reynolds (series editors). Critical Issues in Neuropsychology. Neuropsychology, Neuropsychiatry, Behavioral Neurology. Plenum, New York.

Joseph, R. (1990). The Frontal Lobes. In A. E. Puente and C. R. Reynolds (series editors). Critical Issues in Neuropsychology. Neuropsychology, Neuropsychiatry, Behavioral Neurology. Plenum, New York.

Joseph, R. (1990). The Temporal Lobes. In A. E. Puente and C. R. Reynolds (series editors). Critical Issues in Neuropsychology. Neuropsychology, Neuropsychiatry, Behavioral Neurology. Plenum, New York.hology. Neuropsychology, Neuropsychiatry, Behavioral Neurology. Plenum, New York.

Joseph, R. (1990). Cerebral and cranial trauma. In A. E. Puente & C. R. Reynolds (series editors). Critical Issues in Neuropsychology. Neuropsychology, Neuropsychiatry, Behavioral Neurology. Plenum, New York.

Joseph, R. (1992) The Limbic System: Emotion, Laterality, and Unconscious Mind. The Psychoanalytic Review, 79, 405-456.

Joseph, R. (1992). The Right Brain and the Unconscious. New York, Plenum.

Joseph, R. (1993). The Naked Neuron: Evolution and the Languages of the Body and Brain. New York, Plenum Press.

Joseph, R. (2014) The limbic system and the foundations of emotional experience. In V. S. Ramachandran (Ed). Encyclopedia of Human Behavior. San Diego, Academic Press.

Joseph, R. (1996). Neuropsychiatry, Neuropsychology, Clinical Neuroscience, 2nd Edition. 21 chapters, 864 pages. Williams & Wilkins, Baltimore.

Joseph, R. (1998). The limbic system. In H.S. Friedman (ed.), Encyclopedia of Human health, Academic Press. San Diego.

Joseph, R. (1998). Traumatic amnesia, repression, and hippocampal injury due to corticosteroid and enkephalin secretion. Child Psychiatry and Human Development. 29, 169-186.

Joseph, R. (1998). Flavonoid substance and/or flavone glycosides substance as a treatment for disorders of the brain. United States Department of Commerce: Patent & Trademark Office, March, # 60/080,768.

Joseph, R. (1998). Combined use of Ginko Biloba and Hypericum Perforatum (Saint John's Wort) as a treatment for disorders of the brain. United States Department of Commerce: Patent & Trademark Office, March, # 60/080,769.

Joseph, R. (1998). Olfactory substance and stem cells as a treatment for disorders of the brain. United States Department of Commerce: Patent & Trademark Office, March, # 60/080,770.

Joseph, R. (2016). Frontal lobe psychopathology: Mania, depression, aphasia, confabulation, catatonia, perseveration, obsessive compulsions, schizophrenia. journal of Psychiatry, 62, 138-172.

Joseph, R. (2016). Environmental influences on neural plasticity, the limbic system, and emotional development and attachment, Child Psychiatry and Human Development. 29, 187-203.

Joseph, R. (2016). The neurology of traumatic "dissociative" amnesia. Commentary and literature review. Child Abuse & Neglect. 23, 715-727Joseph, R. (2000). Female Sexuality: The Naked Truth. University Press California.

Joseph, R. (2000). Limbic language/language axis theory of speech. Behavioral and Brain Sciences. 23, 439-441.

Joseph, R. (2000). Fetal brain behavioral cognitive development. Developmental Review, 20, 81-98.

Joseph, R. (2000). The evolution of sex differences in language, sexuality, and visual spatial skills. Archives of Sexual Behavior, 29, 35-66.

Joseph, R. (2001). Biological Substances to Induce Sexual Arousal and as a Treatment for Sexual Dysfunction. United States Department of Commerce: Patent & Trademark Office, January 12, 2001 #60/260,910.

Joseph, R. (2001). Biological Substances to Induce Sexual Arousal, Sexual Behavior, Ovulation, Pregnancy, and Treatment for Sexual Dysfunction. United States Department of Commerce: Patent & Trademark Office, February # 60/.

Joseph, R. (2001). Clinical Neuroscience, 34 chapters, 1,500 pages. Academic Press.

Joseph, R. (2001). The Limbic System and the Soul: Evolution and the Neuroanatomy of Religious Experience. Zygon, the Journal of Religion & Science, 36, 105-136.

Joseph, R. (2002). Biological Substances to Induce Sexual Arousal and as a Treatment for Sexual Dysfunction. Patent Pending: United States Department of Commerce: Patent & Trademark Office, February, 2002 #10/047,906

Joseph, R. (2002/2003). NeuroTheology: Brain, Science, Spirituality, Religious Experience. University Press.

Joseph, R. (2003). Emotional Trauma and Childhood Amnesia. journal of Consciousness & Emotion, 4, 151-178.

Joseph, R. (2011). Origins of Thought: Consciousness, Language, Egocentric Speech and the Multiplicity of Mind "The Universe and Consciousness", Edited by Sir Roger Penrose, FRS, Ph.D., & Stuart Hameroff, Ph.D. Science Publishers, Cambridge, MA.

Joseph, R. (2011). Dreams and Hallucinations: Lifting the Veil to Multiple Perceptual Realities "The Universe and Consciousness", Edited by Sir Roger Penrose, FRS, Ph.D., & Stuart Hameroff, Ph.D. Science Publishers, Cambridge, MA.

Jurgens, U. (2009). The Neural Control of Vocalization in Mammals: A Review. Journal of Voice, 23, 1-10.

Jurgens, U. (1979). Neural control of vocalization in non-human primates. In: Neurobiology of social communication in primates. ed. H. D. Steklis & M. J. Raleigh. Academic Press.

Jurgens, U. (1987). Primate communication: Signalling, vocalizaton. In: ed. G. Adelman. Encyclopedia of Neuroscience. Birkhauser.

Jurgens, U. (1990). Vocal communication in primates. In Kesner, R. P. & Olton, D. S. (eds.). Neurobiology of Comparative Cognition. New Jersey, Erlbaum.

Jurgens, U. (2014). The role of the periaqueductal gray in vocal behaviour. Behavioral Brain Research, 62: 107-117.

Jurgens, U., Kirzinger, A. & von Cramon, D. (1982). The effects of deep-reaching lesions in the cortical face area on phonation. A combined case report and experimental monkey study. Cortex, 18, 125-140.

Jurgens, U., & Muller-Preuss, P. (1977). Convergent projections of different limbic vocalization areas in the squirrel monkey. Experimental Brain Research, 29, 75-83.

Kaada, B. R. (1951). Somato-motor, autonomic and electrocortical responses to electrical stimulation of rhincephalon and other structures in primates, cat, and dog. Acta Physiologica Scandinavica, 24, 1-170.

Kaada, B.R. (1972). Cingulate, posterior orbital, anterior insular and temporal pole cortex. In J. Field, H.W. Magoun, & V.A. Hall (Eds.), Handbook of Physiology, Vol. II. (pp. 1345-1372). Washington, D.C.: American Physiological Society.

Kaada, B. R., Jansen, J., & Andersen, P. (1953). Stimulation of hippocampus and medial cortical areas in unanesthetized cats. Neurology, 3, 844-857.

Kapp, B. C., Whalen, P. J., Supple, W. F., & Pascoe, J. P. (1992). Amygdala contributions to conditioned arousal and sensory information processing. In J. P. Aggleton (Ed). The Amygdala. New York, Wiley-Lis.

Kapp, B. S., Supple, W. F., & Whalen, P. J. (2014). Effects of electrical stimulation of the amygdaloid central nucleus on neocortical arousal in the rabbit. Behavioral Neuroscience, 108, 81-93.

Katche,C. et al., (2010). Delayed wave of c-Fos expression in the dorsal hippocampus involved specifically in persistence of long-term memory storage. PNAS, 107, 349-354.

Kawashima, R., Sugiura, M., Kato, T., et al., (2016). The human amygdala plays an important role in gaze monitoring. Brain, 122, 779-783.

Kelsey, J. E., & Arnold, S. R. (2014). Lesions of the dorsomedial amygdala, but not the nucleus accumbens, reduce the aversiveness of morphine withdrawal in rats. Behavioral Neuroscience, 108, 1119-1127.

Kensinger, E. A. et al., (2011). Amygdala activity at encoding corresponds with memory vividness and with memory for select episodic details. Neuropsychologia, 49, 663-673.

Kesner, R. P. (1992). Learning and memory in rats with an emphasis on the role of the amygdala. In J. P. Aggleton (Ed.). The Amygdala. New York, Wiley-Liss.

Kesner, R.B., & Andrus, R.G. (1982). Amygdala stimulation disrupts the magnitude of reinforcement contribution to long-term memory. Physiological Psychology, 10, 55-59.

Kesner, R. P., & DiMattia, B. V. (1987). Neurobiology of an attribute model of memory. In A. N. Epstein & A. R. Morrison (Eds.), Progress in Psychobiology and Physiological Psychology. San Diego, Academic Press.

Kester, D. B., Saykin, A. J., Sperling, M.R., et al. (1991). Acute effect of anterior temporal lobectomy on musical processing. Neuropsychologia, 29, 703-708.

Kilhstrom, J. F., & Harackiewiz, J. M. (1982). The earliest recollection: A new survey. Journal of Personality, 50, 134-148.

Kilhstrom, J. F., Schacter, D. L., Cork, R. C., et al. (1990). Implicit and explicit memory following surgical anesthesia. Psychological Science, 1, 303-306.

Kilpatrick, D. G., Veronen, L . J., & Best, C. L. (2005). Factors predicting psychological distress among rape victims. In C. R. Figely (Ed.). Trauma and Its Wake. New York, Brunner/Mazel.

Kim, J. J., & Fanselow, M. S. (1992). Modality-specfic retrograde amnesia of fear. Science, 256, 675-677.

Kim, S. et al. (2011). Memory, Visual Discrimination Performance, and the Human Hippocampus. Journal of Neuroscience, 31, 2624-2629.

Kitamura, T. et al. (2009) Adult neurogenesis and modulation of neural circuit function, Cell, 139, 814-827.

Klemm W. R. (1990). Behavioral Inhibition. In W. R. Klemm, & R. P. Vertes (Eds.). Brainstem mechanisms of behavior. Wiley. New York.

Klemm, W. R. (1990). The behavioral readiness response. In W. R. Klemm, & R. P. Vertes (Eds.). Brainstem mechanisms of behavior. Wiley. New York.

Kling, A. (1972). Effects of amygdalectomy on social-affective behavior in non-human primates. In B. E. Eleftherious (Ed.). The Neurobiology of the amygdala (pp 127-170). New York, Plenum.

Kling. A. S. & Brothers, L. A. (1992). The amygdala and social behavior. In J. P. Aggleton (Ed.). The Amygdala. New York, Wiley-Liss.

Kling, A. S., Lloyd, R. L., & Perryman, K. M. (1987). Slow wave changes in amygdala to visual, auditory and social stimuli following lesions of the inferior temporal cortex in squirrel monkey. Behavioral and Neural Biology, 47, 54-72.

Kling, A., & Mass, R. (1974). Alterations of social behavior with neural lesions in nonhuman primates. In B. Holloway (Ed.) Primate aggression, territoriality, and zenophobia, (pp. 361-386). New York: Academic Press.

Kling, A., & Steklis, H.D. (1976). A neural substrate for affiliative behavior in nonhuman primates.

Brain Behavior and Evolution. 13, 216-238.

Klinger, J., & Gloor, P. (1960). The connections of the amygdala and of the anterior temporal cortex in the human brain. Journal of Comparative Neurology, 115, 333-352.

Krettek, J. E., & Price, J. L. (1974). A direct input from the amygdala to the thalamus and the cerebral cortex. Brain Research, 67, 169-174.

Krettek, J.E., & Price, J.L. (1977). Projections from the amygdaloid complex. Journal of Comparative Neurology, 172, 723-752, 687-722.

Krettek, J.E., & Price, J.L. (2014). Amygdala. Journal of Comparative Neurology, 178, 225-254, 255-280.

Krystal, H. (1988). Integration and Self-Healing. Hillsdale, NJ, The Analytic Press.

Krystal, J. H. (1990). Animals models for post traumatic stress disorder. In E. I. Giller, jr. (Ed). Biological Assessment and Treatment of Postraumatic Stress Disorder. Washington: American Psychiatric Press.

Kudielka, B. M., & Wust, S. (2010). Human models in acute and chronic stress: Assessing determinants of individual hypothalamus–pituitary–adrenal axis activity. Stress, 13, 1-14.

Kuehn, L. (1974). Looking down a gun barrel. Perceptual and Motor Skills, 39, 1159-1164.

Kuhar, M. (2015). Cholinergic neurons: septal-hippocampal relationships. In R. L. Isaacson & K. H. Pribram (Eds.). The Hippocampus, pp. 269-283. New York, Plenum.

Kuhar, M. J. (1980). Opioid peptides and receptors in the rat brainstem. In J. A,. Hobson, & M. A. B. Brazier (eds). The reticular formation revisited. Raven Press. New York.

Kuhl, P. K., & Meltzoff, A. N. (1982). Speech as an intermodal object of perception. In A. Yonas (Ed.), The Minnesota Symposium on Child Psychology, (Vol., 20, pp. 235-266). Hillsdale, NJ: Erlbaum.

Kullmann, D. M., & Lamsa, K. P. (2007). Long-term synaptic plasticity in hippocampal interneurons. Nat Rev Neurosci. 2007 Sep;8(9):687-99.

Kumaran D, Maguire EA (2007) Which computational mechanisms operate in the hippocampus during novelty detection? Hippocampus 17:735–748.

Kuraoka, K., & Nakamura, K. (2006). Responses of Single Neurons in Monkey Amygdala to Facial and Vocal Emotions. Journal of Neurophysiology, 97, 1379-1387.

Lang, C., et al., (2004). Transient expansion of synaptically connected dendritic spines upon induction of hippocampal long-term potentiation.Proc Natl Acad Sci. 101(47):16665-70

Lang, S. et al., (2009). Context conditioning and extinction in humans: differential contribution of the hippocampus, amygdala and prefrontal cortex. European Journal of Neuroscience, 29, 823–832.

LeDoux, J. E. (1992). Emotion and the amygdala. In J. P. Aggleton (Ed.). The Amygdala. New York, Wiley-Liss.

LeDoux, J. E. (1996). The emotional brain. New York: Simon & Schuster.

Leibenluft E, et al., (2004).Mothers' neural activation in response to pictures of their children and other children. Biol Psychiatry. 2004 Aug 15;56(4):225-32.

Less, R.S-K, et al. (2009). Activation of CaMKII in single dendritic spines during long-term potentiation. Nature, 458, 299–304.

Lin, D. et al., (2011). Functional identification of an aggression locus in the mouse hypothalamus. Nature 470, 221–226.

Lisman, J. E. & Grace, A. A. (2005). The Hippocampal-VTA Loop: Controlling the Entry of Information into Long-Term Memory. Neuron, 46,703-713.

Lorberbaum JP, et al. (2016). Feasibility of using fMRI to study mothers responding to infant cries. Depress Anxiety. 2016;10(3):99-104.

Lorberbaum JP, et al. (2002) A potential role for thalamocingulate circuitry in human maternal behavior. Biol Psychiatry. 2002 Mar 15;51(6):431-45.

MacLean, P.D. (1949). Psychosomatic disease and the "visceral brain". Recent developments bearing on the Papex theory of emotion. Psychosomatic Medicine, 11, 338-353.

MacLean, P. (1969). The hypothalamus and emotional behavior, in The Hypothalamus. Edited by Haymaker W. Springfield, Thomas.

MacLean, P. (1973). New findings on brain function and sociosexual behavior, in Contemporary Sexual Behavior. Edited by Zubin J, Money J. Baltimore, John Hopkins Press.

MacLean, P. (1990). The Evolution of the Triune Brain. New York, Plenum.

MacLean, P. D. and J. D. Newman (1988). "Role of midline frontolimbic cortex in production of the isolation call of squirrel monkeys." Brain Research 450(1-2): 111-123.

Maggio, N. & Segal, M. (2011). Persistent Changes in Ability to Express Long-Term Potentiation/

Depression in the Rat Hippocampus After Juvenile/Adult Stress. Biological Psychiatry, 69, 748-753.

Magnuson, D. J., & Gray, T. S. (1990). Central nucleus of amygdala and bed nucleus of stria terminalis projections to serotonin or tyrosine hydroxylase immunoreactive cells in the dorsal and median raphe nucleus in the rat. Society of Neuroscience Abstracts, 16, 121.

Magnusson, A., & Stefansson, J. G. (1993). Prevalence of seasonal affective disorder in Iceland. Archives of General Psychiatry, 50, 941-946.

Mann, D. M. A. (1992). The neuropathology of the amygdala in ageing and in dementia. In J. P. Aggleton (Ed.). The Amygdala. (Wiley. New York) .

Manteuffel, G. et al., (2007). Acetylcholine injection into the amygdala elicits vocalization in domestic pigs (Sus scrofa). Behavioural Brain Research, 178, 177-180

Majdic, G. & Tobet, S. (2011). Cooperation of sex chromosomal genes and endocrine influences for hypothalamic sexual differentiation. Frontiers in Neuroendocrinology, 32, 137-145.

Mark, V.H., Ervin, F.R., & Sweet, W.H. (1972). Deep temporal lobe stimulation in man. In B.E. Eleftheriou (Ed.), The Neurobiology of the Amygdala, New York: Plenum Press.

Mark, V. H., Sweet, W. H., & Erwin, F. R. (1972). The effect of amygdalectomy on violent behavior in patients with temporal lobe epilepsy. In E. R. Hitchcock, L. Laitinen, & K. Vaernet (Eds.). Psychosurgery. Springfield, Thomas.

Marshal, L. & Born, J. (2007). The contribution of sleep to hippocampus-dependent memory consolidation. Trends in Cognitive Sciences, 11, 442-450.

McDonald, A. J. (1992). Cell types and intrinsic connections of the amygdala. In J. P. Aggleton (ed.). The Amygdala. New York, Wiley.

McGaugh JL (2000) Memory—a century of consolidation. Science 287:248–251.

Meck, W. H., Church, R. M., & Olton, D. S. (1984). Hippocampus, time, and memory. Behavioral Neuroscience, 98, 3-22.

Mehler, W.R. (1980). Subcortical afferent connections of the amygdala in the monkey. Journal of Comparative Neurology, 190, 733-762.

Milanski, M., et al., (2009). Saturated Fatty Acids Produce an Inflammatory Response Predominantly through the Activation of TLR4 Signaling in Hypothalamus: Implications for the Pathogenesis of Obesity. The Journal of Neuroscience, 14 January 2009, 29(2): 359-370.

Mishkin, M. (1964). Perseveration of central sets after frontal lesions in monkeys. In J. M. Warren & K. Akert (Eds.), The frontal granular cortex and behavior. (pp 219-241). New York: McGraw-Hill.

Mishkin, M. (1972). Cortical visual areas and their interaciton. In A. G. Karczman & J. C. Eccles (Eds.), Brain and human behavior. Berlin: Spinrger-Verlag.

Mishkin, M. (2014). Memory in monkeys severely impaired by combined but not by separate removal of amygdala and hippocampus. Nature, 273, 297-299.

Mishkin, M. (1982). A memory system in the monkey. Philosophical Transactions of he Royal Society of London, 298, 85-92.

Mishkin, M. (1990). Cerebral memory circuits. In Y. Honshai (ed.), Perception, Cognition, & the Brain, Ykult Honsha Co, Tokyo.

Mishkin, M., Malamut, B., & Backevalier, J. (1984). Memories and habits: Two neural systems. In G. Lynch, J. L., McGaugh, & M. N. Weinberger (Eds), Neurobiology of Learning and Memory. New York, Guilford.

Mishkin, M., & Pribram, K. H. (1956). Analysis of the effects of frontal lesion in monkeys, II. Variation of delayed response. Journal of Comparative and Physiological Psychology, 49, 36-40.

Mitchell A. S., Dalrymple-Alford J. C. (2005). Dissociable memory effects after medial thalamus lesions in the rat. Eur. J. Neurosci. 22, 973–985.

Mitchell A. S., et al. (2007a). Dissociable performance on scene learning and strategy implementation after lesions to magnocellular mediodorsal thalamic nucleus. J. Neurosci. 27, 11888–11895.

Morris, J. S., Frith, C. D., Perett, D. I., Rowland, D., Young, A. W., Calder, A. J., & Colan, R. J. (1996). A differential neural response in the human amygdala to fearful and happy facial expression. Nature, 383, 812-815.

Morris RG (2003) Long-term potentiation and memory. Philos Trans R Soc London Ser B 358:643–647.

Morrison, J. H., & Foote, S. L. (1986). Noradrenergic and serotonergic innervation of cortical, thalamic, and tectal visual structures in Old and New World Monkeys. Journal of Comparative Neurology, 243, 117-138.

Morrison, J. H., Hof, P. R., Campbell, M. J., et al. (1990). Cellular pathology in Alzheimer's disease. In S.R. Rapoport, et al. (eds.) Imaging, Cerebral Topography and Alzheimer's disease. New York, Springer.

Motta, S. C. et al., (2009). Dissecting the brain's fear system reveals the hypothalamus is critical for responding in subordinate conspecific intruders. PNAS, 106, 12 4870-4875.

Murphy, G. M., Inger, P., Mark, K., et al., (1987). Volumetric asymmetry in the human amygdaloid complex. Journal of Hirnforsch, 28, 281-289.

Murray, E. A. (1992). Medial temporal lobe structures contributing to recognition memory: The amygdaloid complex versus rhinal cortex. In J. P. Aggleton (Ed.). The Amygdala. New York, Wiley-Liss.

Murray, E. A., & Gaffan, D. (2014). Removal of the amygdala plus subjacent cortex disrupts the retention of both intramodal and crossmodal associative memories in monkeys. Behavioral Neuroscience, 108, 494-500.

Murray, E. A., & Mishkin, M. (2005). Amygdalectomy impairs cross modal associations in monkeys. Science, 228, 604-606.

Nadel, L. (1991). The hippocampus and space revisited. Hippocampus, 1, 221-229.

Nakamura, K., & Ono, T. (1986). Lateral hypothalamus neuron involvement in integration of natural and artifical rewards and cue signals. Journal of Neurophysiology, 55, 163-181.

Nakamura, K., Matsumoto, K., Mikami, A., & Kubota, K. (2014). Visual response properties of single neurons in the temporal pole of behaving monkeys. Journal of Neurophysiology, 71, 1206-140.

Nakazima, S. (1980). The reorganization process of babbling. In T. Murray & J. Murry (Eds.), Infant communication: Cry and early speech. (pp. 272-283). Houston: College-Hill.

Namy, L. L., & Waxman, S. R. (1998). Words and gestures: Infants' interpretations of different forms of symbolic reference. Child Development, 69, 295-308.

Nannis, E. D. & Cowan, P.A. (1987). Emotional understanding: A matter of age, dimension, and point of view. Journal of Applied Developmental Psychology, 8, 289-304.

Nahum, L. et al., (2011)., Rapid consolidation and the human hippocampus: Intracranial recordings confirm surface EEG. Hippocampus, 21, 689-693.

N'Diaye, K. et al., (2009). Self-relevance processing in the human amygdala: Gaze direction, facial expression, and emotion intensity. Emotion, 9, 798-806.

Nee, D. E. & Jonides, J. (2011). Dissociable contributions of prefrontal cortex and the hippocampus to short-term memory: Evidence for a 3-state model of memory. Neuroimage, 54, 1540-1548.

Newman JD. The primate isolation call: a comparison with precocial birds and non-primate mammals. In: Rogers LJ, Kaplan G, editors. Comparative Vertebrate Cognition: Are Primates Superior to Non-Primates? New York: Kluwer Academic/Plenum Publishers; 2004. pp. 171–187.pp. 171–187.

Newman, J. D. (2007). Neural circuits underlying crying and cry responding in mammals. Behavioural Brain Research, 182, 155-165.

Newman, J. D. (2010). Evolution of the communication brain in control of mammalian vocalization. Handbook of Behavioral Neuroscience, 19, 23-28.

Newman JD, Bachevalier J. (1997) Neonatal ablations of the amygdala and inferior temporal cortex alter the vocal response to social separation in rhesus macaques. Brain Res. ;758:180–186.

Niehoff, D. L., & Kuhar, M. J. (2003). Benzodiapine receptors: Localization in the rat amygdala. Journal of Neuroscience, 3, 2091-2097.

Nielsen JM, Sedgwick RP. (1949). Instincts and emotions in an anencephalic monster. J Nerv Ment Dis. 1949;110:387–394.

Nishitani, N., Ikeda, A., Nagamine, T., et al., (2016). The role of the hippocampus in auditory processing studied by event-related electrical potentials and magnetic fields in epilepsy patients before and after temporal lobectomy. Brain, 122, 687-707.

Nishijo, H., Ono, T., & Nishino, H. (1988). Topographic distribution of modality-specific amygdalar neurons in alert monkey. Journal of Neuroscience, 8, 3556-3569.

Nitschke, J. B. et al., (2009). Anticipatory Activation in the Amygdala and Anterior Cingulate in Generalized Anxiety Disorder and Prediction of Treatment Response. Am J Psychiatry, 166, 302-310.

Norman KA, O'Reilly RC (2003) Modeling hippocampal and neocortical contributions to recognition memory: a complementary-learning-systems approach. Psychol Rev 110:611–646.

Numan M, Sheehan TP. (1997). Neuroanatomical circuitry for mammalian maternal behavior. Ann N Y Acad Sci. 1997 Jan 15;807:101-25.

Okada, D, et al. (2009) Input-specific spine entry of soma-derived Vesl-1S protein conforms to synaptic tagging. Science, 324 (904–909.

O'Keefe, J. (1976). Place units in the hippocampus of the freely moving rat. Experimental Neurology, 51, 78-109.

O'Keefe, J., & Bouma, H. (1969). Complex sensory properties of certain amygdala units in the freely moving cat. Experimental Neurology, 23, 384-398.

O'Keefe, J. & Bouma, H. (1969). Complex sensory properties of certain amygdala units in the freely moving cat. Experimental Neurology, 23, 384-398.

Olds, J.A. (1956). A preliminary mapping of electrical reinforcing effects in rat brain. Journal of Comparative and Physiological Psychology, 49, 281-285.

Olds, J. A. & Milner, P. (1954). Positive reinforcement produced by electrical stimulation of septal areas and other regions of the rat brain. Journal of Comparative and Physiological Psychology, 47, 419-427.

Olds, M.E., & Forbes, J.L. (1981). The central basis of motivation: intracranial self-stimulation studies. Annual Review of Psychology, 32, 523-574.

Olmstead, C.E., Best, P.J., & Mays, L.W. (1973). Neural activity in the dorsal hippocampus during paradoxical sleep, slow wave sleep and waking. Brain Research, 60, 381-391.

Olmstead, C. E., Best, P. J., & Mays, L. E. (1973) Neural activity in the dorsal hippocampus during paradoxical sleep, slow wave sleep and waking. Brain Research, 60, 381-391.

Oller, D. K., & Lynch, M. P. (1992). Infant vocalizations and innovation in infraphonology: Toward a broader theory of development and disorders. In C. A. Ferguson, L. Menn, & C. Stoel-Gammon (Eds.), Phonological development: models, research, implications. Academic Press, New York.

Oller, D.K. (1980). The emergence of sounds of speech in infancy. In G. H. Yeni-Komshian, J. F. Kavanagh, & C. A. Ferguson (Eds.), Child phonology, (Vol. 1. pp. 21-35). New York: Academic Press.

Ommaya, A. K., Fass, F., & Yarnell, P. (1968). Whiplash injury and brain damage: An experimental study. Journal of the American Medical Assoation, 204, 285-289.

Ommaya, A. K., et al. (1971). Coup and contrecoup injury. Journal of Neurosurgery, 35, 503-516

O'Neil, J. M. (1982). Gender and sex role conflicts in men's lives. In K. Soloman & M. Levy (Eds.). Men in transition. New York, Plenum.

Ono T., Nishino, H. Sasaki, K., Fukuda, M., & Muramoto, K. (1980). Role of the lateral hypothalamus and the amygdala in feeding behavior. Brain Research Bulletin, 5, 143-149.

Oppenheim, R. W. (1981). Neuronal cell death and some related regressive phenomon during neurogenesis. In W. M. Cowan (ed.). Studies in developmental neurobiology. New York, Oxford U. Press.

Orikasa, C., & Sakuma, Y. (2010). Estrogen configures sexual dimorphism in the preoptic area of C57BL/6J and ddN strains of mice. The Journal of Comparative Neurology, 518, Issue 17, 3618–3629.

Oviatt, S. L. (1980). The emerging ability to comprehend language. Child Development, 51, 97-106.

Packan, D.R., Sapolsky, R.M. (1990). Glucocorticoid endangerment of the hippocampus: tissue, steroid and receptor specificity. Neuroendocrinology 51, 613-618.

Owens, R. E. (2011). Language Development. Allyn & Bacon.

Packard, M. G., Hirsh, R., & White, N. M., (1989). Differential effects of fornix and caudate nucleus lesions on two radial maze tasks: Evidence for multiple memory systems. Journal of Neuroscience, 9, 1465-1472.

Packard, M. G. & White, N. M. (1991). Dissociation of hippocampus and caudate nucleus memory systems by posttraining intracerebral injection of dopamine agonists. Behavioral Neuroscience, 105, 295-306.

Pang PT , et al. (2004) Cleavage of proBDNF by tPA/plasmin is essential for long-term hippocampal plasticity. Science 306:487–491

Pape, H-C & Pare, D. (2010). Plastic Synaptic Networks of the Amygdala for the Acquisition, Expression, and Extinction of Conditioned Fear. Physiol Rev. 90, 419-463.

Pastalkova E , et al. (2006) Storage of spatial information by the maintenance mechanism of LTP. Science 313:1141–1144.

Penfield, W. (1952) Memory Mechanisms. Archives of Neurology and Psychiatry, 67, 178-191.

Penfield, W. (1954). The permanent records of the stream of consciousness. Acta Psychologica, 11, 47-69.

Penfield, W. J., & Boldrey, E. (1937). Somatic motor and sensory representation in the visual cortex of man as studied by electrical stimulation. Brain, 60, 389-443.

Penfield, W., & Evans, J. (1934). Functional defects produced by cerebral lobectomies. Publication of the Associaiton for Research in Nervous and Mental Disease, 13, 352-377.

Penfield, W., & Jasper, H. (1954). Epilepsy and the functional anatomy of the human brain. Boston: Little-Brown & Co.

Penfield, W. & Mathieson, G. (1974). Memory; autopsy findings and comments on the role of the hippocampus in experimental recall. Archives of Neurology, 31, 145-154

Penfield, W., & Milner, B. (1958). Memory deficit produced by bilateral lesions in the hippocampal zone. Archives of Neurology and Psychiatry, 79, 475-497.

Penfield, W., & Perot, P. (1963). The brains record of auditory and visual experience. Brain, 86, 595-695.

Penfield, W., & Rasmussen, T. (1950). The Cerebral Cortex of Man. New York, Macmillan.

Penfield, W., & Roberts, L. (1959). Speech and brain mechanisms. Princeton, New Jersey: Princeton University Press.

Penfield, W., & Welch, K. (1951). Supplementary motor area of cerebral cortex. Clinical and experimental study. Archives of Neurology & Psychiatry, 66, 289-317.

Perryman, K. M., Kling, A. s., & Lloyd, R. L. (1987). Differential effects of inferior temporal cortex lesions upon visual and auditory-evoked potentials in the amygdala of the squirrel monkey. Behavioral and Neural Biology, 47, 73-79.

Pessoa, L. & Adolphs, R. (2010). Emotion processing and the amygdala. Nature Reviews Neuroscience 11, 773-783.

Piekema, C. et al., (2006). The right hippocampus participates in short-term memory maintenance of object–location associations. Neuroimage,33, 374-382.

Poletti, C.E., & Sujatanond, M. (1980). Evidence for a second hippocampal efferent pathway to hypothalamus and basal forebrain comparable to fornix system: a unit study in the monkey. Journal of Neurophysiology, 44, 514-531.

Porrino, L. J., Crane, A. M., & Goldman-Rakic, P. S. (1981). Direct and indirect pathways from the amygdala top the frontal lobe in rhesus monkeys. Journal of Comparative Neurology, 205, 30-48.

Poulos, A. M., et al., (2009). Persistence of fear memory across time requires the basolateral amygdala complex. PNAS, 106, 11737-11741.

Proverbio, A., A. Zani, et al. (2008). "Neural markers of a greater female responsiveness to social stimuli." BMC Neuroscience 9(1): 56.

Proverbio, A. M., S. Matarazzo, et al. (2007). "Processing valence and intensity of infant expressions: the roles of expertise and gender." Scand J Psychol 48(6): 477-85.

Ranote S, et al., (2004). The neural basis of maternal responsiveness to infants: an fMRI study. Neuroreport. 2004 Aug 6;15(11):1825-9.

Ranson, S. W., Kabat, H., & Magoun, H. W. (1935). Autonomic responses to electrical stimulation of the hypothalamus, preoptic region and septum. Archives of Neurology and Psychiatry, 33, 467-477

Rawlins, J. N. P. (2005). Associations across time: The hippocampus as a temporary memory store. Behavioral and Brain Sciences, 8, 479-496.

Remondes, M., & Schuman, E. M. (2004). Role for a cortical input to hippocampal area CA1 in the consolidation of a long-term memory. Nature 431, 699-703.

Represa, A., Temblay, E., & Ben-Ari, Y. (1989). Transient increase of NMDA-Binding sites in human hippocampus during development. Neuroscience Letters, 99, 61-66.

Restivo, L., et al., (2009). The Formation of Recent and Remote Memory Is Associated with Time-Dependent Formation of Dendritic Spines in the Hippocampus and Anterior Cingulate Cortex. The Journal of Neuroscience, 29, 8206-8214.

Reyes, P. F., Golden, G. T., Fagel, P. L., et al., (1987). The prepiriform cortex in dementia of the Alzheimer's type. Archives of Neurology, 44, 644-645.

Reynolds, G. P. (2003). Increased concentrations and lateral asymmetry of amygdala dopamine in schizophrenia. Nature, 305, 527-529.

Riscutia, C. (1973). A study of the Modjokerto infant calvarium. In R. H. Tuttle (Ed.), Paleoanthroplogy, (pp. 373-380). Paris: Mouton Publishers Risold, P. W., & Swanson, L. W. (1996). Structural evidence for functional domains in rat hippocampus. Science, 272, 1484-1486.

Rolls, E. T. (1984). Neurons in the cortex of the temporal lobe and in the amygdala of the monkey with responses selective for faces. Human Neurobiology, 3, 209-222.

Rolls, E. T. (2005). Connections, functions, and dysfunctions of limbic structures, the prefrontal cortex, and hypothalamus. In M. Swash & C. Kennard, (Eds.), The Scientific Basis of Clinical Neurology, London, Livinstone. 201-213.

Rolls, E. T. (1987). Information representation, processing and storage in the brain: analysis at the single neuron level. In J.-P. Changeuz & M. Konishi (Eds.). The Neural and Molecular Bases of Learning. New York, Wiley. 503-540

Rolls, E. T. (1988).Functions of neural networks in the hippocampus and neocortex in memory. In J. H. Byrne & W. O. Berry (eds.). Neural Models of Plasticity: Theoretical and Empirical Approaches. New York, Acaemic Press.

Rolls E. T. (1990a). Functions of neural networks in the hippocampus and of backprojections in the cerebral cortex in memory. In J. L. McGaugh, N. M. Winberger, & G. Lynch (Eds.). Brain Organization and Memory. New York. Oxford University Press.

Rolls, E. T. (1990b). Principles underlying the representation and storage of information in neuronal networks in the primate hippocampus and cerebral cortex. In S. F. Zornetzer, J. L. Davis, & C. Lau (Eds.) An Introduction to Neural and Electronic Networks. San Diego, Academic Press.

Rolls, E. T. (1992). Neurophysiology and functions of the primate amygdala. In J. P. Aggleton (Ed.). The Amygdala. New York, Wiley-Liss.

Rolls, E.T., Burton, M.J., & Mora, F. (1976). Hypothalamic neuronal response associated with the sight of food. Brain Research, 111, 53-66.

Rolls, E. T., Perret, D., Thorpe, S. J., et al. (1979). Responses of neurons in area 7 of the parietal cortex to objects of different significance. Brain Research, 169, 194-198.

Rolls, E. T., & Williams, G. V. (1987). Neuronal activity in the ventral striatum of the primate. In M. B., Carpenter, & A. Jayaraman (Eds.). The basal ganglia. Plenum. New York.

Romanski, L. M., Clugnet, M-C., Bordi, F. & LeDoux, J. E. (1993). Somatosensory and auditory convergence in the lateral nucleus of the amygdala. Behavioral Neuroscience, 107, 444-450.

Romcy-Pereira, R. N. et al., (2009). Sleep-dependent gene expression in the hippocampus and prefrontal cortex following long-term potentiation. Physiology & Behavior, 98, 44-52

Roozendaal, B., & Cools, A. R. (2014). Influence of the noradrenergic state of the nucleus accumbens in basolateral amygdala mediated changes in neophobia of rats. Behavioral Neuroscience, 108, 1107-1118.

Roozendaal, B., et al., (2009). Stress, memory and the amygdala. Nature Reviews Neuroscience. 10, 423-433.

Rosen, J. B. Hitchcock, J. M. Sananes, C. b. Miserendino, M. J. D. & Davis, M. (1991). A direct projection from the central nucleus of the amygdala to the acoustic startle pathway: Anterograde and retrograde tracing studies. Behavioral Neuroscience, 105, 817-825.

Rosen, J. B. & Schulkin, J. (1998). From normal fear to pathological anxiety. Psychological Review, 103, 325-350.

Rubinow, M. J. et al., (2009). Age-related dendritic hypertrophy and sexual dimorphism in rat basolateral amygdala, Neurobiology of Aging, 30, 137-146.

Rule, N.O. et al., (2010). Face value: Amygdala response reflects the validity of first impressions. NeuroImage, 54, 734-741.

Ryan, B. K. et al., (2009). Persistent inhibition of hippocampal long-term potentiation in vivo by learned helplessness stress. Hippocampus, 20, 758-767.

Russell, C. L., K. A. Bard, et al. (1997). "Social referencing by young chimpanzees (Pan troglodytes)." Journal of Comparative Psychology 111(2): 185-193.

Salmaso, N. et al., (2011). Pregnancy and Maternal Behavior Induce Changes in Glia, Glutamate and Its Metabolism within the Cingulate Cortex. PLoS ONE 6(9): e23529.

Sander, K., et al., (2007). FMRI activations of amygdala, cingulate cortex, and auditory cortex by infant laughing and crying. Human Brain Mapping, 28, 1007-1022.

Sander K, Scheich H. (2001) Auditory perception of laughing and crying activates human amygdala regardless of attentional state. Cog Brain Res. 12:181–198.

Sano, K., Mayanagi, S., Sekino, H., et al., (1970). Results of stimulation and destruction of the posterior hypothalamus in man. Journal of Neurosurgery, 33, 689-707.

Sapir, E. (1966). Culture, language and personality. Berkeley. U. California Press.

Sapiro, V. (1990). Women in American society. Mountain View. Mayfield.

Sapolsky, R.M. (1996). Why stress is bad for your brain. Science 273, 749-750.

Sarter, M., & Markowitsch, E. K. (2005). The amygdala's role in human mnemonic processing. Cortex, 21, 7-24.

Sawa, M., & Delgado, J. M. R. (1963). Amygdala unitary activity in the unrestrained cat. Electroencephalography and Clinical Neurophysiology, 15, 637-650.

Sawa, M., Ueki, Y. Arita, M., & Harada, T. (1954). Preliminary report on the amygdalectomy on the psychotIc patients with interpretation or oral-emotional manifestations in schizphrenics. Folia Psychiatrica et Neurological Jaaponica, 7, 309-329.

Sayigh LS, Tyack PL, Wells RS, Scott MD. Signature whistles of free-ranging bottlenose dolphins Tursiops truncates: stability and mother-offspring comparisons. Behav Ecol Sociobiol. 1990;26:247–260.

Schoenknecht, P., et al., (2011). FC12-03 - DTI-based in vivo mapping of subregions within the human hypothalamus. European Psychiatry, 26, Supplement 1,

Schott, B. H. et al., (2011). Fiber density between rhinal cortex and activated ventrolateral prefrontal regions predicts episodic memory performance in humans. PNAS, 108, 5408-5413.

Schutze, I., Knuepfer, M. M., Eismann, A., Stumpf, H., & Stock, G. (1987). Sensory input to single neurons in the amygdala of the cat. Experimental Neurology, 97, 499-515.

Searby A, Jouventin P. Mother-lamb acoustic recognition in sheep: a frequency coding. Proc Roy Soc Lond B. 2003;270:1765–1771.

Segal, M. (1980). The action of serotonin in the rat hippocampus. Journal of Physiology, 303, 375-390.

Seifritz E, Esposito F, Neuhoff JG, Luthi A, Mustovic H, Dammann G, Bardeleben Uv, Radue EW, Cirillo S, Tedeschi G, Di Salle F. (2003) Differential sex-independent amygdala response to infant crying and laughing in parents versus nonparents. Biol Psychiatry. 2003;54:1367–1375.

Scott, S. K., et al. (1997). Impaired auditory recognition of fear and anger following bilateral amygdala lesions. Nature, 385, 254-257.

Sejnowski, T. J., & Tesauro, G. (1990). Building network learning algorithms from Hebbian synapses. In J. L. McGaugh, N. M. Winberger, & G. Lynch (Eds.). Brain Organization and Memory. New York. Oxford University Press.

Seldon, N. R. W., Everitt, B. J., Jarrard, L. E., & Robbins, T. W. (1991). Complementary roles for the amygdala and hippocampus in aversive conditioning to explicit and contextual cues. Neuroscience, 42, 335-350.

Shema, R. et al., (2007). Rapid Erasure of Long-Term Memory Associations in the Cortex by an Inhibitor of PKMζ. Science, 317, 951-953.

Shin L. M. et al., (2009) The role of the anterior cingulate in postraumatic stress and panic disorders. In B. A. Vogt (Ed). Cingulate Neurobiology and disease.

Shizawa Y, Nakamichi M, Hinobayashi T, Minami T. (2005). Playback experiment to test maternal responses of Japanese macaques (Macaca fuscata) to their own infant's call when the infants were four to six months old. Behav Processes. ;68:41–46

Siegel, A. et al., (2010). Limbic, hypothalamic and periaqueductal gray circuitry and mechanisms controlling rage and vocalization in the cat. Handbook of Behavioral Neuroscience, 19, 243-253.

Siegel, S. J., Ginsberg, S. D., Hof, P. R., et al., (1993). Effects of social deprivation in prepubescent rhesus monkeys. Brain Research,619-299-305.

Sidman, R. L., & Rakic, P. (1973). Neural migration with special reference to developing human brain., A review. Brain Research, 62, 1-87.

Sidman, R. L., & Rakic, P. (1982). Development of the human nervous system. In Haymaker, W. & Adams, R. D. (Eds). Histology and Histopathology of the central nervous system. Illinois. Thomas.

Siegel, A., Edinger, H. (1976). Organization of the hippocampal-septal axis. In J.F. DeFrance (Ed.), The Septal Nuclei. New York: Plenum Press.

Siegel, A., Fukushima, T., Meibach, R., Burke, L., Edinger, H., & Weiner, S. (1977). The origin of the afferent supply to the mediodorsal thalamic nucleus: enhanced HRP transport by selective lesions. Brian Research, 135, 11-23.

Siegel, A. & Skog, D. (1970). Effects of electrical stimulation of the septum upon attack behavior elicited from the hypothalamus in the cat. Brain Research, 23, 371-380.

Siegel, J. M., Tomaszewski, K. S., & Nienhus, R. (1986). Behavioral states in the chronic medullary and midpontine cat. Electroencephalogray and Clinical Neurophysysiology, 63, 274-288.

Siegel, J., & Wang, R.Y. (1974). Electroencephalographic, behavioral, and single unit activity produced by stimulation of forebrain inhibitory structures in cats. Experimental Neurology, 42, 28-50.

Sejnowski, T. J., & Tesauro, G. (1990). Building network learning algorithms from Hebbian synapses. In J. L. McGaugh, N. M. Winberger, & G. Lynch (Eds.). Brain Organization and Memory. New York. Oxford University Press.

Seldon, N. R. W., Everitt, B. J., Jarrard, L. E., & Robbins, T. W. (1991). Complementary roles for the amygdala and hippocampus in aversive conditioning to explicit and contextual cues. Neuroscience, 42, 335-350.

Selemon, L. D., Goldman-Rakic P. S., & Tamminga, C. A. (1995). Prefrontal cortex. American Journal of Psychiatry, 152, 5.

Shores, T. J., Seib, T.B., Levine, S. , et al. (1989). Inescapable versus escapable shock modulates long-term potentiation in the rat hippocampus. Science, 244, 224-226.

Sigurdsson, T. et al., (2007). Long-term potentiation in the amygdala: A cellular mechanism of fear learning and memory. Neuropharmacology, 52, 215-227.

Singewald, G. M., et al., (2011). The Modulatory Role of the Lateral Septum on Neuroendocrine and Behavioral Stress Responses. Neuropsychopharmacology, 36, 793–804.

Smith, O., A., DeVito, J. L., & Astley, C. A. 91990). Neurons controlling cardiovascular responses to emotion are located in lateral hypothalamus-perifornical region. American Journal of Physiology, 259, 943-954.

Smith, P. H., Arehart, D. M., Haaf, R. A., & deSaintVictor, C. M. (1989). Expectancies and memory for spatiotemporal events in 5 month old infants. Journal of Experimental Child Psychology, 5, 136-150.

Smith WK. (1945) The functional significance of the rostral cingulate cortex as revealed by its responses to electrical excitation. J Neurophysiol. 8:241–255.

Snow, C. W. & McGaha, C. G. (2002). Infant Development. Prentice Hall.

Spiegler, B. J., & Mishkin, M. (1981). Evidence for the sequential participation of inferior temporal cortex and amygdala in the acquisition of stimulus-reward associations. Behavioural Brain Research, 3, 303-317.

Spitz, R.A. (1945). Hospitalism: an inquiry into the genesis of psychiatric conditions in early childhood. Psychoanalytical Study of the Child. 1, 53-74.

Spitz, R. A., Emde, R. N., & Metcalf, D. R. (1970). Further prototypes of ego formation: A working paper from a research project on early development. Psychoanalytic Study of the Child, 25, 417-441.

Spitz, R. A., & Wolf, K. M. (1946). The smiling response: A contribution to the ontogenesis of social relations. Genetic Psychology Monographs. 34, 57-125.

Sponheimer, M. & Lee-thorp, J. A., (2016). Science, January.

Spoont, M. R. (1992). Modulatory role of serotonin in neural information processing: Implications for human psychopathology. Psychological Bulletin, 112, 330-350.

Squire, L. R. (1981). Two forms of human amnesia: An analysis of forgetting. Journal of Neuroscience, 5, 241-273.

Squire, L. R. (1982). Comparisons between forms of amnesia. Journal of Experimental Psychology. Learning, Memory, and Cognition, 8, 560-573.

Squire, L. (1987). Memory and brain. New York: Oxford University Press.

Squire, L. R. (1992). Memory and the hippocampus: A synthesis from findings with rats, monkeys, and humans. Psychological Review, 99, 195-231.

Squire, L. R., Cohen, N. J., & Nadel, L. (1984). The medial temporal region and memory consolidation. In Weingartner, H., & Parker, E. (Eds). Memory Consolidation.

Squire, L. R., Haist, F., & Shimamura, A. P. (1989). The neurology of memory. Journal of Neuroscience, 9, 828-839.

Squire, L. R., Ojemann, J. g., Miezin, F. M., et al., (1992). Activation of the hippocampus in normal humans. Proceedings of the National Academy of Science, 89, 21-27.

Squire, L. R., Slater, P. C., & Chace, P. M. (2015). Retrograde amnesia. Science, 187, 77-79.

Squire, L.R. & Bayley, P.J. (2007). The neuroscience of remote memory. Curr. Opin. Neurobiol., 17, 185–196.

Squire, E. R. (2006). Lost forever or temporarily misplaced? The long debate about the nature of memory impairment. Learning and Memory, 13, 522-529.

Sroufe, L. A. (1996). Emotional develoment. New York: Cambridge University Press.

Sroufe, L. A. (1997). Psychopathology as an outcome of development. Development and Psychopathology, 9, 251-268.

Sroufe, L. A., Carlson, E., & Shulman, S. (1993). Individuals in relationships: Development from infancy through adolescence. In D. Funder, R. Parke, C. Thomlison-Keasey, & K. Widman (Eds.). Studying lives through time: Personality and development. Academic Press. New York.

Stephan, H., & Andy, O. J. (1977). Quantitative comparisons of the amygdala in insectivores and primates. Acta Anatomy, 98, 130-153.

Stepien, I., & Stamm, J.S. (1970). Impairments on locomotor tasks involving spatial opposition between cue and reward in frontally ablated monkeys. Acta Neurobiologica Experimentalis. 30, 1-12.

Steriade, M. (1964). Development of evoked responses and self-sustained activity within amygdalohippocampal circuits. Electroencephalography and Clinical Neurophysiology, 16, 221-231.

Steriade, M., Datta, S., Pare, D., Oakson, G., & Dossi, R. C. (1990). Neuronal activities in brainstem cholinergic nuclei related to tonic activation processes in thalamocortical sytems. Journal of Neuroscience, 10, 2541-2559.

Strange, B. A. et al., (2008). Emotion-Induced Retrograde Amnesia Is Determined by a 5-HTT Genetic Polymorphism. Journal of Neuroscience, 28, 7036-7039.

Stiles, J. (2008). The Fundamentals of Brain Development: Integrating Nature and Nurture. Harvard University Press.

Stopa, E. G., Koh,m E. T., Sevendsen, C. N., et al., (1991). Computer assisted mapping of immunoreactive mammalian gonadotropin-releasing hormone in adult human basal forebrain and amygdala. Endocrinology, 128, 3199-3207.

Stoof, J. C., Drukarch, B., DE Boer, P., et al. (1992). Regulation of the activity of striatal cholinergic neurons by dopamine. Neuroscience, 47, 755-770.

Stuss, D. T. (2011). Functions of the Frontal Lobes: Relation to Executive Functions. Journal of the International Neuropsychological Soc. 17, 795-765.

Sutor, B., & Hablitz, J. J. (1989). Long term potentiation in frontal cortex. Neuroscience Letters, 97, 111-117.

Suzuki, K., et al., (2010). The role of gut hormones and the hypothalamus in appetite regulation. Endocr J. 57, 359-72.

Swaab, D.F, & Fliers, E. (2005). A sexually dimorphic nucleus in the human brain Science, 228, 1112-1114

Swaab, D.F. & Hoffman M.A. (1988). Sexual differentiation of the human hypothalamus: Ontogeny of the sexually dimorphic nucleus of the preoptic area. Developmental Brain Research, 44, 314-318.

Swaab, D.F., Hoffman, M.A. (1990). An enlarged suprachiasmatic nucleus in homosexual men. Brain Research, 537,141-148.

Swann, A. C., Stokes, P. E., Secunda, S. K., et al. (2014). Depressive mania vs agitated depression. Biogenic amine and hypothalamic-pituitary- adrenocortical function. Biological Psychiatry, 35, 803-813.

Swanson, L. W., & Cowan, W. M. (1979). The connections of the septal region in the cat. Journal of Comparative Neurology, 186, 621-656.

Swayze V., Andreasen, N., Alliger, R., Yuih, W., and Ehrhardt, J. (1992) Subcortical and temporal structures in affective disorder and schizophrenia: A magnetic resonance imaging study. Biological Psychiatry 31: 221-240.

Sweeney, J. E., Lamour, Y., & Bassant, M. H. (1992). Arousal-dependent properties of medial septal neurons in the unanesthetized rat. Neuroscience, 48, 353-362.

Symmes D, Biben M. Maternal recognition of individual infant squirrel monkeys from isolation call playbacks. Am J Primatol. 2005;9:39–46.

Takeuchi, Y. McLean, J. H., & Hopkins, D. a. (1982). Reciprocal connections between the amygdala nd parabachial nuclei. Brain Research, 239, 583-588.

Takeuchi, Y., Satoda, T., & Matshima, R. (1988). Amygdaloid projections for masticatory motoneurons. Brain Research Bulletin, 21, 123-127.

Tanaka, J. et al. (2008). Protein synthesis and neurotrophin-dependent structural plasticity of single dendritic spines. Science, 319, 1683-1687

Thomas, E. & Gunton, D. J. (2011). Kindling of the lateral septum and the amygdala: Effects on anxiety in rats. Physiology & Behaviorm 104, 6530658.

Todd, R. M., & Anderson, A. K. (2009). Six degrees of separation: the amygdala regulates social behavior and perception. Nature Neuroscience 12, 1217 - 1218.

Toscano, J. E. et al., (2009). Interest in infants by female rhesus monkeys with neonatal lesions of the amygdala or hippocampus. Neuroscience, 162, 881-891.

Tronic, E. (2007) The Neurobehavioral and Social-Emotional Development of Infants and Children. W. W. Norton.

Vanderwolf, C. H., & Leung, L.-W.S. (2003). Hippocampal rhythmical slow activity. In W. Seifert (Ed). Neurobiology of the Hippocampus. San Diego, Academic Press.

Vauclair, J. and J. Donnot (2005). "Infant holding biases and their relations to hemispheric specializations for perceiving facial emotions." Neuropsychologia 43(4): 564-571.

Vandewalle G. et al., (2011). Abnormal Hypothalamic Response to Light in Seasonal Affective Disorder. Biological Psychiatry, 70, 954-961

Vertes. R. P. (1981). An analysis of ascending brain stem systems involved in hippocampal synchronizaton and desynchronization. Journal of Neurophysiology, 46, 1140-1159.

Vertes, R. P. (1984). Brainstem control of events of REM sleep. Progress in Neurobiology, 22, 241-288.

Vertes, R. P. (1990). Fundamental of brainstem anatomy: A behavioral perspective. In W. R. Klemm, & R. P. Vertes (Eds.). Brainstem mechanisms of behavior. Wiley. New York.

Vertes, R. P. (1990). Brainstem mechanisms of slow-wave sleep and REM sleep. In W. R. Klemm, & R. P. Vertes (Eds.). Brainstem mechanisms of behavior. Wiley. New York.

Vertes, R. P. (2005). Hippocampal theta rhythm: A tag for short-term memory. Hippocampus, 15, 923-935.

Victor, M. & Agamanolis, J. (1990). Amnesia due to lesions confined to the hippocampus: A clinical-pathological study. Journal of Cognitive Neuroscience, 2, 246-257.

Victor, M., Adams, R. D., & Collins, G. H. (1989). The Wernicke-Korsakoff Syndrome and Related Neurological Disorders due to Alcoholism and Malnutrition. Philadelphia: Davis.

Villarreal, D.M. et al. (2002), NMDA receptor antagonists sustain LTP and spatial memory: active processes mediate LTP decay. Nat. Neurosci., 5. 48–52.

Vitek, J. L., Ashe, J., DeLong, M. R., & Alexander, G. E. (2014). Physiological properties and somatotopic organization of the primate motor thalamus. Journal of Neurophysiology, 71, 1498-1513.

Vochteloo, J. D., & Koolhaas, J. M. (1987). Medial amygdala lesions in male rats reduce aggressive behavior. Physiology and Behavior, 41, 99-102.

Vogt, B. A., Rosene, D. L., & Pandya, D. N. (1979). Thalamic and cortical afferents differentiate anterior from posterior cingulate cortex in the monkey. Science, 204, 205-212.

Vogt, B. A. (2009). Cingulate Neurobiology and disease. Oxford University Press.

Walser ES, Walters E, Hague P. Vocal communication between ewes and their own and alien lambs. Behaviour. 1982;81:140–151.

von Cramon, D. Y., Hebel, N., & Schuri, U. (2005). A contribution to the anatomical basis of thalamic amnesia. Brain, 108, 993-1008.

Vonderache, A. r. (1940). Changes in the hypothalamus in organic disease. Journal of Nervous and Mental Disease, 20, 689-712.

Vonsattel, J-P., Myers, R. H., Stevens, T. J., et al. (1987). Huntington's disease: Neuropathological Grading. In M. B., Carpenter, & A. Jayaraman (Eds.). The basal ganglia. Plenum. New York.

Vygotsky, L. S. (1962). Thought and language. Cambridge: MIT Press.

Walker-Andrews, A. S. (1998). "Emotions and social development: Infants' recognition of emotions in others." Pediatrics 102(5 Suppl E): 1268-71.

Walser ES, Walters E, Hague P. (1982). Vocal communication between ewes and their own and alien lambs. Behaviour. 81:140–151.

Walsh, R. N., Budtz-Olsen, O. E., Penny, J. e., & Cummins, R. A. (1969). The effects of environmental complexity on the histology of the rat hippocampus. Journal of Comparative Neurology, 137, 261-266.

Walters, E., Ch. (2016). Dopaminomimetic psychosis in Parkinson's disease patients. Neurology, 52, S10-S14.

Warburton, E. C. Brown, M. W. (2009). Findings from animals concerning when interactions between perirhinal cortex, hippocampus and medial prefrontal cortex are necessary for recognition memory. Neuropsychologia, 48, 2262-2272.

Warrington, E. K., & Rabin, P. (1971). Visual span of apprehension in patients with unilateral cerebral lesions. Quarterly Journal of Experimental Psychology, 23, 423-431.

Warrington, E. K., & Shallice, T. (1969). The selective impairment of auditory verbal short-term memory, Brain, 92, 885-896.

Warrington, E. K., & Weiskrantz, L. (1970). The amnensic syndrome: Consolitation or retrieval? Nature, 228, 628-630.

Warrington, E. K., & Weiskrantz, L. (1979). Conditioning in amnesic patients. Neuropsychologia, 17, 187-194.

Was-Hockert, O. Lind, J. Vuorenkoski, V. Partanen, T. & Valanne, E. (1968). The infant cry. A spectrographic and auditory analysis. Clinics in Developmental Medicine, 29, 33-73.

Wasman, M., & Flynn, J.P. (1962). Directed attack elicited from the hypothalamus. Archives of Neurology, 6, 220-227.

Wasser, S. K., & Isenberg, D. Y. (1986). Reproductive failure among women: Pathology or adaption? Journal of Psychosomatic Obstetrics and Gynaecology, 5, 153-175.

Watson, D. G., & Humphreys, G. W. (2016). The magic number 4 and temporo-parietal damage.

Cognitive Neuropsychology, 16, 320-333.

Watanabe, E. (1984). Neuronal events correlated with long-term adaption of the horizontal vestibuloocular reflex in the primate flocculus. Brain Research, 297, 169-174.

Waters, E., Matas, L., & Stroufe, L.A. (2015). Infant's reactions to an approaching stranger: description, validation and functional significance of wariness. Child Development, 46, 348-356.

Waters, M. (1997). Science, February 28.

Whalen, P. J. & Phelps, E. A. (2009). The Human Amygdala, Guilford Press.

Wheatley, M.D. (1944). The hypothalamus and affective behavior. Archives of Neurology and Psychiatry, 52, 296-316.

Whitlock, J. R. et al., (2006). Learning Induces Long-Term Potentiation in the Hippocampus. Science, 313, 1093-1097.

Whitlock JR , Heynen AJ , Shuler MG , Bear MF (2006) Learning induces long-term potentiation in the hippocampus. Science 313:1093–1097.

Willshaw, D.J. & Buckingham, J.T. (1990). An assessment of Marr's theory of the hippocampus as a temporary memory store. Philos. Trans. R. Soc. Lond. B Biol. Sci., 329 . 205–215.

Wiltgen, B.J. et al., (2004). New circuits for old memories: the role of the neocortex in consolidation. Neuron, 44, 101–108.

Winson, J. (2005). Brain and Psyche: The Biology of the Unconscious. Anchor Press. New York.

Winson, J. (1986). Behaviorally dependent neuronal gating in the hippocampus. In The Hippocampus. Isaacson, R. L., & Pribram, K. (Eds). New York. Plenum. New York.

Winter, P. Handley, P. Ploog, D. & Schott, D. (1973). Ontogeny of squirrel monkey calls under normal conditions and under acoustic isolation. Behaviour, 47, 230-239.

Wirz-Justice, A., Graw, P., Krauchi, K. et al. (1993). Light therapy in seasonal affective disorder is independent of time of day or circadian phase. Archives of General Psychiatry, 50, 929-937.

Wise, R. J. S., Bernardi, S., Frackowiack, R.S. J., et al. (2003). Serial observations on the pathophysiology of acute stroke. Brain, 106, 197-222.

Wiskrantz, M.L., Mihailovic, L.J., & Gross, C.G. (1962). Effects of stimulation of frontal cortex and hippocampus on behavior in monkeys. Brain, 85, 487-504.

Woolf, N. J., & Butcher, L. L. (1982). Cholinergic projections to the basolateral amygdala. Brain Research Bulletin, 8, 751-763.

Yim, C. Y., & Mogenson, G. J. (1982). Response of nucleus accumbens neurons to amygdala stimulation and its modification by dopamine. Brain Research, 239, 401-415.

Yim, C. Y., & Mogenson, G. J. (2003). Response of ventral pallidal neurons to amygdala stimulation and its modification by dopamine projections to nucleus accumbens. Journal of Neurophysiology, 50, 148-161.

Yingling, C.D., & Skinner, J.E. (1977). Gating of thalamic input to cerebral cortex by nucleus reticularis thalami, In J. Desmedt (Ed.), Attention, voluntary contraction and event related cerebral potentials. (pp. 70-96). Switzerland: S. Kargar.

Zakharenko SS et al. (2001) Visualization of changes in presynaptic function during long-term synaptic plasticity. Nature Neuroscience, 7, 711-717.

Zhang, Q. et al., (2011). Amygdala, an important regulator for food intake. Frontiers in Biology, 6, 82-85.

Zimmerman, M. E. et al., (2008). Hippocampal neurochemistry, neuromorphometry, and verbal memory in nondemented older adults. Neurology, 70, 1594-1600.

Zola-Morgan, S., Amaral, D. G., & Squire, R. (1986). Human amnesia and the medial temporal region. Journal of Neuroscience, 6, 2950-2967.

Zola-Morgan S. & Squire, L. R. (1984). Preserved learning in monkeys with medial temporal lesions: Sparing of motor and cognitive skills. Journal of Neuroscience, 4, 1072-1085.

Zola-Morgan S. & Squire, L. R. (2005). Medial temporal lesions in monkeys impair memory on a variety of tasks sensitive to human amnesia. Behavioral Neuroscience, 99, 22-34

Zola-Morgan S. & Squire, L. R. (1986). Memory impairment in monkeys following lesions of the hippocampus. Behavioral Neuroscience, 100, 155-160.

Zola-Morgan, S., Squire, L. R., Alvarez-Royo, P., & Clower, R. (1991). Independence of memory functions and emotional behavior: Separate contributions of the hippocampal formation and the amygdala. Hippocampus, 1, 207-220.

Zola-Morgan, S., Squire, R., & Amaral, D. G. (1989). Lesions of the hippocampal formation but not lesions of the fornix of the mammillary nuclei produce long-lasting memory impairment in monkeys.

Journal of Neuroscience, 9, 898-913.

Zybrozyna, A. W. (1963). The anatomical basis of patterns of autonomic and behavior responses affected via the amygdala. In W. Bargmann & J. P. Schade (eds.). Progressin brain research, 13. Amsterdam, Elsevier.

Made in the USA
Coppell, TX
04 August 2024

35567155R10155